Fri night & Sat afternoon — Math - Man

STRUCTURAL

ANALYSIS

Jack C. McCormac

Associate Professor of
Civil Engineering
Clemson College

INTERNATIONAL TEXTBOOK COMPANY

Scranton, Pennsylvania

INTERNATIONAL TEXTBOOKS IN CIVIL ENGINEERING

Consulting Editor

RUSSELL C. BRINKER
Professor of Civil Engineering
Texas Western College

PREFACE

This book is presented for the student who is beginning the study of structural theory. It introduces him to the elementary fundamentals of structural analysis for beams, trusses, and frames. Sufficient information is included for a thorough understanding of statically determinate structures and for a first course in statically indeterminate structures. Attention is focused almost entirely upon analysis with only incidental reference given to design.

The analysis of statically determinate structures, based on the laws of statics, is discussed in Chapters 1 to 14. The analysis of statically indeterminate structures based on the laws of statics, the geometry of the structures, and the elastic properties of the structural components is the subject of Chapters 15 to 24. Most of these chapters are relatively short, each containing a few problems of similar nature. Although it would be possible in several instances to combine two or more chapters, the assignments are made simpler by keeping them separate.

Frequent illustrative examples are included, together with a large number of suggested homework problems. If several of these problems are solved in each chapter, the theory involved should become firmly fixed in the reader's mind. Little emphasis is placed on learning formulas, fixed notation systems, or procedures for determining stresses in particular types of structures; rather, the basic fundamentals which apply to all cases are stressed.

Stress analysis is a fascinating field to many of us in structural engineering. This book is presented in the hope that many of its users will be as attracted to stresses and strains as we are.

JACK C. McCORMAC

Clemson, South Carolina
September, 1960

ACKNOWLEDGMENTS

The author gratefully acknowledges the aid he has received from several sources. He is indebted to R. C. Brinker, D. H. McLean, John T. Watkins, B. A. Whisler, C. N. Antoni, W. L. Lowry, and I. A. Trively, who have by their suggestions and criticisms directly contributed to the preparation of this manuscript, and to his own professors, B. B. Williams, Dr. J. B. Wilbur, Dr. C. H. Norris, the late W. M. Fife, and M. J. Holley, who patiently instructed him in their structures classes. The books used in the courses taught by the above men naturally have influenced the enclosed material to some extent. These books were *Structural Theory* by Sutherland and Bowman, *Theory of Simple Structures* by Shedd and Vawter, and *Elementary Structural Analysis* by Wilbur and Norris. Finally, thanks are due Mrs. Fred W. DeBerry, who typed the manuscript.

CONTENTS

Pecos River Bridge, Del Rio, Texas. (Courtesy of R. L. Warren, Del Rio, Texas)

1 | **INTRODUCTION**

1–1. Types of Structures

Structural engineering embraces an extensive variety of structures other than bridges and buildings. There are stadiums, power poles, radio and television towers, cables, arches, water tanks, concrete pavements, and many others. The sizes range from small frames consisting of a few beams and columns to the 1250-ft (foot) high Empire State Building and the Golden Gate Bridge with its 4200-ft suspended span.

To face this wide range of sizes and types of structures, it seems unwise for those entering the structural field to learn to handle only one or two special cases. They should learn the basic fundamentals, which apply not only to all of the structures mentioned in the preceding paragraph but also to structures of types not necessarily considered to lie within the civil engineering field—ships and airplanes, for example.

The laws of statics, which are the fundamentals of all structural analysis, are stressed throughout the text. This emphasis should give the student a solid foundation for more advanced study and convince him that structural theory is not difficult and that it is unnecessary to memorize special cases. Some of the structures to be analyzed may seem to have rather weird shapes. These are included not to confuse the student, but rather to bring out the fact that the basic principles apply to all structures regardless of shape or size.

1–2. Structural Members

The primary types of structural members to be considered are as follows:
Beams are those members which are subjected to bending or flexure. They are usually thought of as being in horizontal positions and loaded with gravity or vertical loads.

Ties are members which are subjected to axial tension only.

Struts (also referred to as columns or posts) are members which are subjected to axial compression only.

1–3. Framed Structures

The truss and rigid frame are the two basic types of structural frames formed from the structural members.

A _truss_ consists of a group of ties and struts so designed and connected that they form a structure which acts as a large beam. The members usually form one or more triangles in a single plane and are so arranged that the external loads are applied at the joints and theoretically cause only axial tension or axial compression in the members. <u>The members are assumed to be connected at their joints with frictionless hinges or pins, which allow the ends of the members freedom to rotate slightly.</u> A common type of truss is shown in Fig. 1–1.

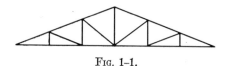

Fig. 1–1.

Trusses lying in one plane will be considered initially; however, framed structures having members not lying in a common plane are discussed in Chapter 14. These frames are called three-dimensional structures or space frames. (Transmission towers and framed domes are two types of space frames frequently seen.)

A *rigid frame* is a structure having moment-resisting joints. The members are rigidly connected at their ends so that no joint translation is possible (i.e., the members at a joint may rotate as a group but may not move with respect to each other). The load-carrying ability of the structure is increased by the ability of the joints to resist moment. Several rigid frames are shown in Fig. 1–2.

Fig. 1–2.

1–4. Classification of Loads

One of the most difficult and yet most important tasks faced by the structural engineer is the estimation of the loads that may be applied to a structure. No loads which may reasonably be expected during the life of the structure may be overlooked. After estimating these loads, the next problem is to determine the worst possible combination of loads that may occur at one time. For instance, would a bridge be subjected to its heaviest traffic, strongest winds, and thickest ice all at the same time, or is some lesser combination more feasible? The various classes of loads are discussed in the following paragraphs.

Dead loads are loads of constant magnitude which remain in one position. They consist of the structural frame's own weight and other loads which are permanently attached to the frame. For a steel-frame building some dead loads are the frame, walls, floors, roof, plumbing, and fixtures.

Cold-storage warehouse, Grand Junction, Colorado. (Courtesy of American Institute of Steel Construction, Inc.)

To design a structure, it is necessary for the weights or dead loads of the various parts to be estimated for use in the stress calculations. The exact sizes and weights of the parts are not known until the stress analysis is made and the members of the structure are selected. The weights, as determined from the actual design, must be compared with the estimated weights. If large discrepancies are present, it will be necessary to repeat the analysis and design with the use of better estimated weights.

Reasonable estimates of structure weights may be obtained by referring to similar type structures or to various formulas and tables available in most civil engineering handbooks. An experienced designer can estimate very closely the weights of most structures and will spend little time repeating designs because of poor estimates.

Live loads are loads which do not remain in one position and which may change in magnitude. Simply stated, all loads which are not dead loads are live loads. Live loads which move under their own power are said to be *moving loads,* such as trucks, people, and cranes, while those loads which may be moved are *movable loads,* such as furniture, warehouse materials, and snow. (A detailed discussion of truck and train loads is presented in Chapter 13.)

In the colder states, snow and ice loads are often of importance. For roof designs, snow loads of from 10 to 40 psf (pounds per square foot) are used; the magnitude depends primarily on the slope of the roof and to a lesser degree on the character of the roof surface. The larger loads are used for flat roofs; the smaller ones are used for sloped roofs. Snow tends to slide off sloped roofs, particularly roofs with metal or slate surfaces. A load of approximately 10 psf might be used for 45° (degree) slopes and a 40-psf load for flat roofs. Studies of snowfall records in areas with severe winters may indicate the occurrence of snow loads even greater than 40 psf.

It is possible for snow to cover either an entire roof or only a portion of it. For a roof truss, such as the one shown in Fig. 1–1, there may be a heavy snow on both sides with no wind, but it seems illogical to have a full snow on both sides and a full wind blowing on one side at the same time. At full wind load it is assumed that the snow has substantially been blown from the windward side but remains on the leeward side. All load possibilities are considered in finding the most critical stresses in each of the members of the truss.

Bridges are generally not designed for snow loads, since the loads are usually not appreciable. In any case, it is doubtful that a full load of snow and maximum traffic are present at the same time. Bridges and towers are sometimes covered with layers of ice from 1 to 2 in. (inches) thick. The weight of the ice runs up to about 10 psf. Another factor to be considered is the increased surface area of the ice-coated members as it pertains to wind loads.

Impact loads are caused by the vibration of moving or movable loads. It is obvious that a crate dropped on the floor of a warehouse or a truck bouncing on uneven pavement of a bridge causes greater stresses than occur if the loads are applied gently and gradually. Impact loads are equal to the difference between the magnitude of the loads actually caused and the magnitude of the loads had they been dead loads. Several expressions which are commonly used is estimating impact are given in Chapter 13.

Lateral loads are of two main types: wind and earthquake. The accurate determination of the most critical wind loads on a building or bridge is an extremely involved problem; however, sufficient information is available today to permit satisfactory estimates on a reasonably simple basis.

The actual effect of wind on a building is to cause pressures against vertical surfaces on the windward side, pressures or suctions on inclined surfaces on the windward side, and suction on all surfaces on the leeward side. Many persons have noted the effects of suction on the leeward sides of buildings during severe windstorms when shingles or other coverings have been lifted from the roof.

During the passing of a tornado or hurricane a sharp reduction in atmospheric pressure occurs. This decrease in pressure is not reflected inside airtight buildings, and the inside pressures, being greater than the external pressures, cause outward forces against the roofs and walls. Nearly everyone has heard stories of the walls of a building "exploding" outward during a storm.

For many years the usual practice has been to assume buildings loaded with a wind pressure of from 20 to 30 psf on vertical surfaces (20 psf is calculated to correspond to a 77.8-mph (miles per hour) wind). Somewhat higher loads per square foot for exposed surfaces of bridges have been used because bridges are usually located in more unprotected sites. The practice has been to consider a moving pressure of approximately 30 psf applied to $1\frac{1}{2}$ times the area of the bridge in elevation.

For estimating wind loads normal to sloping roof surfaces, various expressions have been used through the years. One of the very common ones is that of a French army officer, Colonel Duchemin. In his expression P_n represents pressure normal to the surface, P is the pressure if surface were vertical, and α is the angle between the wind and the roof surface.

$$P_n = P\frac{2\sin\alpha}{1+\sin^2\alpha}$$

This formula has been used to a great extent. Although it is known to give pressures larger than necessary, it still leaves a great deal to be desired. Colonel Duchemin conducted his experiments for wind on inclined surfaces representing roofs but did not include the effect of the remainder of the building on the forces produced on the roof. An obvious example of a case not correctly pictured by his formula is the windward side of a roof with a slope of less than 30° where a suction occurs.

For a period of ten years Committee 31 of the American Society of Civil Engineers (ASCE) made studies of wind behavior; they submitted their final report, *Wind Bracing in Steel Buildings* in 1940.[1] They recommended a standard wind load of 20 psf for vertical surfaces of buildings up to

[1] *Transactions of the ASCE,* vol. 105, p. 1713, 1940.

300 ft above ground level and an increase of 2.5 psf for each additional 100 ft of height, with special consideration to be given to areas subject to tornadoes and hurricanes. For other portions of gable-roofed buildings the following values were recommended:

1) A 12-psf suction on flat surfaces.
2) A 9-psf suction on walls parallel to wind direction.
3) A 9-psf suction on all leeward surfaces.
4) A pressure or suction on windward surfaces depending on their slopes as follows: a 12-psf suction from 0 to 20°, a 12-psf suction at 20° decreasing uniformly to 0 psf at 30°, a 0-psf pressure at 30° increasing uniformly to 9 psf at 60°, and a 9-psf pressure above 60°.

Should the location of these surfaces lie above 300 ft, the forces are to be increased in the same proportion as the pressures on windward vertical surfaces. These pressures and suctions were recommended for buildings which are normally airtight and are to be used in combination with the outward pressures produced inside the buildings. The committee recommended 4.5 psf pressing outward against walls and roofs of airtight buildings and other values for buildings which are not airtight. Suggested wind forces were also given for buildings with rounded roofs.

Although the values presented by this committee were a great improvement over the ones obtained by the Duchemin and other formulas, considerable room for improvement remained. During the past several years another ASCE committee has studied the available data on wind forces. Their findings were published in 1958 in a series of papers *Wind Forces on Structures*[2] and include several interesting and well-written articles. These papers suggest that, rather than assume the pressures and suctions recommended by Committee 31 for any structure, more realistic values can be obtained by taking into account the shape of a particular structure. Tables of shape coefficients, which were developed from the aerodynamic characteristics of various types of structures, are included. It is recommended that a shape coefficient be selected from the tables for the structure under consideration and be used together with the estimated maximum wind velocity for the particular geographic locality. The procedure for determining the actual wind forces is explained in the reports.

The estimation of wind forces cannot by any means be classified as an exact science. Much research needs to be done on the factors causing poor wind estimates. Perhaps the inaccuracies introduced thereby are not serious for massive stationary structures, but imagine their importance for large flexible frames such as long-span bridges. There are many factors needing intensive study: the strongest winds are often accompanied by the heaviest precipitation, which causes substantial changes in the forces; pressures and suctions have been assumed to be equal across

[2] *Proceedings of the ASCE*, vol. 84, no.ST4, 1958.

a particular surface, whereas recent tests show they may vary considerably; the presence of surrounding buildings affect wind forces; etc.

Earthquakes can occur anywhere in the world, but in the United States they are most common along the West Coast, and in California in particular. In areas where earthquakes are fairly frequent, studies have shown they cause some movement or acceleration of the ground surface. The acceleration can be broken down into horizontal and vertical components; the effect of the latter probably is negligible. The horizontal components, however, are of such magnitude that buildings erected in earthquake areas should be designed on the basis of loads which include some estimate for these forces. The forces to be reckoned with are usually taken as a percentage (5 to 10 per cent) of the weight of the building and its contents, and they are applied as a set of horizontal loads at the different floor levels. In computing the weight of the building, the total dead load plus from 25 to 50 per cent of the live load is required by building specifications. The effect of the horizontal acceleration increases with the distance above the ground because of the "whipping effect" of the earthquake, and the loads should be increased accordingly. Obviously, towers, water tanks, and penthouses on building roofs occupy precarious positions during an earthquake.

Longitudinal loads are another type of load that needs to be considered in designing some structures. Stopping a train on a railroad bridge or a truck on a highway bridge causes longitudinal forces to be applied. It is not difficult to imagine the tremendous longitudinal force developed when the driver of a 40-ton trailer truck traveling 60 mph suddenly has to apply the brakes while crossing a highway bridge.

There are other longitudinal load situations, such as ships running into docks and the movement of traveling cranes in building frames.

Selection of Design Loads. To estimate the values of live loads for which structures should be proportioned, reference can be made to publications by several organizations for suggested minimum loadings. As examples there are:

1) For railroad bridges, American Railway Engineering Association (AREA).

2) For highway bridges, American Association of State Highway Officials (AASHO).

3) For buildings, National Board of Fire Underwriters (NBFU) and the Building Code Committee of the Department of Commerce.

These specifications will on many occasions clearly prescribe the loads for which structures are to be designed. Despite the availability of this information, the engineer's ingenuity and knowledge of the situation are often needed to predict what loads the structure will have to support in years to come. The failure of engineers in designing bridges during the

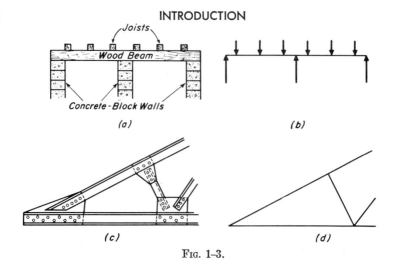

Fɪɢ. 1–3.

last few decades to accurately predict the loads, i.e., traffic, which would have to be supported during the estimated lives of the bridges has resulted in a great amount of replacement with wider and stronger structures.

1–5. Line Diagrams

To calculate the stresses in a structure with reasonable simplicity, it is necssary to replace the actual structure with a series of lines representing the center lines of the members. This convenient representation does cause discrepancies from actual conditions, but the errors are generally within reasonable limits.

Line diagrams represent actual structures examples of which can probably be found in the reader's neighborhood, wherever he lives, and the reader is encouraged to attempt to visualize the make-up of the actual structures so represented. Figure 1–3 (a) shows a series of wood joists supported by a wood beam which itself is supported by concrete-block walls. A line diagram for the beam, its supports, and the loads applied to it is drawn in Fig. 1–3 (b). The load transferred from a joist to the beam is spread over the width of the joist, but the line diagram has only an arrow acting at the center of the joist. A similar condition is the support supplied by the walls to the beam.

A drawing of a portion of a common steel roof truss as it is frequently assembled can be seen in Fig. 1–3 (c), while (d) represents the line diagram for the truss.

1–6. Slide-Rule Computations

Slide-rule computations equivalent to three- and perhaps four-place logarithms are probably far more accurate than the estimates of material strengths and magnitudes of loads used for structural analysis and design. The common materials dealt with in structures (wood, steel, concrete, and a few others) have ultimate strengths which can only be estimated. The loads applied to structures may be known within a few hundred pounds or no better than a few thousand pounds. It therefore seems inconsistent to require stress computations of greater accuracy than those obtainable with the slide rule.

Several partly true assumptions will be made about the construction of trusses: truss members are connected with frictionless pins, the deformation of truss members under load is so slight as to cause no effect on member stresses, etc. These deviations from actual conditions emphasize that it is useless to carry stress analysis to many decimal places.

1–7. Checks on Problems

A definite advantage of stress analysis is the possibility of making mathematical checks on the analysis by some method other than the one initially used, or by the same method from some other position on the structure. A person should be able in nearly every situation to determine if his work has been done correctly.

All of us, unfortunately, have the weakness of making exasperating mistakes, and the best that can be done is to keep them to the absolute minimum. The application of the simple arithmetical checks suggested in the following chapters will eliminate many of these costly blunders. The best structural engineer is not necssarily the one who makes the fewest mistakes initially but is probably the one who discovers the largest percentage of his mistakes.

2 |
REACTIONS

2-1. Equilibrium

A body at rest is said to be in equilibrium. The resultant of the external loads on the body and the supporting forces or reactions is zero. Not only is the sum of the horizontal forces equal to zero and the sum of the vertical forces equal to zero, but the sum of the moments of those forces about any point in that plane is also equal to zero. The three equations of statics are as follows:

$$\Sigma H = 0 \qquad \Sigma V = 0 \qquad \Sigma M = 0$$

These equations cannot be proved algebraically; they are merely statements of Sir Isaac Newton's observation that for every action on a body at rest there is an equal and opposite reaction. Whether the structure under consideration is a beam, a truss, a rigid frame, or some other type of assembly supported by various reactions, the equations of statics must apply if the body is to remain in equilibrium.

2-2. Moving Bodies

The statement was made in the preceding section that a body at rest is in equilibrium. It is possible, however, for an entire structure to move and yet be in equilibrium. An airplane or ship moves, but its individual parts do not move with respect to each other.

For a moving body, additional forces must be included for the equations of statics to be applicable. These are the inertia forces, and with them included the body may be considered to be acted upon by a set of forces in equilibrium for purposes of stress analysis.

2-3. Calculation of Unknowns

To identify a force completely, there are three unknowns that must be determined; they are the magnitude, direction, and line of action of the force. All of these values are known for external loads, but for a reaction only the point of application and perhaps the direction are known.

The total number of unknowns that can be determined by the equations of statics is controlled by the number of equations available. It does not make any difference how many reactions a structure has or how many unknowns each reaction has; there are three equations of statics and they can be used to determine but three unknowns for each structure. The determination of more than three unknowns requires additional equations or methods to use in conjunction with the statics equations. It will be seen that in some few instances, owing to special construction features, equations of condition are available in addition to the usual equations.

2–4. Types of Support

Structural frames may be supported by hinges, rollers, fixed ends, or links. These supports are discussed in the following paragraphs:

A *hinge* or pin-type support (represented herein by the symbol 〰️) is assumed to be connected to the structure with a frictionless pin. This type of support prevents movement in a horizontal and a vertical direction but does not prevent slight rotation about the hinge. There are two unknown forces at a hinge: the magnitude of the force required to prevent horizontal movement and the magnitude of the force required to prevent vertical movement. (The support supplied at a hinge may also be referred to as an inclined force which is the resultant of the horizontal force and the vertical force at the support. Two unknowns remain: the magnitude and direction of the inclined resultant.)

A *roller* type of support (represented herein by the symbol 〰️) is assumed to offer resistance to movement only in a direction perpendicular to the supporting surface beneath the roller. There is no resistance to slight rotation about the roller or to movement parallel to the supporting surface. The magnitude of the force required to prevent movement perpendicular to the supporting surface is the one unknown. Rollers may be installed in such a manner that they can resist movement either toward or away from the supporting surface.

A *fixed-end* support (represented herein by the symbol ▮—) is assumed to offer resistance to rotation about the support and to movement vertically and horizontally. There are three unknowns: the magnitude of the force to prevent horizontal movement, the magnitude of the force to prevent vertical movement, and the magnitude of the force to prevent rotation.

A *link* type of support (represented herein by the symbol ▮○—○) is quite similar to the roller in its action because the pins at each end are assumed to be frictionless. The line of action of the supporting force must be in the direction of the link and through the two pins. One unknown is present: the magnitude of the force in the direction of the link.

2–5. Statically Determinate Structures

The discussion of supports showed there are three unknown reaction components at a fixed end, two at a hinge, and one at a roller or link. If, for a particular structure, the total number of reaction components

The Chesapeake Bay Bridge illustrating beam spans, plate girder spans, deck truss, cantilever construction and suspension construction, all included in this structure. (Courtesy of Bethlehem Steel Company)

equals the number of equations available, the unknowns may be calculated, and the structure is then said to be statically determinate externally. Should the number of unknowns be greater than the number of equations available, the structure is statically indeterminate externally; if less, it is unstable externally.

The internal arrangement of some structures is such that one or more equations of condition is available. The arch of Fig. 3–5 has an internal pin (or hinge) at C. The internal moment at this "frictionless" pin is zero because no rotation can be transferred between the adjacent parts of the structure. A special condition exists because the internal moment at the pin must be zero regardless of the loading. A similar statement cannot be made for any continuous section of the beam.

By definition, a hinge transmits no rotation, and the three equations of statics plus a $\Sigma M = 0$ equation at hinge C are available to find the four unknown reaction components at A and B. The omission of a member in the truss of Fig. 15–3 will be shown to give another condition equation. If the number of condition equations plus the three equations of statics equals the number of unknowns, the structure is statically determinate; if more, it is statically indeterminate; and if less, it is unstable.

TABLE 2–1.
STATICAL CLASSIFICATION OF STRUCTURES

Structure	Sketch of Structure	Number of Unknowns	Number of Equations	Statical Condition
a		3	3	Statically determinate (referred to as a simple beam)
b		5	3	Statically indeterminate to second degree (a continuous beam)
c		2	3	Unstable
d		3	3	Statically determinate (a cantilever beam)
e		6	3	Statically indeterminate to third degree (a fixed-ended beam)
f		4	3	Statically indeterminate to first degree (a propped beam)
g		3	3	Statically determinate
h		4	4	Statically determinate
i		7	3	Statically indeterminate to fourth degree
j		5	5	Statically determinate

Several structures are classified in Table 2–1 as to their statical condition. The beam c supported on its ends with rollers, is stable under vertical loads but is unstable under inclined loads. A structure may be stable under one arrangement of loads, but if it is not stable under any

other conceivable set of loads, it is unstable. This condition is sometimes referred to as *unstable equilibrium*. The structure j has two internal
hinges and thus two equations of condition. There are five equations
available and five unknown reaction components; the structure is statically
determinate. If one of the supporting hinges were changed to a roller,
the structure would become unstable.

2–6. Geometric Instability

The ability of a structure to adequately support the loads applied to it
is dependent not only upon the number of reaction components but also
upon the arrangement of those components. It is possible for a structure
to have as many or more reaction components than there are equations
available and yet be unstable. This condition is referred to as *geometric
instability*.

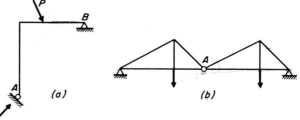

Fig. 2–1.

The frame of Fig. 2–1 (*a*) has three reaction components, and three
equations available for their solution; however, a study of the moment
situation at B shows the structure to be unstable. The line of action of
the reaction at A passes through B, and unless the line of action of the
force P passes through the same point, the sum of the moments about B
cannot equal zero. There is no resistance to rotation about B, and the
frame will immediately begin to rotate. It may not collapse, but it will
rotate until a stable situation is developed, when the line of action of the
reaction at A passes some little distance from B. Of prime importance to
the engineer is for a structure to hold its position under load. One that
does not do so is unstable.

Another geometrically unstable structure is shown in Fig. 2–1 (*b*).
Four equations are available to compute the four unknown reaction components, but rotation will instantaneously occur about the hinge at A.
After a slight deflection vertically of A, the structure will probably become stable.

2–7. Sign Convention

What particular sign convention is used for tension, compression, and
so forth, is of little consequence as long as a consistent system is used.

The author uses the following signs in his computations.

1) For *tension* a positive sign is used, the thought being that pieces in tension become longer or have plus lengths.

2) A negative sign is used for pieces in *compression* because they are compressed or shortened and therefore have minus lengths.

3) For clockwise *moments* a positive sign is usually used; for counter-clockwise moments, a negative sign. This system is of even less importance than the tension and compression system, the important thing being to use the same sign convention in taking moments throughout each complete problem to avoid confusion.

4) On many occasions it is possible to determine the direction of a *reaction* by inspection, but where it is not possible, a statics equation may be written by assuming a direction. If upon solution of the equation the numerical value for the reaction is positive, the assumed direction was correct; if negative, the assumed direction was incorrect.

2–8. Horizontal and Vertical Components

It is a good plan to compute the vertical and horizontal components of inclined forces for use in making calculations. If this practice is not followed, the perpendicular distances from the lines of action of inclined forces to the point where moment is being taken will have to be found. The calculation of these distances is often difficult, and the possibility of making mistakes in setting up the equations is greatly increased.

2–9. Free-Body Diagrams

For a structure to be in equilibrium each and every part of the structure must be in equilibrium. If the statics equations are applicable to an entire structure, they must also be applicable to any part of the structure, no matter how large or how small.

It is therefore possible to draw a diagram of any part of a structure and apply the statics equations to that part. The result, called a *free-body diagram*, must include all of the forces applied to that portion of the structure. These forces are the external reactions and loads and the internal forces applied from the adjoining parts of the structure.

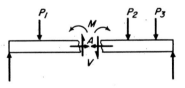

FIG. 2–2.

A simple beam is cut into two free bodies in Fig. 2–2. The internal forces—shear, moment, and axial—are assumed to be in the directions indicated by the arrows on the left free body. The corresponding forces on the right free body are by necessity in opposite directions from those on the left. Should the left-hand side of a beam tend to move up with respect to the right-hand side, the right side must pull down with an equal and opposite force if equilibrium is present.

Isolating certain sections of structures and considering the forces applied to those sections is the basis of all stress analysis. It is doubtful that this procedure can be overemphasized to the student. He will discover over and over that free-body diagrams open the way to the solution of structural problems.

2–10.   Reactions by Proportions

The calculation of reactions is fundamentally a matter of proportions. To illustrate this point, reference is made to Fig. 2–3 (a). The load P is three-fourths of the distance from the left-hand support A to the right-hand support B. By proportions, the right-hand support will carry three-fourths of the load and the left-hand support will carry the remaining one-fourth of the load.

Similarly, for the beam of Fig. 2–3 (b), the 10^k (kilo pound) load is one-half of the distance from A to B and each support will carry half of it, or 5^k. The 20^k load is three-fourths of the distance from A to B. The B support will carry three-fourths of it, or 15^k, and the A support will carry one-fourth or 5^k. In this manner the total reaction at the A support was found to be 10^k and the total reaction at the B support 20^k.

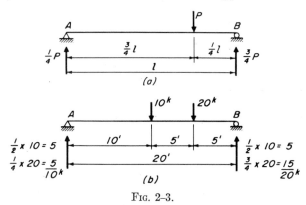

Fig. 2–3.

2–11.   Reactions Calculated by Equations of Statics

Reaction calculations by the equations of statics are illustrated by Examples 2–1 to 2–3. In applying the $\Sigma M = 0$ equation, a point may usually be selected as the center of moments so that the lines of action of all but one of the unknowns pass through the point. The unknown is determined from the moment equation, and the other reaction components are found by applying the $\Sigma H = 0$ and $\Sigma V = 0$ equations.

The beam of Example 2–1 has three unknown reaction components,

Mississippi River Bridge, St. Paul, Minnesota. (Courtesy of
Kenneth M. Wright Studios, St. Paul, Minnesota)

vertical and horizontal ones at A and a vertical one at B. Moments are taken about A to find the value of the vertical component at B. All of the vertical forces are equated to zero, and the vertical reaction component at A is found. A similar equation is written for the horizontal forces applied to the structure, and the horizontal reaction component at A is found to be zero.

The solutions of reaction problems may be checked by taking moments about the other support, as illustrated in Example 2–1. For future examples space is not taken to show the checking calculations. *A problem, however, should be considered incomplete until a mathematical check of this nature is made.*

The roller of the frame of Example 2–3 is supported by an inclined surface. The statics equations are still applicable, because the direction of the reaction at B is known (perpendicular to the supporting surface). If the direction of the reaction is known, the relationship between the vertical component, the horizontal component, and the reaction itself are known. Here the reaction has a slope of 4 vertically to 3 horizontally (4:3), which is the reverse of the slope of the supporting surface of 3:4. Moments are taken about the left support, which gives an equation including the horizontal and vertical components of the reaction at the inclined roller. But both components are in terms of that reaction; therefore, only one unknown, R_{Bj} is present in the equation and its value is easily obtained.

EXAMPLE 2–1. Compute the reaction components for the beam shown in Fig. 2–4.

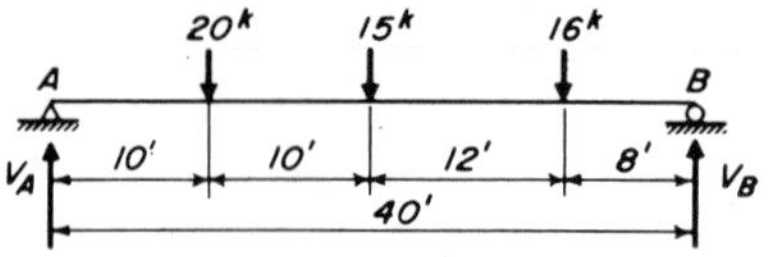

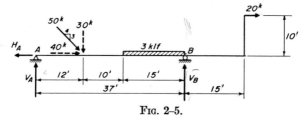

FIG. 2–4.

Solution: $\Sigma M_A = 0$

$$(20)(10) + (15)(20) + (16)(32) - 40\ V_B = 0$$
$$V_B = 25.3^k \uparrow$$

$\Sigma V = 0$
$$20 + 15 + 16 - 25.3 - V_A = 0$$
$$V_A = 25.7^k \uparrow$$

Checking: $\Sigma M_B = 0$
$$(V_A)(40) - (20)(30) - (15)(20) - (16)(8) = 0$$
$$V_A = 25.7^k \uparrow$$

EXAMPLE 2–2. Find all reaction components in the structure shown in Fig. 2–5.

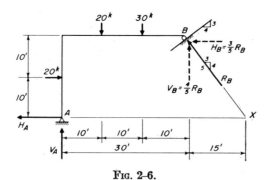

FIG. 2–5.

Solution: $\Sigma M_A = 0$
$$(30)(12) + (3 \times 15)(29.5) + (20)(10) - (V_B)(37) = 0$$
$$V_B = 51^k \uparrow$$

$\Sigma V = 0$
$$30 + 45 - 51 - V_A = 0$$
$$V_A = 24^k \uparrow$$

$\Sigma H = 0$
$$40 + 20 - H_A = 0$$
$$H_A = 60^k \leftarrow$$

EXAMPLE 2–3. Compute the reactions for the frame shown in Fig. 2–6.

FIG. 2–6.

Solution: $\Sigma M_A = 0$

$$(20)(10)+(20)(10)+(30)(20)-(H_B)(20)-(V_B)(30)=0$$
$$200+200+600-(\tfrac{3}{5}R_B)(20)-(\tfrac{4}{5})(R_B)(30)=0$$
$$R_B=27.8^k \ \nwarrow$$

$V_B=\tfrac{4}{5}R_B=22.2^k \uparrow$
$H_B=\tfrac{3}{5}R_B=16.7^k \leftarrow$
$\Sigma V=0$
$\quad 20+30-22.2-V_A=0$
$\quad\quad\quad V_A=27.8^k \uparrow$
$\Sigma H=0$
$\quad 20-16.7-H_A=0$
$\quad\quad\quad H_A=3.3^k \leftarrow$

Alternate Solution: Should the line of action of R_B be extended until it intersected a horizontal line through A, at point X, another convenient location for taking moments would be available. Moments are taken at point X, and only one unknown appears in the equation. This method may be simpler than the previous solution.

$$\Sigma M_X = 0$$
$$(V_A)(45)+(20)(10)-(20)(35)-(30)(25)=0$$
$$V_A=27.8^k \uparrow$$

Problems

2-1. Determine which of the structures shown in the accompanying illustration are statically determinate, statically indeterminate (including the degree of indeterminacy), and unstable as regards outer forces.

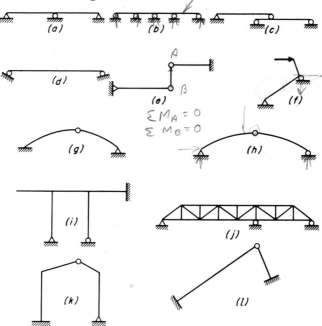

Prob. 2-1.

2–2 to 2–12. Compute the reactions for the structures.

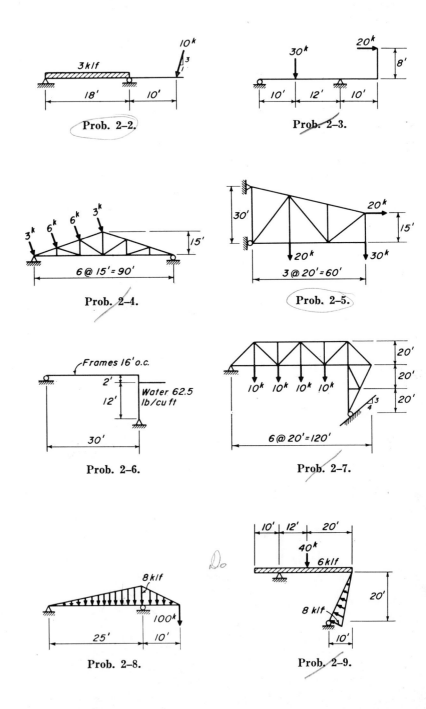

Prob. 2–2.

Prob. 2–3.

Prob. 2–4.

Prob. 2–5.

Prob. 2–6.

Prob. 2–7.

Prob. 2–8.

Prob. 2–9.

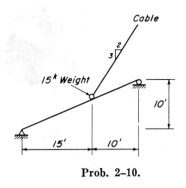

Prob. 2–10.

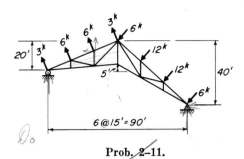

Prob. 2–11.

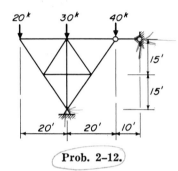

Prob. 2–12.

3 | REACTIONS FOR CANTILEVER AND ARCH-TYPE CONSTRUCTION

3–1. The Simple Cantilever

The simple cantilever pictured in Example 3–1 has three unknown reaction components supporting it at the fixed end; they are the forces required to resist horizontal movement, vertical movement, and rotation. They may be determined with the equations of statics as illustrated in the example.

EXAMPLE 3–1. Find all reaction components for the cantilever beam shown in Fig. 3–1.

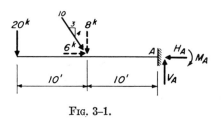

FIG. 3–1.

Solution: $\Sigma V = 0$
$$20 + 8 - V_A = 0$$
$$V_A = 28^k \uparrow$$
$\Sigma H = 0$
$$6 - H_A = 0$$
$$H_A = 6^k \leftarrow$$
$\Sigma M_A = 0$
$$(20)(20) + (8)(10) - M_A = 0$$
$$M_A = 480'^k \ \rotatebox{0}{$\curvearrowright$}$$

3–2. Cantilever Structures

Moments in structures which are simply supported increase rapidly as the spans become longer. It will be seen that bending increases approximately in proportion to the square of the span length. Stronger and more expensive structures are required to resist the greater moments. For very long spans, moments are so large that it becomes economical to introduce special types of structures which will reduce the moments. One of these types is cantilever construction as illustrated in Fig. 3–2.

A cantilever type of structure is substituted for the three simple beams

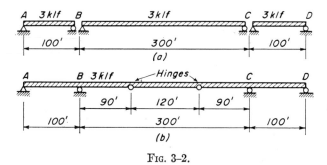

FIG. 3-2.

of Fig. 3-2 (a) by making the beam continuous over the interior supports B and C and introducing hinges in the center span as indicated in (b). An equation of condition ($\Sigma M_{\text{hinge}} = 0$) is available at each of the hinges so introduced, giving a total of five equations and five unknowns. The structure is statically determinate.

The moment advantage of cantilever construction is illustrated in Fig. 3-3. The diagrams give the variation of moment in each of the structures of Fig. 3-2 due to a uniform load of 3 klf (kilopounds per linear foot) for the entire spans. The maximum moment for the cantilever type is seen to be considerably less than that for the simple spans, which permits lighter and cheaper construction. The plotting of moment diagrams is fully explained in the next chapter.

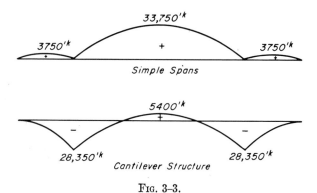

FIG. 3-3.

3-3. Reaction Calculations for Cantilever Structures

Cantilever construction consists essentially of two simple beams, each with an overhanging or cantilevered end

with another simple beam in between supported by the cantilevered ends:

The first step in determining the reactions for a structure of this type is to isolate the center simple beam and compute the forces necessary to support it at each end. Secondly, these forces are applied as downward loads on the respective cantilevers, and as a final step the end beam reactions are determined individually. Example 3–2 illustrates the entire process.

EXAMPLE 3–2. Calculate all reactions for the cantilever structure of Fig. 3–4.

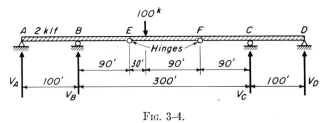

FIG. 3–4.

Solution: By isolating the center section from the two end sections,

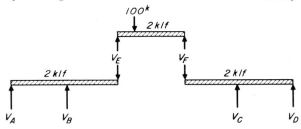

By computing reactions for center beam,

$$\Sigma M_E = 0$$
$$(100)(30) + (2 \times 120)(60) - 120V_F = 0$$
$$V_F = 145^k$$
$$\Sigma V = 0$$
$$100 + 240 - 145 - V_E = 0$$
$$V_E = 195^k$$

By computing reactions for left-end beam,

$$\Sigma M_A = 0$$
$$(2 \times 190)(95) + (195)(190) - 100V_B = 0$$
$$V_B = 731.5^k \uparrow$$
$$\Sigma V = 0$$
$$380 + 195 - 731.5 - V_A = 0$$
$$V_A = 156.5^k \downarrow$$

Similarly, the reactions for the right-end beam are found to equal

$$V_C = 636.5^k \uparrow$$
$$V_D = -111.5^k \downarrow$$

Structural arch construction, U.S.A.F. hangar, Edwards Air Force Base, California. (Courtesy of Bethlehem Steel Company)

3–4. Three-hinged Arches

The reactions for structures discussed previously, which had horizontal supports, were vertical and parallel under vertical loading. Arches are structures which produce horizontal converging reactions under vertical load. They tend to flatten out under load and must be fixed against horizontal movement at their supports.

Arches may be constructed with three hinges, two hinges, one hinge (very rare), or no hinges (quite common in concrete construction). The three-hinged type is discussed here because it is the only statically determinate one.

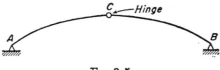

Fig. 3–5.

Examination of the three-hinged arch pictured in Fig. 3–5 reveals there are two reaction components at each support, or a total of four. Three equations of statics and one condition equation ($\Sigma M_c = 0$, where the subscript c means crown hinge) are available to find the unknowns.

The arch of Example 3–3 is handled by taking moments at one of the supports to obtain the vertical reaction component at the second support. Because the supports are on the same level, the horizontal reaction component at the second support passes through the point where moments are being taken. When one vertical reaction component has been found, the other may be obtained with the $\Sigma V = 0$ equation. The horizontal reaction components are obtained by taking moments at the crown hinge of the forces either to the left or to the right. The only unknown appearing in either equation is the horizontal reaction component on that side, and the equation is solved for its value. The other horizontal component is found by writing the $\Sigma H = 0$ equation for the entire structure.

The computation of reactions for the arch of Example 3–4 is slightly more complicated because the supports are not on the same level. Taking moments at one support results in an equation involving both the horizontal and vertical components of reaction at the other support. Moments may be taken about the crown hinge of the forces on the same side as those two unknowns. The resulting equation contains the same two unknowns. Solving the equations simultaneously gives the values of the components, and the application of the $\Sigma H = 0$ and $\Sigma V = 0$ equations results in the values of the remaining components.

EXAMPLE 3–3. Find all reaction components for the three-hinged arch shown in Fig. 3–6.

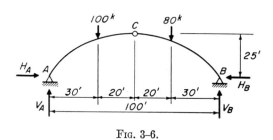

FIG. 3–6.

Solution: $\Sigma M_A = 0$
$$(100)(30) + (80)(70) - 100V_B = 0$$
$$V_B = 86^k \uparrow$$
$\Sigma V = 0$
$$100 + 80 - 86 - V_A = 0$$
$$V_A = 94^k \uparrow$$
ΣM_C to left $= 0$
By using free-body sketch shown,
$$(94)(50) - (100)(20) - 25H_A = 0$$
$$H_A = 108^k \rightarrow$$
$\Sigma H = 0$
$$108 - H_B = 0$$
$$H_B = 108^k \leftarrow$$

EXAMPLE 3–4. In the structure diagrammed in Fig. 3–7 determine reaction components at both supports.

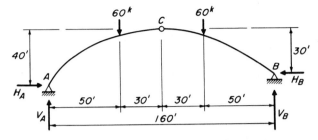

Fig. 3–7.

Solution: $\Sigma M_A = 0$
$$(60)(50) + (60)(110) - 10H_B - 160V_B = 0$$
$$10H_B + 160V_B = 9600 \qquad (1)$$

ΣM_C to right $= 0$
$$(60)(30) + 30H_B - 80V_B = 0$$
$$30H_B - 80V_B = -1800 \qquad (2)$$

Solving Eqs. 1 and 2 simultaneously gives

$$H_B = 85.7^k \leftarrow$$
$$V_B = 54.6^k \uparrow$$
$$\Sigma H = 0$$
$$85.7 - H_A = 0$$
$$H_A = 85.7^k \rightarrow$$
$$\Sigma V = 0$$
$$60 + 60 - 54.6 - V_A = 0$$
$$V_A = 65.4^k \uparrow$$

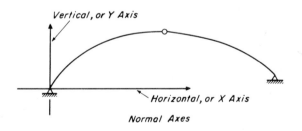

Normal Axes

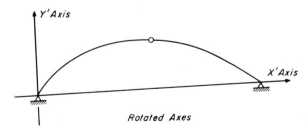

Rotated Axes

Fig. 3–8.

The reactions for the arch of Example 3–4 may be computed without using simultaneous equations. The horizontal and vertical axes (on the basis of which the $\Sigma H = 0$ and $\Sigma V = 0$ equations are written) are so rotated that the horizontal axis passes through the two supporting hinges (Fig. 3–8). Components of forces can be computed parallel to the X' and Y' axes, and the $\Sigma X' = 0$ and $\Sigma Y' = 0$ equations applied, but the computations are rather inconvenient.

3–5.   Uses of Arches and Cantilever Structures

Three-hinged steel arches are used for short and medium-length bridge spans up to approximately 600 ft. They are used for buildings where large clear spans are required underneath, as for hangars, field houses, and armories. Steel two-hinged arches are generally economical for bridges from 600 to 900 ft in length, one exceptional span being over 1600 ft long. Concrete hingeless arches are used for bridges of from 100- to 400-ft spans. Cantilever-type bridges are used for spans of from approximately 500 ft up to very long spans such as the 1800-ft center span of the Quebec bridge.

An arch is a structure which requires foundations capable of resisting the large thrusts at the supports. In arches for buildings, it is possible to carry the thrusts by tying the supports together with steel rods as illustrated in Fig. 3–9, with steel sections, or even specially designed floors.

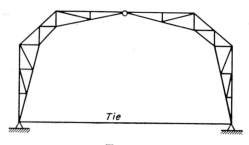

FIG. 3–9.

For many locations, the three-hinged arch is selected over the indeterminate arches because of poor foundation conditions with the possibility of settlement. It will become evident in later chapters that foundation settlement may cause severe stress changes in indeterminate structures.

The fact that cantilever-type construction reduces bending moments for long spans has been previously demonstrated. Arch-type construction also reduces moments, because the reactions at the supports act in such a way that they tend to cause bending in the arch in a direction opposite to that caused by the downward loads.

Problems

3–1 to 3–12. Determine the reactions for the structures.

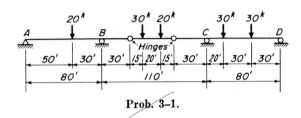

Prob. 3–1.

3–2. The cantilever structure of Prob. 3–1 with each of the interior hinges moved 10 ft toward the nearest supports (*B* and *C*).

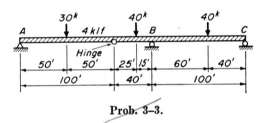

Prob. 3–3.

3–4. The beam of Prob. 3–3 with the interior hinge moved to a point 60 ft from support *B*.

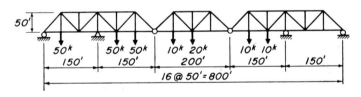

Prob. 3–5.

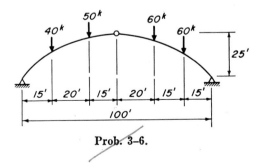

Prob. 3–6.

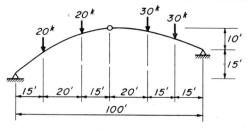

Prob. 3–7.

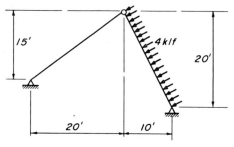

Prob. 3–8.

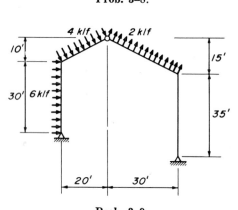

Prob. 3–9.

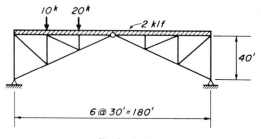

Prob. 3–10.

3–11. The arch of Prob. 3–10 with the panels changed to 40 ft each and the uniform load increased to 3 klf.

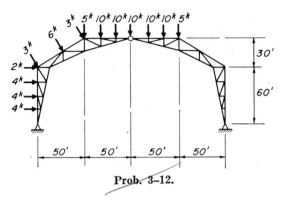

Prob. 3–12.

4 | SHEAR AND MOMENT DIAGRAMS

4-1. Introduction

An important phase of structural engineering is the understanding of shear and moment diagrams and their construction. It is doubtful that there is any other point at which careful study will give more reward in structural knowledge. These diagrams, from which values of shear and moment at any point in a beam are immediately available, are very convenient in design.

To examine the internal conditions of a structure, a free body must be taken out and studied to see what forces have to be present if the body is to be held in place, or in equilibrium. Shear and bending moment are two actions of the external loads on a structure which need to be understood to properly study the internal forces.

Shear is defined as the algebraic summation of the external forces to the left or to the right of a section which are perpendicular to the axis of the beam. It is considered to be positive if the sum of the forces to the left is up or the sum of the forces to the right is down. The calculations for shear at two sections in a simple beam are given in Example 4-1. In each case the summations are made both to the left and to the right to prove that identical results are obtained. It is often convenient to find a shear by considering the side of the section which has the least number of loads.

EXAMPLE 4-1. Find the shear at sections a–a and b–b, Fig. 4-1.

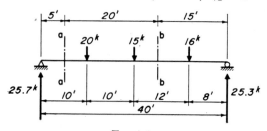

FIG. 4-1.

Solution: Shear at section a–a:
$V_{a\text{-}a}$ to left $= 25.7^k \uparrow$, or $+25.7^k$
$V_{a\text{-}a}$ to right $= 20+15+16-25.3 = 25.7^k \downarrow$, or $+25.7^k$
Shear at section b–b:
$V_{b\text{-}b}$ to left $= 25.7-20-15 = 9.3^k \downarrow = -9.3^k$
$V_{b\text{-}b}$ to right $= 16-25.3 = 9.3^k \uparrow = -9.3^k$

Bending moment is the algebraic sum of the moments of all of the external forces to the left or to the right of a particular section, the moments being taken about an axis through the centroid of the cross section. A positive sign indicates the moment to the left is clockwise or the moment to the right is counterclockwise. A study of Fig. 4–7 shows that positive moment at a section causes tension in the bottom fibers and compression in the top fibers of the beam at the section. Should the member under consideration be a vertical member, a fairly standard sign convention is to consider the right-hand side of the member to be the bottom side.

The bending moments at sections a–a and b–b in the beam of Example 4–1 are computed as follows:

Moment at section a–a:

M_{a-a} to left $= (25.7) (5) = 128.5'^k$), or $+128.5'^k$

M_{a-a} to right $= (25.3) (35) - (16) (27) - (15) (15) - (20) (5) = 128.5'^k$),
or $+128.5'^k$

Moment at section b–b:

M_{b-b} to left $= (25.7) (25) - (20) (15) - (15) (5) = 267.5'^k$), or $+267.5'^k$

M_{b-b} to right $= (25.3) (15) - (16) (7) = 267.5'^k$), or $+267.5'^k$

4–2. Shear Diagrams

Shear diagrams are quite simple to draw in most cases. The standard method is to start with the left end of the structure and work to the right. As each concentrated load or reaction is encountered, a vertical line is drawn to represent the quantity and direction of the force involved. Between the forces a horizontal line is drawn to indicate no change in shear.

Where uniform loads are encountered, the shear is changing at a constant rate per foot and can be represented by a straight but inclined line on the diagram. When an ordinate on the shear diagram is above the line, a positive shear is indicated, because the sum of the forces to the left of that point is up. A shear diagram for a simple beam is drawn in Example 4–2.

EXAMPLE 4–2. Draw a shear diagram for the beam shown in Fig. 4–2.

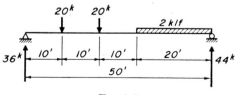

FIG. 4–2.

Solution:

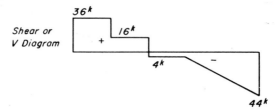

The moments at various points in a structure necessary for plotting a bending-moment diagram may be obtained by algebraically taking moments at those points, but the procedure is quite tedious if there are more than two or three loads applied to the structure. The method developed in the next section is much more practical.

4–3. Moment Diagrams

The moments at various points in a structure necessary for plotting a bending-moment diagram may be obtained by algebraically taking moments at those points, but the procedure is quite tedious if there are more than two or three loads applied to the structure. The method developed in the next section is much more practical.

4–4. Relationships of Loads, Shears, and Bending Moments

There are significant mathematical relations between the loads, shears, and moments in a beam. These relations are discussed in the following paragraphs with reference to Fig. 4–3.

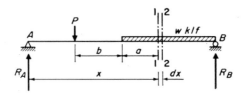

Fig. 4–3.

The shear and moment at section 1–1 may be written as follows:

$$V_{1-1} = R_A - P - wa$$

$$M_{1-1} = R_A x - P(a+b) - \frac{wa^2}{2}$$

The shear and moment at section 2–2 a distance dx to the right of section 1–1 are:

$$V_{2-2} = V_{1-1} + dV = R_A - P - wa - w\,dx$$

$$M_{2-2} = M_{1-1} + dM = R_A x - P(a+b) - \frac{wa^2}{2} + V_{1-1}dx - \frac{w\,dx^2}{2}$$

From these equations the changes in shear and moment in a dx distance are seen to equal:

$$\frac{dV}{dx} = -w$$

$$\frac{dM}{dx} = V \quad \text{omitting the infinitesimal } \frac{w\,dx^2}{2}$$

These two relationships are very useful to the structural engineer. The first indicates that the rate of change of shear at any point equals the load per unit of distance at the point, meaning that the slope of the shear curve at any point is equal to the load at that point. The second equation indicates that the rate of change of moment at any point equals the shear. This relationship means that the slope of the bending-moment curve at any point equals the shear.

The procedure for drawing shear and moment diagrams, to be described in Sec. 4–5, is based on the above equations and is applicable to all structures regardless of loads or spans. Before the process is described, it may be well to examine the equations more carefully. A particular value of dV/dx or dM/dx is good only for the portion of the structure where the function is continuous. For instance, in the beam of Example 4–4 the rate of change of shear from A to B equals the uniform load, 4 klf. At the 30^k load, which is assumed to act at a point, the rate of change of shear and the slope of the shear diagram are infinite, and a vertical line is drawn on the shear diagram to represent a concentrated load. The rate of change of moment from A to B has been constant, but at B the shear changes decidedly, as does the rate of change of moment. In other words, an expression for shear or moment from A to B is not the same as the expression from B to C beyond the concentrated load. The equations of the diagrams are not continuous beyond a point where the function is discontinuous.

4–5. Moment Diagrams Drawn from Shear Diagrams

The change in moment between two points on a structure has been shown to equal the shear between those points times the distance between them $(dM = V\ dx)$; therefore, the change in moment equals the area of the shear diagram between the points.

The relationship between shear and moment greatly simplifies the drawing of moment diagrams. To determine the moment at a particular section, it is only necessary to compute the total area beneath the shear curve, either to the left or to the right of the section, taking into account the algebraic signs of the various segments of the shear curve. Shear and moment diagrams are self-checking. If they are initiated at one end of a structure, usually the left, and check out to the proper value on the other end, the work is probably correct.

The rate of change of moment at a point has been shown to equal the shear at that point. Whenever the shear passes through zero, the rate of change of moment must be zero, and the moment is at a maximum or a minimum. If the moment diagram is being drawn from left to right and the shear diagram changes from positive to negative, the moment will reach a positive maximum at that point. Beyond the point it begins to diminish as the negative shear area is added. If the shear diagram changes from negative to positive, the moment reaches a negative maximum and then begins to taper off as the positive shear area is added.

When shear and moment diagrams are drawn for inclined members, the components of loads and reactions perpendicular to the centroidal axes of the members are used, and the diagrams are drawn parallel to the members. Examples 4–3 to 4–5 illustrate the procedure for drawing shear and moment diagrams for ordinary beams. In studying these diagrams, particular emphasis should be given to their shapes under uniform loads, between concentrated loads, etc.

EXAMPLE 4–3. Draw shear and moment diagrams for the beam shown in Fig. 4–4.

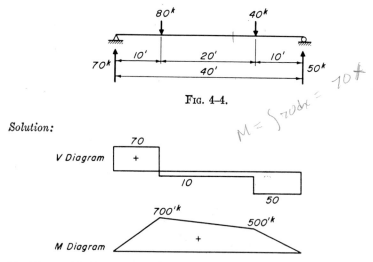

FIG. 4–4.

EXAMPLE 4–4. Draw shear and moment diagrams for the structure shown in Fig. 4–5.

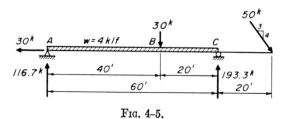

FIG. 4–5.

Solution:

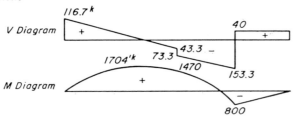

EXAMPLE 4–5   Draw shear and moment diagrams for the cantilever-type structure shown in Fig. 4–6.

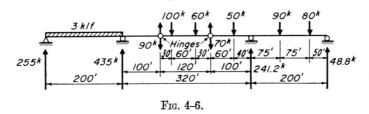

FIG. 4–6.

Solution:

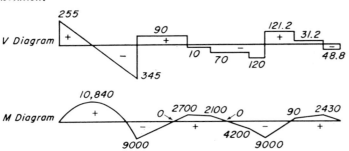

Some structures have rigid arms fastened to them. If horizontal or inclined loads are applied to these arms, a twist or moment will be suddenly induced in the structure at the point of attachment. The fact that moment is taken about an axis through the centroid of the section becomes important because the lever arms of the forces applied must be measured to that centroid. To draw the moment diagram at the point of attachment, it is necessary to figure the moment an infinitesimal distance to the left of the point and then add the moment applied by the arm. The moment exactly at the point of attachment is discontinuous and cannot be figured, but the moment immediately beyond that point is available.

The usual sign convention for positive and negative moments will apply in deciding whether to add or subtract the induced moment. It can be seen in Fig. 4–7 that forces to the left of a section which tend to cause clockwise moments produce tension in the bottom fibers (+ moment), while those forces to the left that tend to cause counterclockwise moments produce tension in the upper fibers (− moment). Similarly, a counterclockwise moment to the right of the section produces tension in the bottom fibers; a clockwise moment, tension in the upper fibers.

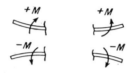

FIG. 4–7.

Shear and moment diagrams are shown in Example 4–6 for a beam that has a moment induced at a point by a rigid arm to which a couple is applied. The moment diagram is drawn from left to right. Considering the moment of the forces to the left of a section through the beam immediately after the rigid arm is reached, it can be seen that the couple causes a clockwise or positive moment, and its value is added to the moment obtained by summation of the shear-diagram areas up to the attached arm.

The beam of Example 4–7 is a continuous beam which cannot be analyzed by the equations of statics. The reactions have been computed by a method to be discussed in a later chapter, and the shear and moment diagrams have been drawn to show that the load, shear, and moment relationships are applicable to all structures.

EXAMPLE 4–6. Draw shear moment diagrams for the beam shown in Fig. 4–8.

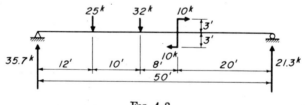

FIG. 4–8.

Solution:

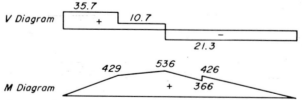

EXAMPLE 4–7. Draw the shear and moment diagrams for the continuous beam shown in Fig. 4–9, for which the reactions are given.

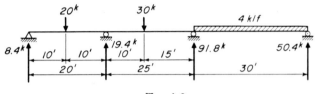

FIG. 4–9.

Solution:

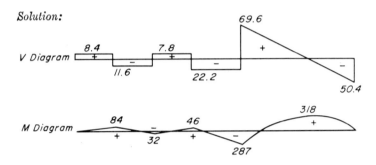

Problems

4–1 to 4–23. Draw shear and moment diagrams for the structures.

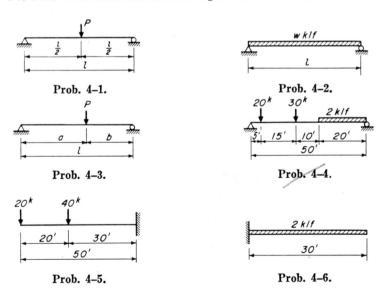

Prob. 4–1.

Prob. 4–2.

Prob. 4–3.

Prob. 4–4.

Prob. 4–5.

Prob. 4–6.

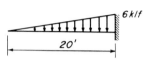

Prob. 4–7.

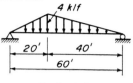

Prob. 4–8.

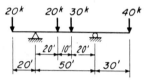

Prob. 4–9.

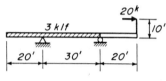

Prob. 4–10.

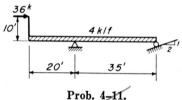

Prob. 4–11.

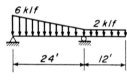

Prob. 4–12.

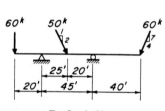

Prob. 4–13.

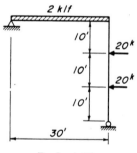

Prob. 4–14.

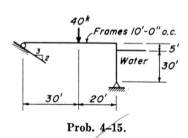

Prob. 4–15.

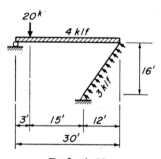

Prob. 4–16.

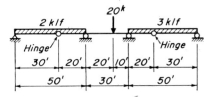

Prob. 4-17.

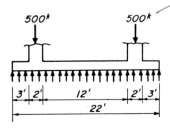

The figure for this problem represents two concrete columns supported by a concrete beam (or footing) along the ground. Assume soil pressure uniformly distributed and neglect footing weight.

Prob. 4-18.

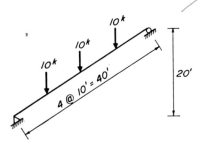

Prob. 4-19.

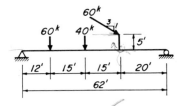

Prob. 4-20.

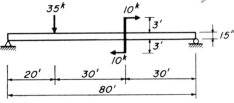

Prob. 4-21.

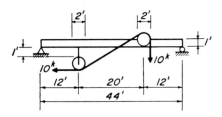

Prob. 4-22.

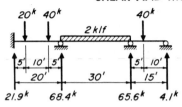

Moment at fixed end$= -86'^{k}$; other reactions as shown.

Prob. 4–23.

5 | **INTRODUCTION TO TRUSSES**

5–1. General

An Italian architect, Andrea Palladio (1518–1580), is believed to have developed the first trusses. His extensive writings on architecture include detailed descriptions and drawings of several wooden trusses quite similar to those in use today.[1]

A truss is defined in Chapter 1 as a structure formed by a group of members arranged in the shape of one or more triangles. Because the members are assumed to be connected with frictionless pins, the triangle is the only stable shape. Study of the truss of Fig. 5–1 (a) shows that it is impossible for the triangle to change shape under load unless one or more of the sides is bent or broken. Figures of four or more sides are not stable and may collapse under load, as seen in Fig. 5–1 (b) and (c).

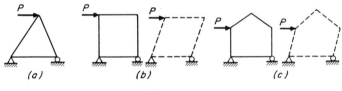

(a) (b) (c)

Fig. 5–1.

These structures may be deformed without a change in length of any of their members. It will be seen in Chapter 8 that there are many stable trusses which include one or more figures which are not triangles. A careful study, however, will show they consist of separate groups of triangles which are connected together according to definite rules, forming nontriangular but stable figures in between.

5–2. Assumptions for Truss Analysis

The following assumptions are made in order to simplify the analysis of trusses:

1) Truss members are connected together with frictionless pins. (Pin connections are used for very few trusses erected today, and no pins are frictionless. A heavy riveted or welded joint is a far cry from a frictionless pin.)

[1] Sheiry, *Elements of Structural Engineering* (Scranton, Penna.: International Textbook Company, 1944), Chap. 4.

2) Truss members are straight. (If they were not straight, the axial stresses would cause them to have bending moments.)

3) The deformations of a truss under load, caused by the changes in lengths of the individual members, are not of sufficient magnitude to cause appreciable changes in the over-all shape and dimensions of the truss. Special consideration may have to be given to some very long and flexible trusses.

4) Members are so arranged that the loads and reactions are applied only at the truss joints. Examination of roof and bridge trusses will prove this statement to be generally true. In roof trusses the beams, columns, and bracing frame directly into the truss joints. Roof loads are transferred to trusses by horizontal beams, called purlins, that span the distance between the trusses. The roof is supported directly by the purlins or by rafters, or subpurlins, which run parallel to the trusses and are supported by the purlins. The purlins are placed at the truss joints unless the top-chord panel lengths become exceptionally long, in which case it is sometimes economical to place purlins in between the joints, although some bending will be developed in the top chords. The loads supported by a highway bridge are transferred to the trusses at the joints by beams running underneath the roadway as shown in Fig. 12–1 and described in Sec. 12–2.

5–3. Effect of Assumptions

The effect of the foregoing assumptions is to produce an ideal truss, whose members have only axial stresses. A member with axial stress only is subject to a push or pull with no bending present, as illustrated in Fig. 5–2. (Even if all of the assumptions were perfectly true, there would be some bending in a member caused by its own weight.)

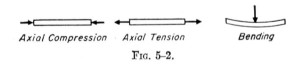

Axial Compression   Axial Tension   Bending

Fig. 5–2.

Stresses obtained on the basis of these simplifying assumptions are very satisfactory in most cases and are referred to as *primary stresses*. Structures are sometimes analyzed without the aid of some or all of these assumptions. The stresses so obtained are said to be *secondary stresses*.

5–4. Truss Notation

A common system of denoting the members of a truss is shown in Fig. 5–3. The joints are numbered from left to right, the bottom joints having

L (for lower) prefixes and the top joints having U (for upper) prefixes. Should there be, in more complicated trusses, joints in between the lower and upper joints, they may be given M (for middle) prefixes.

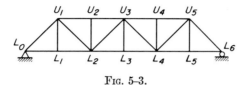

FIG. 5–3.

The various members of a truss are often referred to by the following names, reference being made to Fig. 5–3:

1) _Chords_ are those members forming the outline of the truss, such as members U_1U_2 and L_4L_5.

2) _Verticals_ are named on the basis of their direction in the truss, such as members U_1L_1 and U_3L_3.

3) _Diagonals_ also are named on the basis of their direction in the truss, such as members U_1L_2 and L_4U_5.

4) _Web members_ include the verticals and diagonals of a truss, and most engineers consider them to include the end diagonals, or _end posts_, such as L_0U_1 and U_5L_6.

5–5. Common Types of Roof Trusses

Several types of roof trusses are shown in Table 5–1, together with some comment about each. The minimum span for which they are used depends on a relative study of economy between beams and trusses. Where spans of 40 or 50 ft are required, trusses usually begin to compete favorably. There are many kinds of roof trusses in use because of the different slopes, spans, and types of roofing material that are used. Only a few of the common ones are presented here. The student is referred to the three-hinged arch roof of Fig. 3–9 for another type of roof truss frequently used.

There are so many factors entering into deciding the best lateral spacing of roof trusses that it is difficult to give one steadfast rule. It is desirable to space the trusses uniformly for a given section of a building or, even better, for the entire building so that as many trusses as possible will be identical. Trusses are probably spaced from 12 to 20 ft for 50- or 60-ft spans and from 15 to 24 ft for longer spans up to 90 or 100 ft.

5–6. Common Types of Bridge Trusses

Several of the more common types of bridge trusses in use today are shown in Table 5–2.

TABLE 5-1

COMMON TYPES OF ROOF TRUSSES

Type	Sketch of Truss	Material	Miscellaneous
Pratt		Generally steel, sometimes wood or wood and steel	Maximum spans approximately 90 ft
Howe		Generally wood (tension members sometimes steel rods)	Maximum spans approximately 90 ft
Fink		Generally steel	Web members may be arranged in several different ways; spans limited to approximately 70 ft
Bowstring		Generally steel	Used frequently for warehouses, super-markets, garages, etc.; spans may be as large as 90 or 100 ft
Saw tooth		Wood or steel	Steep faces support skylights facing the north for more even light; used where numerous columns are not objectionable.

A saving in steel for trusses can be realized by varying the depth in approximate proportion to the bending moment, as illustrated by the Parker truss of Table 5–2. The pound price, however, goes up, and the so-called curved-chord trusses do not become economical until spans are approximately 200 ft or more.

Studies have shown that the best economy for bridge trusses is obtained when the diagonals are kept at an angle of roughly 45° with the horizontal and when the ratio of depth to span varies from 1:5 to 1:8, approximately. When these requirements are followed for spans above 300 ft, trusses will have very long panels.

If the panels are very long, compression members become quite large because of their great unsupported length, and the floor systems between panel points become heavy and expensive. The desired panel lengths and diagonal slopes are obtained for longer spans if the Baltimore or K truss is used.

The roadway for a bridge may be supported by the bottom chords, by the top chords, or somewhere in between. If it is supported by floor beams

TABLE 5–2

COMMON TYPES OF BRIDGE TRUSSES

Type	Sketch of Truss	Material	Miscellaneous
Pratt		Steel	Used moderately to-day; probably has been used more in past than any other type of bridge truss; spans up to 200 ft
Howe		Wood or wood with steel verticals	Used a great deal in past but very little at present
Warren		Steel	Very common; spans up to 200 ft
Parker		Steel	For spans above 180 or 200 ft up to 350 or 360 ft; more economical than parallel-chord trusses above 200 ft
Baltimore		Steel	Used for spans over 300 ft
K Truss		Steel	Used for spans over 300 ft

running between the bottom-chord joints and there is room for overhead lateral bracing above the roadway, the bridge is said to be a *through bridge*. Where the roadway is carried to the top-chord joints or where it rests directly on the top-chord joints, the bridge is said to be a *deck bridge*. Sometimes the roadway may be in between the top and bottom chords and the bridge may be called a *half-through bridge* or *pony* type. In this type there is not room for overhead lateral bracing.

Where the deck structure is possible, several advantages are present. The floor system can be placed directly on top of the trusses, permitting a much simpler connection problem. The trusses may be closer together, and there is less lateral bending in the floor, allowing it to be lighter and cheaper. There is an unlimited overhead and lateral clearance available. These factors indicate a more economical structure; however, the under-clearance requirements of bridges very often rule out the deck bridge or make the through type more economical.

The lower economical span limits for bridge trusses are difficult to establish because the upper economical spans for beam bridges vary considerably. Beam bridges are normally used up to 50 or 60 ft for railroad

Willard Bridge over Kansas River north of Willard, Kansas. (Courtesy of
American Institute of Steel Construction, Inc.)

bridges and up to 100 or 120 ft for highway bridges. Plate girders, however, are often erected for much longer spans, particularly where continuous and deck-type construction is used. For this latter case some
highway bridges have been built with spans well over 200 ft.

TRUSS ANALYSIS BY METHOD
OF JOINTS

6–1. Use of Sections

An indispensble part of truss analysis, as in beam analysis, is the separation of the truss into two parts with an imaginary section. The part of the truss on one side of the section is removed and studied independently. The loads applied to this free body include the axial stresses of the members which have been cut by the section and any loads and reactions which may be applied externally.

Application of the equations of statics to isolated free bodies enables one to determine the stresses in the cut members if the free bodies are carefully selected so that the sections do not pass through too many members whose stresses are unknown. There are only three equations of statics, and no more than three unknowns may be determined from any one section.

After he has analyzed a few trusses, the student will have little difficulty in selecting satisfactory locations for his sections in most cases. He is not encouraged to remember specific sections for specific trusses, although he will probably unconsciously fall into such a habit as time goes by. At this stage of the game he needs to consider each case individually without reference to other, similar trusses.

6–2. Horizontal and Vertical Components

It is convenient to work with horizontal and vertical components in the computation of stresses of truss members, as in the computation of reactions. The $\Sigma H = 0$ and $\Sigma V = 0$ equations of statics are generally written on the basis of a pair of axes which are horizontal and vertical. Because the stresses in truss members are determined successively across a truss, much time will be saved if the vertical and horizontal components of stresses in inclined members are recorded for use in applying the equations to other members. The use of components is clearly illustrated in the example problems of the sections to follow.

6–3. Arrow Convention

The sign convention for tensile and compressive stresses ($+$ and $-$, respectively) has previously been mentioned. Arrows are also used throughout the text to represent the character of stresses. The arrows indicate what members are doing to resist the axial forces applied to them by the remainder of the truss. For example, if a truss is compressing a certain member from each end ($\rightarrow$ ——— $\leftarrow$),the member will push back against the compressive forces ($\leftarrow$———$\rightarrow$). This arrow convention is used for members in compression. The arrow convention for a member in tension is just the opposite, because a member which is being pulled or stretched from the ends ($\leftarrow$ ——— $\rightarrow$) will resist by pulling back ($\rightarrow$——— $\leftarrow$).

Ford Automobile Assembly Plant, Milpitas, California. (Courtesy of American Institute of Steel Construction, Inc.)

After some practice in the analysis of trusses, it is possible to determine by examination the character of the stresses in many of the members of a truss. The student should often try to picture whether a member is in tension or compression before making the actual calculations. In this way a better understanding of the action of trusses under load will be obtained. The following paragraphs will show it is possible to determine entirely by mathematical means the character as well as the numerical value of stresses.

6–4. Method of Joints

An imaginary section may be completely passed around a joint in a truss, regardless of its location, completely isolating it from the remainder of the truss. The joint has become a free body which is in equilibrium under the forces applied to it. The equations $\Sigma H = 0$ and $\Sigma V = 0$ may be applied to the joint to determine the unknown stresses in members meeting there. It is evident that no more than two unknowns can be determined at a joint with these two equations.

A person learning the method of joints may find it necessary to draw a free-body sketch for every joint in a truss which he is analyzing. After he has computed the stresses in two or three trusses, he will find it necessary to draw the diagrams for very few joints, because he will be able to easily visualize the free bodies involved. The most important thing for the beginner to remember is that he is interested in only one joint at a time. He must keep his mind away from the loads and stresses at other joints. His only concern is with the forces at the one joint on which he is working. The method of joints is illustrated by Example 6–1.

Example 6–1. By using the method of joints, find all stresses in the truss shown in Fig. 6–1.

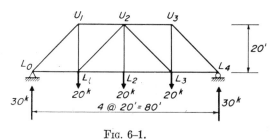

Fig. 6–1.

Solution: Considering joint L_0,

$$\Sigma V = 0$$
$$30 - L_0 U_{1Y} = 0$$
$$L_0 U_{1Y} = 30^k \text{ compression}$$

An examination of the joint shows a vertical reaction of 30^k acting upward. The equation $\Sigma V = 0$ indicates that the members meeting there must supply 30^k downward. A member which is horizontal, such as $L_0 L_1$, can have no vertical component of stress; therefore, $L_0 U_1$ must supply the entire amount and 30^k will be its vertical component. The arrow convention shows that $L_0 U_1$ is in compression. From its slope (20:20, or 1:1) the horizontal component can be seen to be 30^k also.

$$\Sigma H = 0$$
$$-30 + L_0 L_1 = 0$$
$$L_0 L_1 = 30^k \text{ tension}$$

The application of the $\Sigma H = 0$ equation shows L_0U_1 to be pushing horizontally to the left against the joint with a force of 30^k. For equilibrium, L_0L_1 must pull to the right away from the joint with the same force. The arrow convention shows the stress is tensile.

Considering joint U_1,
$$\Sigma V = 0$$
$$30 - U_1L_1 = 0$$
$$U_1L_1 = 30^k \text{ tension}$$

The stress in L_0U_1 has previously been found to be compressive with vertical and horizontal components of 30^k each. Since it is pushing upward at joints U_1 with a force of 30^k, U_1L_1 (the only other member at the joint that has a vertical component) must pull down with a force of 30^k in order to satisfy the $\Sigma V = 0$ equation.

$$\Sigma H = 0$$
$$30 - U_1U_2 = 0$$
$$U_1U_2 = 30^k \text{ compression}$$

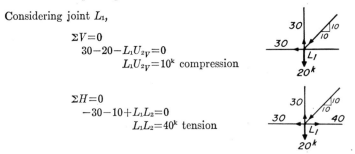

Member L_0U_1 is pushing to the right horizontally with a force of 30^k. For equilibrium U_1U_2 is pushing back to the left with 30^k.

Considering joint L_1,

$$\Sigma V = 0$$
$$30 - 20 - L_1U_{2V} = 0$$
$$L_1U_{2V} = 10^k \text{ compression}$$

$$\Sigma H = 0$$
$$-30 - 10 + L_1L_2 = 0$$
$$L_1L_2 = 40^k \text{ tension}$$

The stresses in all of the truss members may be calculated in a similar manner with the following results:

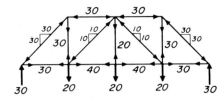

The resultant stresses for inclined members may be determined from the square root of the sum of the squares of the vertical and horizontal components of stress. An easier method is to write ratios comparing the resultant axial stress of a member and its horizontal or vertical component with the true length of the member and its horizontal or vertical component. By letting S, H, and V represent the stress and its components and l, h, and v the length and its components, the ratios of Fig. 6–2 are developed.

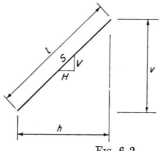

FIG. 6–2.

$$S = \sqrt{H^2 + V^2}$$

The method of joints may be used conveniently to com[pute]
in all of the members of many trusses. The trusses of Ex[amples]
6–3 and the problems at the end of the chapter fall int[o]
There are, however, a large number of trusses which need
by a combination of the method of joints with the method
the following chapter. The author likes to calculate as ma[ny]
possible in a truss by using the method of joints. At joints
a little difficulty, he takes moments, as described in the next
then continues his calculations as far as possible by joints un[til]
another point of difficulty, where he takes moments again, etc

EXAMPLE 6–2. Find all stresses in the truss of Fig. 6–3.

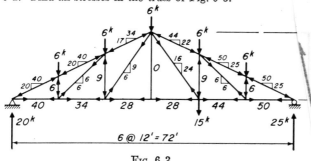

FIG. 6–3.

EXAMPLE 6–3. Find all stresses in the truss of Fig. 6–4.

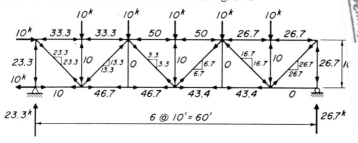

FIG. 6–4.

Problems

6–1 to **6–18.** Compute the stresses in all of the members of the trusses by using the method of joints.

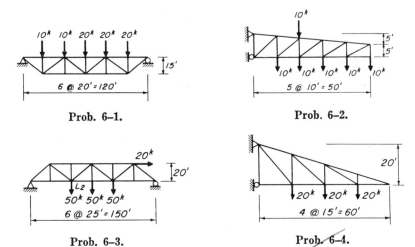

Prob. 6–1.   Prob. 6–2.

Prob. 6–3.   Prob. 6–4.

6–5. Rework Prob. 6–1 with the depth of the truss changed from 15 to 10 ft.

6–6. Rework Prob. 6–2 with the panels changed from 5 @ 10′ to 5 @ 8′.

6–7. Rework Prob. 6–3 with the 50^k load at L_2 removed.

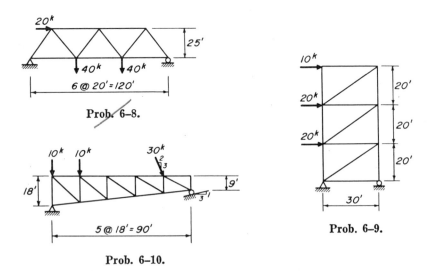

Prob. 6–8.

Prob. 6–10.   Prob. 6–9.

6–11. Rework Prob. 6–10 with the supporting surface beneath the roller changed to a 45° slope.

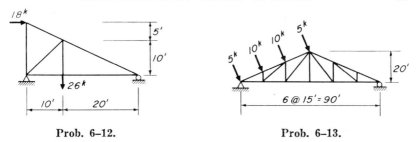

Prob. 6–12.   **Prob. 6–13.**

6–14. Rework Prob. 6–13 with the assumption that wind loads are in accordance with Committee 31's recommendations (Chapter 1). Trusses are 16 ft on center.

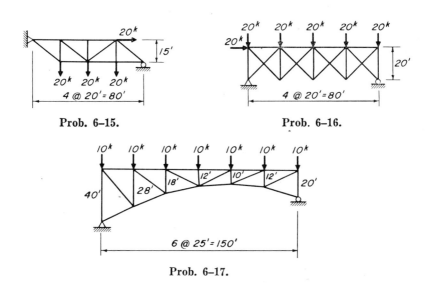

Prob. 6–15.   **Prob. 6–16.**

Prob. 6–17.

6–18. Rework Prob. 6–17 with the panels changed from 6 @ 25' to 6 @ 20'.

7 | TRUSS ANALYSIS BY MOMENTS AND SHEARS

7–1. Method of Moments

The equilibrium of free bodies is the basis of stress computation by the method of moments as it is by the method of joints. To obtain the value of the stress in a particular member, an imaginary section is passed completely through the truss to divide it into two free bodies. A section is placed to cut the member whose stress is desired and as few other members as possible.

The moment of all the forces applied to the free body under consideration about any point in the plane of the truss is zero. If it is possible to take moments of the forces about a point so that only one unknown stress appears in the equation, the value of the stress can be obtained. This objective can usually be attained by selecting a point along the line of action of one or more of the stresses of the other members. Some familiar trusses have special locations for placing sections which greatly simplify the work involved. These cases will be discussed in the chapters to follow.

One advantage of the method of moments is that, if the stress in only one member of a truss is desired and the member is not near the end of the truss, it may be obtained directly in most cases without first determining the stresses in other members. If the method of joints were used, it would be necessary to calculate the stresses in the members joint by joint from the end of the truss until the member in question was reached.

7–2. Stresses in Members Cut by Sections

Should tension and compression members actually be cut, the results would be as described in the following paragraphs and as pictured in Fig. 7–1.

1) A tension member is being stretched, and should it be cut would tend to resume its original length, leaving a gap at the section. A tension member pulls away from the free body, Fig. 7–1 (a).

2) A compression member has been shortened, and should it be cut in half would tend to resume its original length, i.e., try to expand. A compression member pushes against the free body, Fig. 7–1 (a).

A truss is divided into two free bodies in Fig. 7–1 (b). Members U_1U_2 and L_1U_2 are assumed to be in compression, and member L_1L_2 is assumed

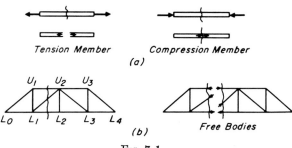

Fig. 7–1.

to be in tension. On the basis of these assumptions the directions of the stresses on the two free bodies are shown.

7–3. Application of the Method of Moments

Examples 7–1 to 7–5 illustrate in detail the computation of stresses with the $\Sigma M = 0$ equation. In writing the moment equation, it is to be noted that the unknown stress may be assumed to be tension or compression. If the mathematical solution yields a positive number, the character of stress is the opposite of that which was assumed. The numerical answer is correct regardless of the sign.

It is probably simpler to always assume the unknown stress to be in tension, i.e., pulling away from the free body. If the solution yields a positive number, the stress is tensile; if a negative number, compressive. Therefore, the sign always agrees with the normal sign convention of + for tension and − for compression. This practice is followed in the illustrative problems throughout the text.

EXAMPLE 7–1. Find the stresses in members L_1L_2 and U_2U_3, Fig. 7–2, by moments.

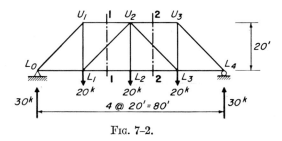

Fig. 7–2.

Solution: Member L_1L_2. Section *1–1* is passed through the truss, and the part of the truss to the left of the section is considered to be the free body. The forces acting on the free body are the 30^k reaction, the 20^k load at L_1, and the axial stresses in the members cut by the section (U_1U_2, L_1U_2, and L_1L_2). Moments of these forces are taken about U_2, which is the point of intersection of L_1U_2 and U_1U_2. The moment equation contains one unknown stress, L_1L_2, and its value may be found by solving the equation.

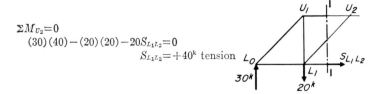

$$\Sigma M_{U_2} = 0$$
$$(30)(40) - (20)(20) - 20 S_{L_1 L_2} = 0$$
$$S_{L_1 L_2} = +40^k \text{ tension}$$

Member $U_2 U_3$. Section 2–2 is passed through the truss, and the portion of the truss to the right of the section is considered to be the free body. Members $U_2 U_3$, $U_2 L_3$, and $L_2 L_3$ are cut by the section. Taking moments at the intersection of $L_2 L_3$ and $U_2 L_3$, at L_3, eliminates the two members from the equation because the lines of action of their stresses pass through the center of moments. The stress in $U_2 U_3$ is the only unknown appearing in the equation, and its value may be determined.

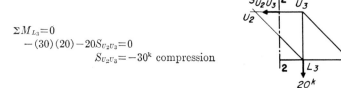

$$\Sigma M_{L_3} = 0$$
$$-(30)(20) - 20 S_{U_2 U_3} = 0$$
$$S_{U_2 U_3} = -30^k \text{ compression}$$

EXAMPLE 7–2. Find the stresses in all of the members of the truss shown in Fig. 7–3. Use both the method of joints and the method of moments as convenient.

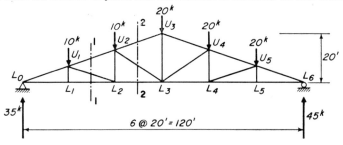

FIG. 7–3.

Solution: The stresses of members meeting at L_0 and L_1 are quickly determined by the method of joints. To calculate the stress in $U_1 U_2$, section 1–1 is passed and moments are taken at L_2. Because $U_1 U_2$ is an inclined member, the stress is resolved into its vertical and horizontal components. The components of a stress may be assumed to act anywhere along its line of action. It is convenient in this case to break the force down into its components at joint U_2, because the vertical component will pass through the center of moments and the moment equation may be solved for the horizontal component of stress.

$$\Sigma M_{L_2} = 0$$
$$(35)(40) - (10)(20) + 13.33 H_{U_1 U_2} = 0$$
$$H_{U_1 U_2} = -90^k \text{ compression}$$

By joints, the unknown stresses in members meeting at U_1 and L_2 may now be obtained. Section 2–2 is passed through the truss, and moments are taken at L_3 to find the stress in U_2U_3. By knowing this stress, the remaining stresses in the truss can be found by joints with the results shown.

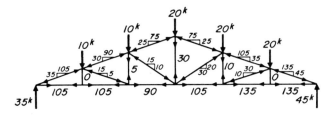

EXAMPLE 7–3. Determine the stresses in all of the members of the truss shown in Fig. 7–4.

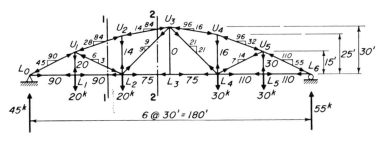

FIG. 7–4.

Solution: $\Sigma M_{L_2}=0$; free body to left of section *1–1*:

$$(45)(60)-(20)(30)+25\,H_{U_1U_2}=0$$
$$H_{U_1U_2}=-84 \text{ compression}$$

$\Sigma M_{U_3}=0$; free body to left of section *2–2*:

$$(45)(90)-(20)(30)-(20)(60)-30L_2L_3=0$$
$$L_2L_3=+75 \text{ tension}$$

EXAMPLE 7–4. Determine the stresses in all of the members of the Fink truss shown in Fig. 7–5.

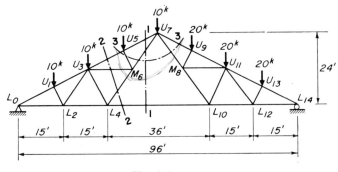

FIG. 7–5.

Solution: The stresses in members meeting at joints L_0, L_2, and U_1 can be found by the methods of joints and moments without any difficulty. At each of the next two joints, U_3 and L_4, there are three unknown stresses which can not be determined directly with sections. It is necessary to compute the stresses in some members further over in the truss and then work back to these joints. The sections numbered *1–1*, *2–2*, and *3–3* may be used to advantage. From the first of these sections the stresses in any of the three members cut may be obtained by moments. By using section *2–2* and taking moments at U_3, the stress in L_4M_6 may be found. It is important to note that four members have been cut by the section and only two of them pass through the point where moments are being taken; however, the stress in one of these members, L_4L_{10}, was previously found with section *1–1*, and only one unknown is left in the equation. The remaining stresses in the truss may be calculated by the usual methods. These two sections are sufficient for analyzing the truss, but should another approach be desired, a section such as *3–3* may be considered. From this section the stress in U_3M_6 can be found, because all of the other members cut by the section pass through U_7. The stresses in all of the truss members are as shown.

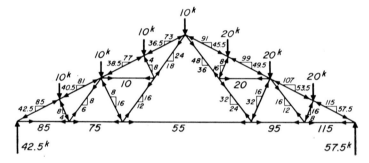

EXAMPLE 7–5. Calculate the stress in member *cg* of Fig. 7–6.

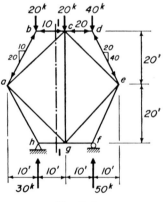

FIG. 7–6.

Solution: The stress in the member in question cannot be determined immediately by joints or moments. It is necessary to know the stress values for several other members before the value for *cg* can be found. The stresses in members *ba*, *bc*, *dc*, and *de* may be found by joints as shown, and the stress in member *ac* can be found by moments. Considering section *1–1* and the free body to the left, moments may be taken about g. By noting that the stress in bc is in compression and pushes against the free body from the outside and by assuming member ac to be in tension, the following equation may be written. The stress is broken into its vertical and horizontal components at c.

$$\Sigma M_g = 0$$
$$(30)(10) - (20)(10) - (10)(40) + (H_{ac})(40) = 0$$
$$H_{ac} = +7.5 \text{ tension}$$

By having the stress in ac, the stresses in ce and cg can be determined by joints as shown.

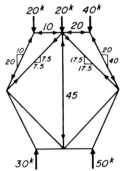

7–4. Method of Shears

It should be obvious by this time that if a vertical section is passed through a truss and divides it into two separate free bodies, the sum of the vertical forces to the left of the section must be equal and opposite in direction to the sum of the vertical forces to the right of the section. The summation of the forces to the left or to the right of a section has been defined as the shear.

The inclined members cut by a section must have vertical components of stress equal and opposite to the shear along the section, because the horizontal members can have no vertical components of stress. For parallel-chord trusses there is only one inclined member in each panel, and the vertical component of stress in that inclined member must be equal and opposite to the shear in the panel. The vertical components of stress are computed by shears for the diagonals of the parallel-chorded truss of Example 7-6.

EXAMPLE 7-6. Determine the vertical components of stress in the diagonals of the truss shown in Fig. 7-7. Use the method of shears.

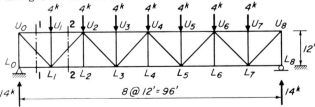

Fɪɢ. 7-7.

Solution: By considering section *1–1* and free body to the left,

Shear to the left=14^k ↑
$V_{U_0L_1}$=14^k ↓ tension (pulling away
    from free body)

By considering section *2–2* and free body to the left,

Shear to left=10^k ↑
$V_{L_1U_2}$=10^k ↓ compression (pushing
    against free body)

The vertical components of stress in all the diagonals are as follows:

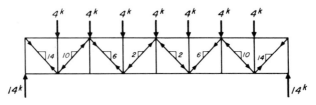

Non parallel-chord trusses have two or more diagonals in each panel, and they all may have vertical components of stress; however, their sum must be equal and opposite to the shear in the panel. If all but one of the diagonal stresses in a panel are known, the remaining one may be determined by shears, as illustrated in Example 7–7.

EXAMPLE 7–7. Referring to the truss of Example 7–3, sections *1–1* and *2–2*, and assuming that the stresses in the chords U_1U_2 and U_2U_3 are known, find the vertical components of stress in U_1L_2 and L_2U_3 by the method of shears.

Solution: By considering section *1–1* and free body to the left,

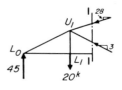

Shear to left=25^k ↑
$V_{U_1U_2}$=28^k ↓
$V_{U_1L_2}$=3^k ↑ compression

By considering section *2–2* and free body to the right,

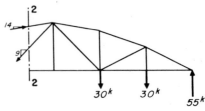

Shear to right=5^k ↓
$V_{U_2U_3}$=14^k ↑
$V_{L_2U_3}$=9^k ↓ tension

Problems

7–1 to 7–20. Determine the stresses in all of the members of the trusses.

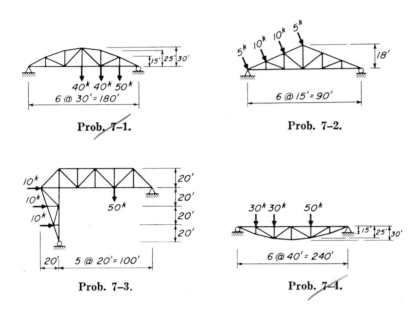

Prob. 7–1.

Prob. 7–2.

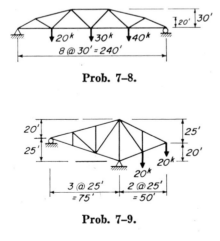

Prob. 7–3.

Prob. 7–4.

7–5. Rework Prob. 7–1 with a uniform load of 6 klf for the entire span applied to the truss in addition to the loads shown.

7–6. Rework Prob. 7–3 with the horizontal 10^k loads doubled.

7–7. Rework Prob. 7–4 with the panels changed from 6 @ 40′ to 6 @ 30′.

Prob. 7–8.

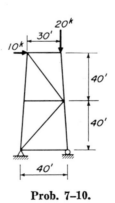

Prob. 7–9.

Prob. 7–10.

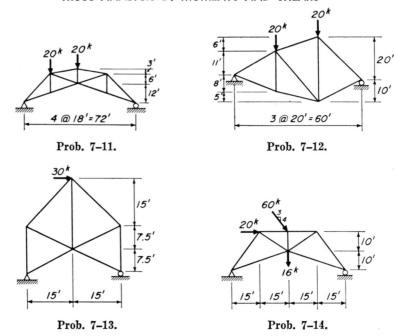

Prob. 7–11.   Prob. 7–12.

Prob. 7–13.   Prob. 7–14.

7–15. Rework Prob. 7–12 with the supporting surface beneath the roller having a slope of 1 vertically to 2 horizontally.

7–16. Rework Prob. 7–14 with the 20^k load removed and the 16^k load doubled.

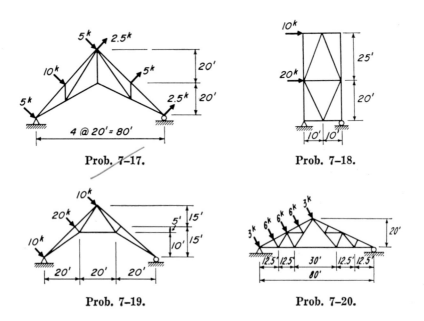

Prob. 7–17.   Prob. 7–18.

Prob. 7–19.   Prob. 7–20.

7-21 to 7-24. Determine the stresses in the designated members.

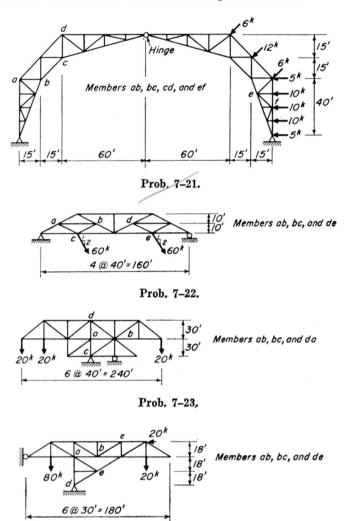

Prob. 7-21.

Members ab, bc, cd, and ef

Prob. 7-22.

Members ab, bc, and de

Prob. 7-23.

Members ab, bc, and da

Prob. 7-24.

Members ab, bc, and de

8 | TRUSS TYPES AND STABILITY

8–1. Arrangement of Truss Members

A detailed discussion of the assembly of trusses has been delayed until this chapter so that the student will have had some contact with the elementary types. The background should enable him to better understand the material to follow.

The triangle has been shown to be the basic shape from which trusses are developed because it is the only stable shape. Other shapes such as the ones shown in Fig. 8–1 (a) and (b) are obviously unstable and may possibly collapse under load. Structures such as these can, however, be made stable by one of the following methods:

1) Addition of members so that the shapes are made to consist of triangles. The structures of Fig. 8–1 (a) and (b) are stabilized in this manner in (c) and (d), respectively.

2) Using a member to tie the unstable structure to a stable support. Member AB performs this function in Fig. 8–1 (e).

3) Making some or all of the joints of an unstable structure rigid, so they become moment-resisting. A figure with moment-resisting joints, however, does not coincide with the definition of a truss (i.e., members connected with frictionless pins, etc.).

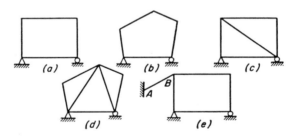

Fig. 8–1.

8–2. Statical Determinancy of Trusses

The simplest form of truss, a single triangle, is illustrated in Fig. 8–2 (a). To determine the unknown stresses and reaction components for this truss, it is possible to isolate the joints and write two equations, $\Sigma H = 0$ and $\Sigma V = 0$, for each. From experience obtained in the last few chapters, the student should have little difficulty in making the necessary calculations.

The single-triangle truss may be expanded into a two-triangle one by the addition of two new members and one new joint. In Fig. 8–2 (b), triangle ABD is added by installing new members AD and BD and the new joint D. A further expansion with a third triangle is made in part (c) of the figure by the addition of members BE and DE and joint E. For each of the new joints (D and E) a new pair of equations is available for calculating the two new-member stresses. As long as this procedure of expanding the truss is followed, the truss will be statically determinate internally. Should new members be installed without adding new joints, such as member CE in Fig. 8–2 (d), the truss will become statically indeterminate because no new joint equations are made available to find the new-member stresses.

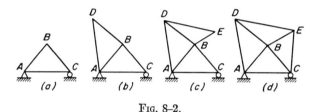

FIG. 8–2.

From the foregoing information an expression can be written for the relationship which must exist between the number of joints and the number of members and reaction components for a particular truss if it is to be statically determinate internally. (The identification of externally determinate structures has previously been discussed.) In the following discussion, $m =$ number of members, $j =$ number of joints, and $r =$ number of reaction components.

If the number of equations available $(2j)$ is sufficient to obtain the unknowns, the structure is statically determinate, from which the following relation may be written.

$$2j = m + r$$

Or as more commonly written,

$$m = 2j - r$$

Before an attempt is made to apply this equation, it is necessary to have a structure which is stable externally or the results are meaningless; therefore, r is the least number of reaction components required for external stability. Should the structure have more external reaction components than necessary for stability (and thus be statically indeterminate externally), the value of r remains the least number of reaction components required to make it stable externally. This statement means that

r will equal 3 for the usual statics equations plus the number of any additional condition equations which may be available.

It is possible to build trusses which have too many members to be analyzed by statics, in which case they are statically indeterminate internally, and m will exceed $2j-r$ because there are more members present than are absolutely necessary for stability. The extra members are said to be redundant members. If m is 3 greater than $2j-r$, there are three redundant members, and the truss is internally statically indeterminate to the third degree. Should m be less than $2j-r$, there are not enough members present for stability.

A brief glance at a truss will usually show if it is statically indeterminate. Trusses having members which cross over each other or members which serve as the sides for more than two triangles may quite possibly be indeterminate. The $2j-r$ expression should be used, however, if there is any doubt about the determinancy of a truss, because it is not difficult to be fooled. Figure 8–3 shows several trusses and the application of the expression to each. The small circles on the trusses indicate the joints.

Little explanation is necessary for most of the structures shown, but some remarks may be helpful for a few. The truss of Fig. 8–3 (e) has five reaction components and is statically indeterminate externally to the second degree; however, two of the reaction components could be removed and leave a structure with sufficient reactions for stability. The least number of reaction components for stability is 3, m is 21, and j is 12; applying the equation $m=2j-r$ yields

$$21=24-3=21 \qquad \text{statically determinate internally}$$

The truss of Fig. 8–3 (j) is externally indeterminate because there are five reaction components and only four equations available. With r equal to 4 the structure is shown to be determinate internally. The three-hinged arch of Fig. 8–3 (k) has four reaction components, which is the least number of reaction components required for stability; so r equals 4. Application of the equation shows the arch to be determinate.

In the chapters pertaining to the analysis of indeterminate structures it will be seen that the values of the redundants may be obtained by applying certain simultaneous equations. The number of simultaneous equations equals the total number of redundants, whether internal, external, or both. It therefore may seem a little foolish to distinguish between internal and external determinancy. The separation is particularly questionable for some types of internally and externally redundant trusses, where no solution of the reactions is possible independently of the member stresses, and vice versa.

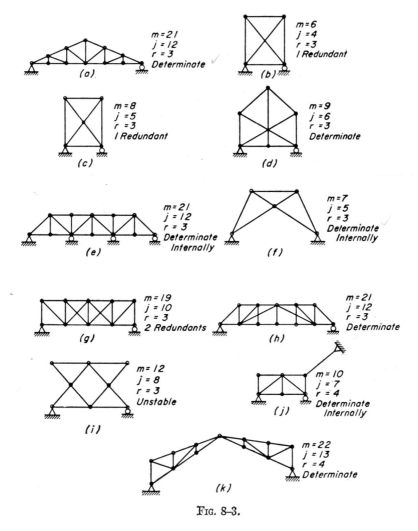

FIG. 8-3.

If a truss is externally determinate and internally indeterminate, the reactions may be obtained by statics. If the truss is externally indeterminate and internally determinate, the reactions are dependent upon the internal-member stresses and may not be determined by a method independent of those stresses. If the truss is externally and internally indeterminate, the solution of the stresses and reactions will be performed simultaneously. (For any of these situations, it may be possible to obtain a few stresses here and there by joints without going through the indeterminate procedure necessary for complete analysis.) This entire subject is discussed in detail in later chapters.

8–3.   Simple Trusses

The first step in forming a truss has been shown to be the connecting of three members at their ends to form a triangle. Subsequent figures are formed by adding two members and one joint; the new members meet at the new joint and each is pinned at its opposite ends into one of the existing joints. Trusses formed in this way are said to be *simple trusses*.

8–4.   Compound Trusses

A *compound truss* is a truss made by connecting two or more simple trusses. The simple trusses may be connected by three nonparallel non-concurrent links, by one joint and one link, by a connecting truss, by two or more joints, etc. An almost unlimited number of trusses may be formed in this way. The Fink truss shown in Fig. 8–4 (a), consisting of the two cross-hatched trusses connected by one joint and one link, is one example. Other compound trusses are shown in Fig. 8–4 (b) and (c). The $2j-r$ equation applies equally well to compound trusses and simple trusses.

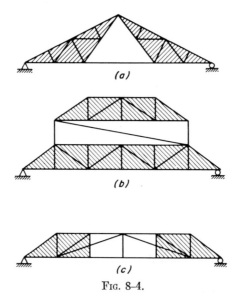

(a)

(b)

(c)

Fig. 8–4.

Another type of compound truss is the subdivided truss; an example is shown in Fig. 8–5 (a). Analysis of subdivided trusses is discussed in detail in Chapter 9. The subdivided truss of Fig. 8–5 (a) may be considered to consist of the large truss of (b) with the small trusses of (c) superimposed on it. In fact, the truss analysis may be handled in exactly this manner, as described in Chapter 9.

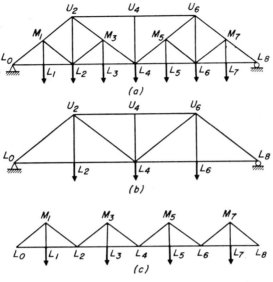

FIG. 8-5.

8-5. Complex Trusses

There are a few trusses which are statically determinate but which do not have the requirements necessary to fall within the classification of either simple or compound trusses. These are referred to as *complex trusses*. The members of simple and compound trusses are so arranged that sections may be passed through three members at a time, moments taken at the intersection of two of them, and the stress found in the third.

Complex trusses may not be analyzed in this manner. Not only does the method of moments result in failure, but the methods of shears and joints are also of no avail. The difficulty lies in the fact that there are three members meeting at almost every joint, and therefore there are too many unknowns at every location in the truss to pass a section and obtain the stress in any member directly by the equations of statics. Two complex trusses are shown in Fig. 8-6. The number of joints and members is sufficient for them to be statically determinate.

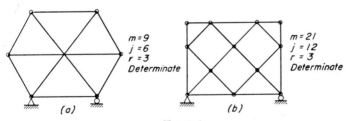

FIG. 8-6.

One method of computing the stresses in complex trusses is to write simultaneous equations for two times the number of joints minus r in the structure. Solution of the equations, however, is so tedious that the method is of little practical value.

Another method, applicable to many complex trusses, is the one of assuming the stress in one of the truss members. A convenient member is selected and given a stress of X. Stresses in the surrounding members are computed in terms of X. The process is continued until it is possible to pass a section completely through the truss and write one of the equations of statics for the free body, so the only members appearing in the equation have stresses which have been calculated in terms of X. Solution of the resulting equation will give the value of X, and the other stresses may be determined by statics. This method is not easy to apply in many complex trusses.

For a more comprehensive discussion of complex trusses, the reader may refer to the method of substitute members described in *Theory of Structures* by Timoshenko and Young.[1]

Generally speaking, there is little need for complex trusses because it is possible to select a simple or compound truss which will serve the purpose equally well.

8–6. Stability

The following paragraphs discuss several situations which may cause a structure to be unstable.

Less than $2j-r$ Members. A truss which has less than $2j-r$ members is obviously unstable internally, but a truss may have as many or more than $2j-r$ members and still be unstable. The truss of Fig. 8–7 (a) satisfies the $2j-r$ relationship and is statically determinate and stable; however, if the diagonal in the second panel is removed and added to the first panel as shown in Fig. 8–7 (b), the truss is unstable even though the number of members remains equal to $2j-r$. The part of the truss to the left of panel 2 can move with respect to the part of the truss to the right of panel 2, because panel 2 is a rectangle. (As previously indicated, a rectangular shape is unstable unless restrained in some way.)

Similarly, addition of diagonals to panels 3 and 4, as shown in Fig. 8–7 (c), will not prevent the truss from being unstable. There are two more than $2j-r$ members, and the truss is statically indeterminate to the second degree, but it is unstable because panel 2 is unstable.

Trusses Consisting of Figures Which Are Not All Triangles. As the student becomes more familiar with trusses, he will be able in most cases to tell with a brief glance if a truss is stable or unstable. For the present,

---

[1] New York: McGraw-Hill Book Company, Inc., 1945.

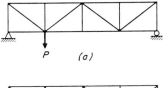

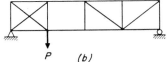

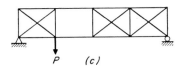

Fig. 8-7.

though, it may be a good idea for him to study trusses in detail if he thinks there is any possibility of instability. One indication that instability may be present is when a truss does not consist entirely of triangles. The trusses of Fig. 8-7 (b) and (c) fall in this category.

The fallacy of this idea is that the number of perfectly stable trusses which can be assembled not entirely consisting of triangles is endless. As an example consider the truss of Fig. 8-8 (a). The basic triangle ABC has been extended by the addition of joint D and members AD and CD and a stable truss maintained, even though figure ABCD is not a triangle. Joint D is firmly held in position and cannot move without changing the length of one or more members. Compound trusses such as the ones of Figs. 8-3 (h) and (i) and the subdivided types of Chapter 9 often present a nontriangular but stable situation. Another example is presented in Fig. 8-8 (b). Structures of these types have the joints around the nontriangular figures tied to the rest of the truss so that they are not free to move. If a truss consists of figures which are not all triangles, it should be carefully examined to see if any of the joints can possibly move in any direction without causing changes in length of one or more of the truss members.

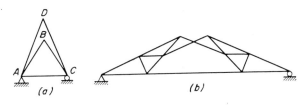

Fig. 8-8.

Analysis as Means of Finding Instability. The members of a truss must be arranged to support the external loads. What will satisfactorily support the external loads is a rather difficult question to answer with only a glance at the truss under consideration, but an analysis of the structure will always provide the answer. If the structure is stable, the analysis will yield reasonable results, but if it is unstable, the analysis will never balance.

Unstable Supports. A structure cannot be stable if its supports are unstable. To be stable, it must be supported by at least three nonparallel, nonconcurrent forces. This subject has been previously discussed in Chapter 2.

8–7. Equations of Condition

On some occasions two or more separate structures are connected together so that only one type of force can be transmitted through the connection. The three-hinged arch and cantilever types of structures of Chapter 3 have been shown to fall into this class, because they are connected with interior hinges unable to transmit rotation.

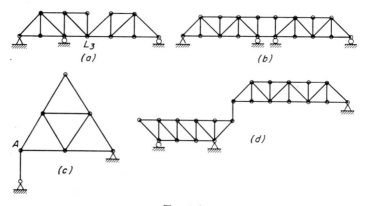

Fig. 8–9.

Perhaps the simplest way to produce a hinge in a truss is by omitting a chord member in one of the panels, as shown in Fig. 8–9 (*a*). It is obvious that the moment of all the external forces on the part of the structure to the left or the right of the pin connection at joint L_3 must be zero. The truss is statically determinate because there are three statics equations and one condition equation available for calculating the four reaction components.

The omission of members in some other situations may produce equations of condition. A diagonal of the truss of Fig. 8–9 (*b*) has been omitted between the two interior supports. With no members in the panel able to have a vertical component of stress, no shear can be transmitted through the panel, and an equation of condition is available. The supports on each side of the usually unstable rectangular shape prevent it from collapsing.

Practically speaking, the bars mentioned as being omitted are probably not omitted at all, because they would detract from the appearance of the structure and might be useful in its erection. They are frequently assembled so they can be adjusted to be inactive in the completed truss. The Wichert truss, discussed in Chapter 15, is a continuous truss which has omitted verticals (actually omitted) over the interior supports; each omission provides an equation of condition.

Figure 8–9 (c) and (d) presents two more situations in which equations of condition are produced. In the first of these figures, there are four reaction components, and the structure may appear to be statically indeterminate externally; however, the joint at A, Fig. 8–9 (c) is pin-connected and cannot transmit rotation. This equation of condition makes the structure determinate externally. Figure 8–9 (d) shows two separate trusses which are connected by a link. The link makes available two equations of condition, because rotation may not be transmitted at either end.

Problems

8–1 to 8–19. Classify the structures as to their internal and external stability and determinancy. For indeterminate structures include the degree of redundancy internally or externally.

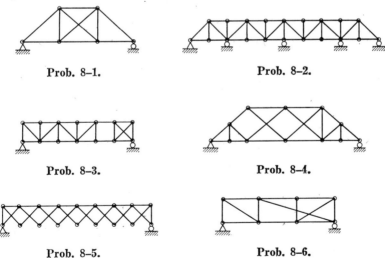

Prob. 8–1.   Prob. 8–2.

Prob. 8–3.   Prob. 8–4.

Prob. 8–5.   Prob. 8–6.

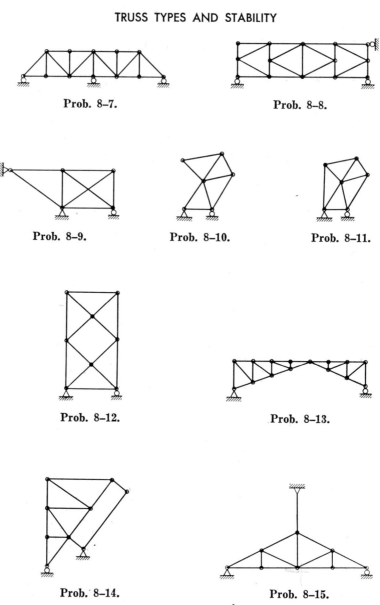

Prob. 8–7.

Prob. 8–8.

Prob. 8–9.

Prob. 8–10.

Prob. 8–11.

Prob. 8–12.

Prob. 8–13.

Prob. 8–14.

Prob. 8–15.

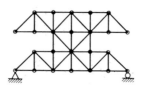

Prob. 8–16.

Prob. 8–17.

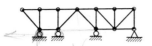

Prob. 8–18.

GIVES ONE CONDITION

Prob. 8–19.

9 | SUBDIVIDED TRUSSES

9–1. Reasons for Subdivision

In Chapter 5, the statement was made that it is desirable to keep bridge truss diagonals at angles of approximately 45° with the horizontal and to vary truss depths from one-fifth to one-eighth of their spans (the flatter trusses being used for the longer spans). To maintain these relationships for long-span steel trusses, it becomes necssary to have very wide and deep panels. With large panels the unsupported lengths of chords and diagonals become excessive and the weight of the floor system increases greatly. The Pratt truss of Fig. 9–1 illustrates these disadvantages. For this truss the following facts are evident:

1) Ratio of depth to span=1:8.
2) Diagonals at 45° with horizontal.
3) Unsupported length of top chord members=50 ft.
4) Unsupported length of diagonals=70.7 ft.
5) Unsupported length of floor system=50 ft.

The moments in bridge floor systems longer than 20 to 25 ft are excessive. A floor system would have to be exceptionally heavy, thus expensive, to span a distance of 50 ft between panel points from which it receives its support. The increased weight of the floor system would

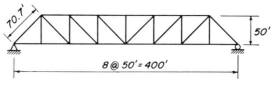

Fig. 9–1.

produce corresponding increases in the stresses, sizes, and cost of the supporting trusses. Long diagonals and chords subject to compression must be made quite heavy because of the danger of buckling. A large compressive load is not required to buckle a 70 ft column even though the cross-sectional area of the column may be quite large.

9–2. Trusses with Multiple Web Systems

Toward the end of the nineteenth century, these problems were solved with multiple web system trusses such as the ones shown in Fig. 9–2. These trusses reduced lengths of members and floor systems, but they

Brown's Bridge, Forsyth and Hall Counties, Gainesville, Georgia. (Courtesy of American Institute of Steel Construction, Inc.)

introduced other disadvantages: they are inconvenient to analyze, because they are statically indeterminate, and they are somewhat expensive to construct. For these reasons they are almost extinct today. The student who is interested in their analysis by an approximate method may refer to the text *Stresses in Framed Structures* by Hool and Kinne.

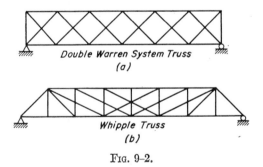

Double Warren System Truss
(a)

Whipple Truss
(b)

Fig. 9–2.

9–3. Subdivided Trusses

Subdivided trusses are more satisfactory for long-span trusses than are the multiple web system trusses. The Pratt truss of Fig. 9–1 may be subdivided by the addition of the members shown in Fig. 9–3.

The resulting truss is a subdivided Pratt, or Baltimore, truss. The newly added members are referred to as subdiagonals or subverticals and may also be referred to as sub-struts (if they are compression members) or sub-ties (if they are tension members).

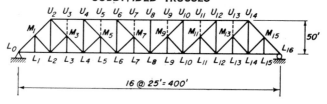

FIG. 9–3.

The subverticals (M_3L_3, $M_{11}L_{11}$, etc.) transfer the loads at their panel points (L_3 and L_{11}) by tension to the main diagonals. The subdiagonals (L_2M_3, $M_{11}L_{12}$, etc.) prevent the diagonals from being bent laterally by the tensile loads applied from the subverticals.

Subdivision reduces the unsupported length of the floor system between panel points by one-half; therefore, the bending moment, which varies approximately as the square of the span length, becomes approximately one-fourth of its former value. The unsupported lengths of the main diagonals are one-half as long as they were, which in design will allow them to be considerably smaller, particularly if they are subject to compression. Members U_3M_3, U_5M_5, and so forth (shown with dotted lines) are sometimes used to reduce the unsupported lengths of top-chord members.

Other types of subdivided trusses are shown in Fig. 9–4 (a) and (b). Figure 9–4 (c) shows a K truss, with its unusual arrangement of members, which accomplishes the same purpose as ordinary subdivided trusses and will probably have smaller secondary stresses.

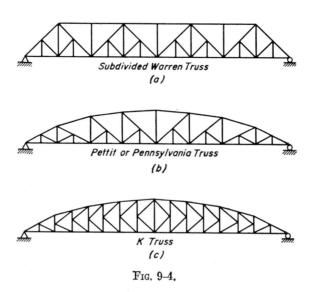

Subdivided Warren Truss
(a)

Pettit or Pennsylvania Truss
(b)

K Truss
(c)

FIG. 9–4.

9–4. Disadvantages of Subdivision

Several advantages of subdivision have been discussed in the preceding paragraphs. However, subdivision introduces three main disadvantages that accompany the advantages. They are:

1) Higher pound prices of steel.
2) Less attractive trusses.
3) Higher secondary stresses in many cases.

9–5. Analysis of Baltimore Truss; "Secondary-Truss" Method

A subdivided truss may be considered to consist of a main truss and a series of smaller, or "secondary," trusses connected together to form a compound truss. It may be analyzed by removing the smaller trusses from the larger and conducting an analysis of each truss individually. The stresses of the actual subdivided truss may be determined by adding the stresses of the secondary truss members to the stresses of the corresponding members of the main truss. For this discussion the Baltimore truss of Fig. 9–5 is considered.

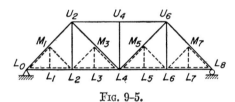

Fɪɢ. 9–5.

The new members added to the main truss are the subdiagonals and subverticals. Members L_0L_1, L_0M_1, L_1L_2, etc. are parts of both trusses, but for purposes of stress analysis each of these members may be assumed to consist of two parts, one part serving the main truss and one part serving the secondary truss.

The stresses computed for the main truss are correct for members which have no corresponding secondary members. Stresses for U_2U_4, M_5U_6, U_2L_2, etc., in the main truss are the final stresses in the actual subdivided truss. To find the final stresses in members having corresponding secondary members such as M_3L_4, L_4L_5, and M_7L_8, it is necessary to add the two stresses.

The secondary-truss method is admittedly not the quickest way to analyze subdivided trusses, but it is occasionally of value in analyzing some special types of truss. The multiple web system trusses of Fig. 9–2 may be analyzed by separating them into primary and secondary trusses. (They are statically indeterminate, and assumptions must be made to

make the analysis even after the trusses are separated.)   Example 9–1
illustrates the secondary-truss method.

EXAMPLE 9–1. Determine the stresses in the members of the Baltimore truss of
Figs. 9–6 by the secondary-truss method.

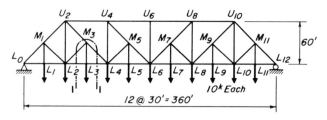

FIG. 9–6.

Solution: The secondary trusses are removed from the main truss, and the stresses
in the main truss are computed.   With the removal of the subverticals the inter-
mediate panel points (L_1, L_3, L_5, etc.) are removed, and the loads which were initially
applied at these panel points must be moved proportionately to the main panel
points on each side.

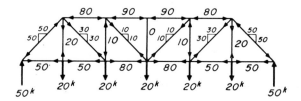

The secondary trusses are identical as to loading and dimensions, and the analysis
of only one of them is shown.

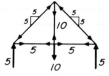

The final stresses are found by adding the stresses of the members of the secondary
trusses to the corresponding members of the main truss.

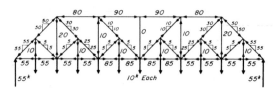

9–6. Analysis of Baltimore Truss as a Single Truss

The Baltimore truss of Example 9–1 may be analyzed as a single truss with little difficulty by the methods of joints and moments with no new information presented; however, there is available one short cut which will appreciably expedite the analysis.

The stress in each subvertical obviously equals the load applied to the panel point below. If no load is applied at the panel point, the subvertical can have no stress.

It is desired to find a simple method of calculating the stress in the subdiagonal L_2M_3, so the horseshoe-shaped section $1-1$, Fig. 9–6, is passed around joints M_3 and L_3 as shown in Fig. 9–7.

Considering the free body enclosed by the horseshoe, the imaginary section can be seen to pass through five different members (L_2L_3, L_2M_3, U_2M_3, M_3L_4, and L_3L_4). Moments are taken about L_4 to find the stress in L_2M_3 because the lines of action of the stresses in all of the cut members, except L_2M_3, pass through this joint.

$$\Sigma M_{L_4} = 0$$
$$- (10)(30) - (L_2M_{3_v})(60) = 0$$
$$L_2M_{3_v} = -5^k \text{ compression}$$

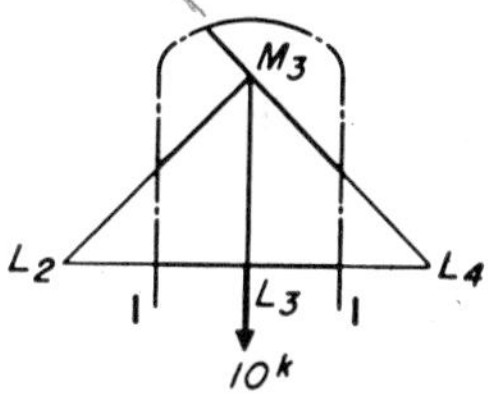

Fig. 9–7.

The moment equation shows that the vertical component of stress in the subdiagnoal equals one-half of the subpanel load and is compression. This statement is always true if the subpanel point lies midway between the main panel points. Should the subpanel point not lie at the mid-point (quite unusual because the purpose of the subvertical is to reduce as much as possible the unsupported length of the floor system), the value of the vertical component may be determined by moments as described for this truss.

With this simplification the stresses for the subverticals and sub-diagonals of the truss can be quickly written in. The remaining stresses can be computed by the method of joints. Should the subdivided truss under consideration have nonparallel chords, it may be necessary to use the method of moments for a few chord members to complete the solution.

9–7. Analysis of K Truss

The short panels of the K truss eliminate the necessity for subverticals to help support the floor system. The stresses may be found by joints and moments with little difficulty, but as with the Baltimore truss some simplifications of the analysis are available.

For the discussion to follow, the K truss of Example 9–2 is considered. The stress in chord member U_2U_3 may be found by passing section *1–1* and taking moments at L_2, because the lines of action of the stresses in all of the members cut by the section except U_2U_3 pass through that joint.

$\Sigma M_{L_2}=0$ (free body to left of section)
$$(70)(80) - (20)(40) + (U_2U_3)(40) = 0$$
$$U_2U_3 = -120^k \text{ compression}$$

A complete analysis may be made by using sections of the same nature as *1–1* in each panel for finding chord stresses and determining the stresses in the other members by joints. Another simplification, however, can be found by studying the middle joints. By passing a section completely around joint M_1, the free body of Fig. 9–8 (*a*) is obtained. Unless an inclined external load is applied at M_1 (highly improbable), the horizontal components of stress in M_1U_2 and M_1L_2 must be equal numerically and opposite in character. If one diagonal is in tension, the other is in compression. The numerical relationship between their vertical components depends upon their respective slopes. If they have the same slopes, as is usually the case, the components are equal. The two possible stress situations in these members are presented in Fig. 9–8 (*b*) and (*c*). The vertical components of stress in these diagonals act in the same direction in opposing the shear in the panel, regardless of which diagonal is in tension and which is in compression. The vertical components are both acting down or are both acting up; there is no other possible combination.

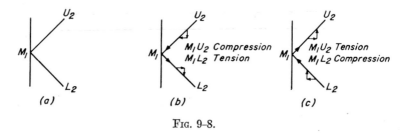

(a)   (b)   (c)

Fɪɢ. 9–8.

The slopes of the diagonals of the truss of Example 9–2 are equal and their vertical components will be equal. Passing section *2–2*, as shown in Fig. 9–9, will permit the calculation of the diagonal stresses in the panel by considering the free body to the right of the section.

The K trusses often have nonparallel chords, and the inclined chord has a vertical component of stress which must be included in considering the forces resisting shear in a panel. Stresses in sloping chords may be determined by taking moments.

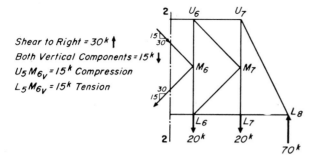

Shear to Right = 30^k ↑
Both Vertical Components = 15^k ↓
$U_5 M_{6v} = 15^k$ *Compression*
$L_5 M_{6v} = 15^k$ *Tension*

Fig. 9–9.

EXAMPLE 9–2. Find the stresses in all of the members of the K truss shown in Fig. 9–10.

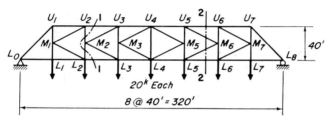

Fig. 9–10.

Solution: The final stresses are as shown.

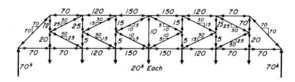

Problems

9–1 to 9–12. Analyze the subdivided trusses.

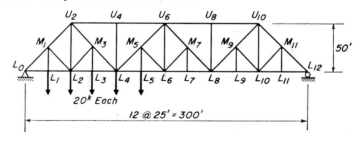

Prob. 9–1.

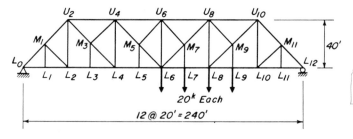

Prob. 9-2.

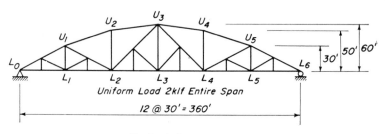

Prob. 9-3.

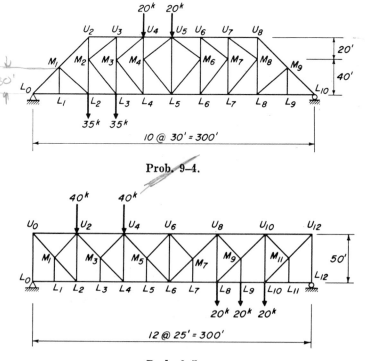

Prob. 9-4.

Prob. 9-5.

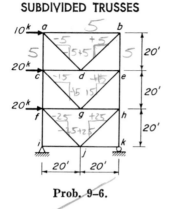

Prob. 9-6.

Diagonals in Each Panel have Same Slope

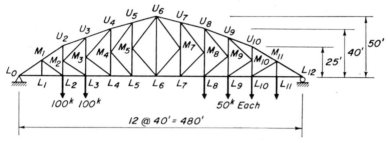

Prob. 9-7.

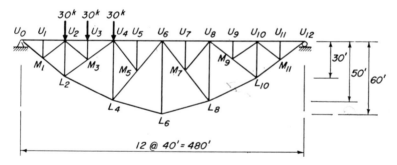

Prob. 9-8.

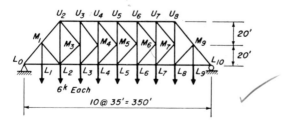

Prob. 9-9.

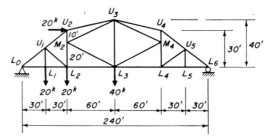

Prob. 9–10.

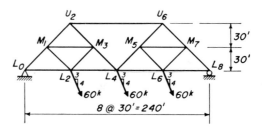

Prob. 9–11.

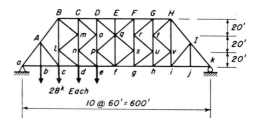

Prob. 9–12.

10 |

GRAPHIC STATICS

10–1. General

Reactions and stresses for all types of structural frameworks may be determined from carefully constructed geometric figures as well as by the algebraic methods discussed in earlier chapters. The solution of these and other statics problems by graphical methods is known as *graphic statics.*

There are several situations in which graphical solutions are of advantage. Most nonparallel chord trusses may be analyzed by graphics as quickly, if not more quickly, than by algebraic methods. The advantage becomes even greater for very complicated types of trusses, such as towers, which are often quite difficult to analyze by the former methods. The author believes that the "brainwork" necessary for most graphical analysis is less than that required for algebraic analysis of the same structures. The simplicity of the method permits companies, such as steel fabricators, to use draftsmen for much of their analysis. The draftsmen may be completely unfamiliar with the theory of graphic statics and of algebraic solutions and yet be able to make the analyses because they have memorized the few simple steps involved. The situation pictured here is not altogether desirable, but it is occasionally encountered.

Countless steel design and fabricating offices all over the country use graphics every day for the analysis of roof trusses such as the Bowstring and the Pratt. This common application of graphics makes it necessary for structural engineers to be completely familiar with the process.

10–2. Basic Concepts

Complete mastery of the elementary concepts of graphics can be obtained immediately, because only basic mechanics principles are involved. These principles are reviewed in the following paragraphs.

Force Representation. A force is completely identified when its magnitude, direction, and point of application are known. A fully identified force may be represented with a line or vector. The line is drawn parallel to the force, with an arrow representing its direction, and to a scaled length representing its magnitude. Representation of forces with fine penciled lines seems to indicate that they are concentrated at fine points. The loads are actually distributed over relatively large areas, and the lines merely represent their centers of gravity.

Combination of Forces. It may be convenient to replace a group of forces with a single force, referred to as the resultant of the forces. Two or more nonparallel forces intersecting at one point, such as the stresses in a group of truss members meeting at a joint, may be graphically combined into one resultant. The forces P_1 and P_2 of Fig. 10–1 are combined

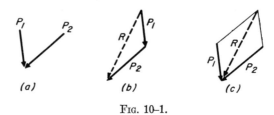

FIG. 10–1.

with a force triangle in (b) and with a force parallelogram in (c). The magnitude of the resultant force R can be obtained by scaling it with the same scale used to draw P_1 and P_2 initially.

A group of four forces is combined into one resultant in Fig. 10–2. An arbitrary point was selected as the starting position, and successive lines were drawn representing each of the forces, the lines being parallel to the actual forces and scaled to the proper magnitude. The order in which the forces are considered is immaterial. They are drawn in completely different orders in Fig. 10–2 (b) and (c), but the resultant is the same in magnitude and direction in each case. The resultant was found by drawing a line (dashed in the figure) from the starting to the ending point.

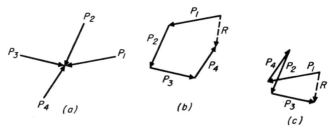

FIG. 10–2.

The resultant of all of the forces applied to a body in equilibrium is zero, and the starting and ending points of the polygon of forces coincide. Each of the joints of a stable truss is in equilibrium, and the resultant of all of the loads and stresses at a joint is zero.

Resolution of Forces. Not only can two or more forces which meet at a point be combined into one resultant force, but any single force may itself be broken down arbitrarily into two or more components the resultant of which is the force. Force P_1 is resolved into components a and b in Fig. 10–3.

Rigid Bodies in Equilibrium. The structures considered in this text are assumed to be in equilibrium or at rest, and the summation of all the forces applied to any one of them is zero. Furthermore, they are assumed to be rigid bodies, which will not deform under load. The application of load to any body causes some deformation, but it is usually so small as to be negligible in its effect on the stresses of the body.

FIG. 10–3.

10–3. Bow's Notation

A convenient system for numbering the members, loads, and reactions of a truss is shown in Fig. 10–4. This system is known as Bow's notation and consists in placing a number in each of the triangles of a truss and a letter in the space between each of the external loads and reactions. By this method each of the members can be designated by the letters or numbers on each side of it; examples are members *B-1*, *E-6*, *6-7*, and *9-10* in the truss shown. Similarly, each of the external forces is designated by a pair of letters, such as loads *B-C* and *H-A* and reaction *G-H*. Bow's notation is more satisfactory for graphics than the joint-numbering sys-

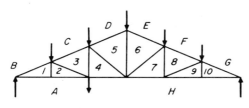

FIG. 10–4.

tem used in the earlier chapters, where the joints were numbered L_0, L_1, U_1, U_2, etc. To use the joint system it would be necessary to give additional letters or numbers to the external loads and reactions on the structure.

10–4. The Force Polygon

Three forces (P_1, P_2, and P_3) acting on a rigid, nondeforming body are represented in Fig. 10–5 (*a*). For the body to be in equilibrium there must be another force applied to it: a reaction equal and opposite to the resultant of the three loads. A force polygon is drawn in Fig. 10–5 (*b*)

for all four forces. This polygon should be carefully examined, because
it illustrates the following two important facts:

 1) The polygon closes because the forces are in equilibrium.

 2) The arrows on the forces follow each other successively around the
polygon.

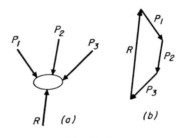

FIG. 10–5.

10–5. Force Polygons for Individual Joints of a Truss

 Two or more forces meet or intersect at each joint of a truss. If the
truss is in equilibrium, each and every joint of the truss is in equilibrium,
and the resultant of all the forces at any joint is zero; therefore, a force
polygon drawn for any joint must close. It will be seen in the following
paragraphs that, if one or two, but not more than two, stresses meeting
at a joint are unknown, they may be determined by drawing a force
polygon.

 Figure 10–6 presents a truss for which the stresses are to be determined
graphically. Truss reactions may be determined algebraically or graphically (as described later in the chapter), but for the usual loading conditions they are determined so easily by algebraic methods that a graphical
solution would waste time. A procedure closely related to the algebraic
method of joints is used to calculate the stresses in truss members by
graphic statics. Joints are taken out one by one and a diagram (or force
polygon) is drawn for each, which in effect applies the equations of statics
that set the horizontal forces equal to zero and the vertical forces equal
to zero. Force polygons are shown in Fig. 10–6 for each of the joints on
the left-hand side of the truss. Because the truss and loading are symmetrical on each side, it is unnecessary to consider the right-hand side of
the truss. The polygons are prepared as described in the following paragraphs.

 Joint L_0. There are three forces at the joint, a 15^k reaction and two
unknown member stresses. The magnitude and character of the two
stresses may be determined by drawing a force polygon for the joint.
The order in which the forces are considered in drawing a separate poly-

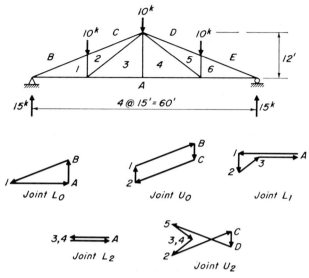

Fɪɢ. 10–6.

gon for each joint is of little importance, but in drawing a combined polygon for an entire truss (to be described) it is essential for the forces to be taken successively in a clockwise order or in a counterclockwise order. To form the proper habit, the individual polygons are drawn by taking the forces one by one as they are encountered in a clockwise order. The forces at joint L_0 in a clockwise order are A-B, B-1, and 1-A. If they were taken in a counterclockwise order, they would be B-A, A-1, and 1-B.

A scaled line is drawn to represent the reaction A-B. In going clockwise around the joint from A to B the line must go up 15^k. Stress B-1 is a force applied at the joint acting to the right or left and parallel to the member, so a light construction line is drawn through B in this direction. Stress 1-A acts either to the right or left parallel to the member and, because the polygon must close for equilibrium, ends up at A, the starting point of the polygon. In going around the polygon one goes from A to B to 1 and back to A, making it obvious that 1 can be at only one point: the intersection of the two construction lines. The force polygon for joint L_0 is complete and may be darkened with the pencil.

The arrow on force A-B was up, and since the arrows on a force polygon must follow each other successively around the polygon, the directions of forces B-1 and 1-A are known. The character of the two stresses is now obvious from the arrows on the polygon. Stress B-1 is acting to the left and pushing against L_0 (compression), and 1-A is to the right pulling away from L_0 (tension). Their magnitudes are available by scaling.

Joint U_1. There are three unknown stresses at joint L_1, and they cannot be determined conveniently at the present time. Joint U_1 is therefore considered next; it has only two unknowns. The members are again taken in a clockwise order around the joint, and the member previously denoted as *B-1* at joint L_0 has become *1-B*.

The stress in *1-B*, which was determined by the force polygon for L_0, is compressive and is pushing against the joints at each of its two ends. Its value is scaled off by going to the right and parallel to the member. A line representing load *B-C* is scaled downward 10^k from *B*. Through point *C* a line is drawn parallel to member *C-2*; and through point *1* a line is drawn parallel to member *2-1*, their intersection being point *2*. The directions and magnitudes of all the forces at joint U_1 are now known. Stress *C-2* is to the left pushing against the joint and is compressive, while stress *2-1* is pushing up against the joint and also is compressive.

Joint L_1. The determination of stress *2-1* at joint U_1 leaves only two unknown stresses at Joint L_1, which permits the construction of a force polygon there. Member *A-1* is taken first; its magnitude and direction are available from the polygon for joint L_0. The stress is tensile and pulls away from the joint to the left. Member *1-2* is in compression and pushes down against the joint. After the known stresses are drawn in, a line is drawn through point *2* parallel to member *2-3*, and another line is drawn through *A* parallel to member *3-A*. Their intersection is point *3*, which in this case lies along the previously drawn line, *A-1*. The force polygon starts at *A*, goes left to *1*, down to *2*, up to *3*, and right to *A* again.

Other Joints. The other joints for which polygons have been prepared, L_2 and U_2, are handled in a similar manner.

10–6. The Maxwell Diagram

The preparation of separate force polygons for each of the joints in a truss wastes considerable time and space, because it is necessary to repeat lines used in previous polygons. For instance, the stress *1-A* in the polygon for L_0 is redrawn as *A-1* in the polygon for L_1; the stress *C-2* at U_1 is repeated as *2-C* at U_2; etc. The force polygons for all of the joints of a truss may be combined in one large diagram in which each stress is represented with only one line. The combined drawing is the *Maxwell diagram* (sometimes called the reciprocal polygon diagram), which is drawn by the identical methods used for the individual-joint polygons. A Maxwell diagram is draw in Fig. 10–7 for the same roof truss considered in Fig. 10–6, and its preparation is described in the following paragraphs. The stresses and loads at each of the joints are taken in a clockwise order, although the same numerical results would be obtained by taking them in a counterclockwise order. A step-by-step construction of the diagram is presented in Fig. 10–7.

Joint L_0. The diagram for joint L_0 is drawn in Fig. 10–7 exactly as in Fig. 10–6 except that no attempt is made to place arrows on the lines; they would be confusing and are unnecessary in determining the character of the stresses. The forces have been considered successively around the joint in a clockwise order; therefore, it is known that in going from *B* to *1* on the Maxwell diagram the line goes to the left. Force *B-1* acts to the left and pushes against the joint (compression). On continuing around the joint, the next force is *1-A*. In going from *1* to *A* on the diagram the line goes to the right and the stress is pulling away from the joint (tension).

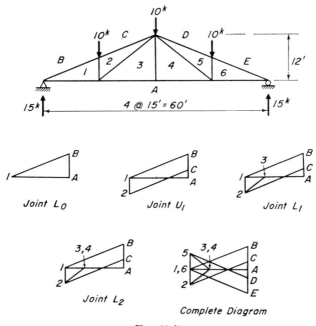

Fig. 10–7.

Joint U_1. The polygon for joint U_1 is drawn as a continuation of the one for L_0. On starting around the joint clockwise, the first force encountered is *1-B*, which was previously developed on the diagram. The next force is the load *B-C*, and it is represented by a 10^k line downward. Finally, a line is drawn through *C* parallel to *C-2* and another line parallel to *2-1* is drawn through *1*, their intersection being point *2*. The diagram shows *C-2* is to the left, pushes against the joint, and is compressive. Similarly, the direction from *2* to *1* on the diagram is up; the force pushes against the joint; and member *2-1* is in compression.

Joint L_1. By using the figure prepared for joints L_0 and U_1 and going clockwise around L_1, the first stresses encountered are *A-1* and *1-2*. The lines representing these stresses are already on the diagram. A line is drawn through point *2* parallel to *2-3*, and another line is drawn through *A* parallel to *3-A*. The intersection of the two is point *3*.

Other Joints. The other joints are handled in the same manner; each is an extension of the previous diagram. If the Maxwell diagram is accurately drawn, results of a high degree of accuracy, satisfactory for any design work, will be obtained. Sharp pencils, careful scaling of distances, and great care in drawing parallel lines are essential. Most drafting offices have equipment to facilitate the construction of parallel lines, but in the absence of special equipment a T square and a pair of large triangles (or, better, a pair of adjustable triangles) will produce satisfactory results.

10–7. Sample Problems

Figures 10–8 to 10–10 illustrate the analysis of three different types of trusses by graphic statics. The procedure is identical with the one used for analyzing the truss of Fig. 10–7, but a few explanatory remarks may be helpful.

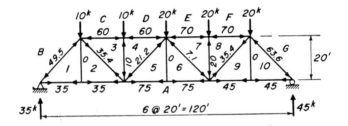

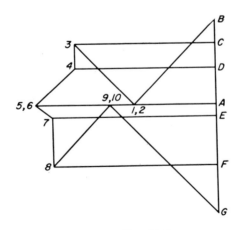

Fig. 10–8.

The hinge reactions for the trusses of Figs. 10–9 and 10–10 have been broken down into their vertical and horizontal components as shown. If resultant hinge reactions were used, the results would be the same. In Fig. 10–9, A-B is the vertical reaction component and B-C is the horizontal reaction component. Should the resultant of the two components be used, it would coincide with the dotted line A-C in the figure. The reactions for all three trusses have been obtained algebraically.

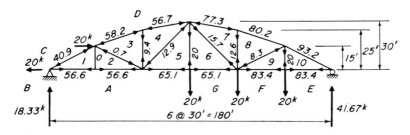

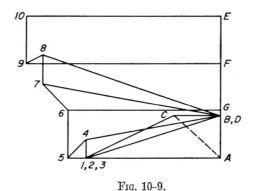

Fig. 10–9.

The reader should note the manner in which the bottom panel point loads are handled in Fig. 10–9. Upon reaching joint L_3, having constructed the polygons for the joints on the left-hand side of the truss up to L_3, it is noted that point A is already located on the diagram. Because the forces are being considered as encountered in a clockwise direction around the joints, the 20^k load is lettered G-A. On going from G to A, a line is drawn 20^k downward to the existing point A; therefore, a bottom-chord load is seemingly handled in exactly the opposite manner from a top-chord load.

Experience with the Maxwell diagram will show that all of the loads and reactions may be laid off initially in constructing the diagram. The student, however, is not encouraged to try this procedure until he has practiced several problems, because he may confuse the loads, particularly when top and bottom panel points of a truss are loaded.

The character and magnitude of each of the stresses as obtained from the Maxwell diagram are indicated on the truss members in Figs. 10–8 to 10–10.

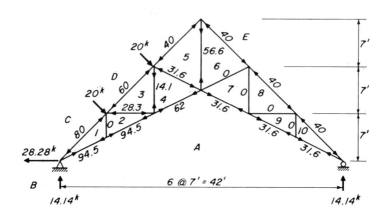

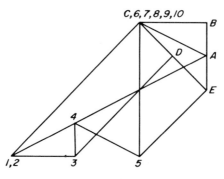

FIG. 10–10.

10–8. Substitute Members

The Maxwell diagram can be drawn quite easily for simple trusses, but the work is a little more difficult for compound trusses. It may be possible to handle several joints of a compound truss by the usual methods, but there will come a time when each of the subsequent joints will have three unknown member stresses. The Fink truss of Fig. 10–11 (a) is an outstanding example. The lines representing the stresses in members meeting at joints L_0, U_1, and L_2 are quickly drawn, but there are three unknown stresses meeting at each of the next two joints, U_3 and L_4. These stresses may not be determined by the graphical methods discussed to date unless one of the unknowns is otherwise determined.

One solution to the problem is to algebraically compute the stresses in one of the unknown members and draw its proper position on the diagram. In Fig. 10–11 (b) the diagram has been developed for joints L_0, U_1, and L_2, and it is assumed that the stress in member D-5 has been calculated algebraically to be 69.8^k in compression. Starting around U_3 in a clockwise direction, 3-2 is known, 2-C is known, and C-D is drawn downward 10^k from C. The stress in member D-5 is compressive and pushing against the joint, so 69.8^k is scaled off to the left parallel to the member to point 5 as shown in Fig. 10–11 (b). With D-5 represented on the diagram the stresses in 5-4 and 4-3 can be obtained by the usual graphical methods. The diagram is completed for the left half of the truss, which is symmetrical as to both dimensions and loading about the center line. The completed diagram is the same as Fig. 10–11 (d) with point X and the dotted line X-6 omitted.

Another method of handling joints in a compound truss having three unknown stresses is the method of substitute members. By this method two of the members of the truss at the difficult joints are assumed to be replaced with a single member, leaving only two unknowns at one of the joints. This substitution permits the continuation of the diagram, although several fictitious stresses will be obtained in the undisturbed members of the truss as well as in the substitute member. Eventually, however, a stress which is correct for the original truss will be obtained. Having obtained a correct stress, it will be possible to work back through the joints of the original truss and find the correct stresses in all of the members.

The truss of Fig. 10–11 (a) is considered in the following discussion, and it is assumed that the Maxwell diagram has been constructed for joints L_0, L_2, and U_1. Members 4-5 and 5-6 are replaced with a single member running from L_4 to U_5, as shown by the dotted line in Fig. 10–11 (c). The triangle to the left of the member is given the letter X. The insertion of a fictitious member in place of the two members leaves only two unknowns at joint U_3, D-X, and X-3. These stresses, correct only for the fictitious truss, can be obtained with the Maxwell diagram. Although not correct for the actual truss, they are useful because they permit the graphical determination of the stresses E-6 and 6-X at joint U_5. The stress in E-6 is the same for both trusses and is the key to finding the remaining stresses in the original truss.

A study of section 1-1 in Fig. 10–11 (a) and (c) shows the stress E-6 to be unchanged by the insertion of the substitute member. To determine the stress in this member algebraically, moments can be taken about joint L_4 of the forces acting on the free body to the left of the section.

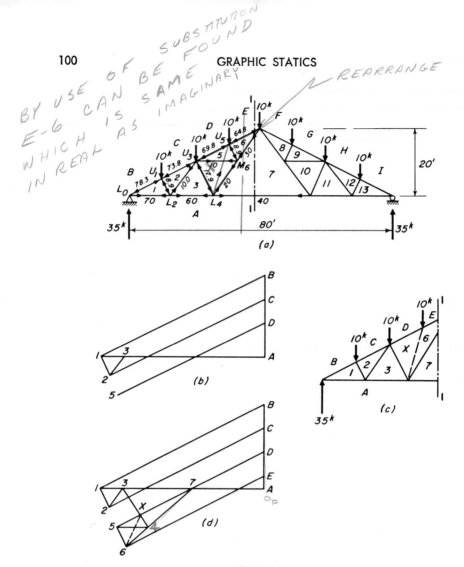

FIG. 10–11.

The resulting moment equation is the same with either truss; therefore, the graphically obtained value of *E-6* in the fictitious truss is correct. Now that *E-6* has been established, the truss with the substitute member is abandoned and the original truss is reconsidered. At joint U_5 the stresses in *6-5* and *5-D* are graphically determined; then the diagram is drawn for joint U_3, which has only two unknowns, *5-4* and *4-3*. No other difficulties will be encountered in completing the drawing for the remainder of the truss. The point *X* is only a construction point and is not used subsequently; it may be erased to prevent possible confusion in scaling stress values. Figure 10–11 (*d*) shows the complete Maxwell diagram for the left half of the truss.

There are several other compound trusses which require algebraic or substitute-member assistance for complete analysis. The procedure is the same as the one used for the Fink truss, although some trusses may require substitute members (or algebraic computations) in more than one location. Two precautions must be kept in mind when a substitute member is used: a) The removal of the actual truss members and replacement with the substitute member must leave a stable truss. b) The arrangement must allow the computer to determine the correct stress in a member of the original truss. In some cases it may be necessary to go two or three joints before a true stress can be obtained.

10–9. Graphical Determination of Reactions; Non-parallel Loads

For a structure to be in equilibrium, the resultant of the applied external loads must coincide with the resultant of the reactions and be equal in magnitude and opposite in direction. Similarly, the resultant of any group of reactions and loads on a structure must be equal and opposite to the resultant of the remaining reactions and loads.

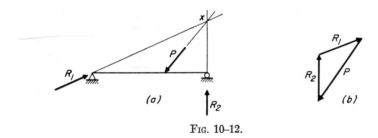

FIG. 10–12.

The load P on the simple beam of Fig. 10–12 (a) produces the reactions R_1 and R_2. The direction of the left-hand reaction R_1 at the hinge is not known, but the right-hand reaction R_2 is vertical, since it is perpendicular to the horizontal supporting surface beneath the roller. If the lines of action of P and R_2 are extended, they will intersect at some point x. The only remaining force on the beam is R_1, and it must pass through x and be equal and opposite to the resultant of P and R_2. If R_1 did not pass through the point, the statics equation $\Sigma M = 0$ of the forces acting on the beam taken about x could not be satisfied.

The direction of R_1 is known, since the line of action passes through the left hinge and point x. Having the directions of all three forces and the magnitude of one, it is possible to determine the magnitude of the other two by drawing a force polygon, Fig. 10–12 (b).

The beam of Fig. 10–13 (a) has two loads, P_1 and P_2. These loads are combined into one resultant $R_{1\text{-}2}$ with a force triangle in Fig. 10–13 (b).

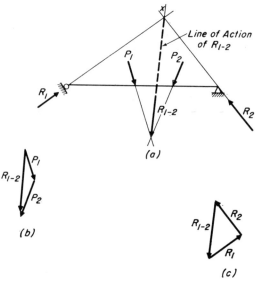

FIG. 10–13.

The line of action of the resultant is indicated by the dotted line in (a). The problem is now the same as the one handled in Fig. 10–12. The resultant of the loads is extended until it intersects the line of action of the roller reaction R_1 at x. The line of action of the right-hand reaction R_2 must also pass through x. A force polygon is drawn in Fig. 10–13 (c), and the magnitudes of R_1 and R_2 can be determined by scaling.

10–10. Graphical Determination of Resultant of Series of Parallel Loads

The beams of Figs. 10–12 and 10–13 had conveniently supported loads whose lines of action made fairly large angles with each other. This relationship made it possible to determine the resultants of the loads at the points of intersection of the lines of action. The resultants, having considerable inclination, were intersected with the lines of action of the roller reactions within the confines of an ordinary size sheet of paper, which permitted the determination of the reactions.

When a structure is loaded with a series of forces which are parallel, the method discussed in Sec. 10–9 cannot be applied successfully. Although the magnitude of the resultant is easily found from a force polygon, the fact that the lines of action of the forces do not intersect makes the location of the resultant something of a problem. Even if the forces are not parallel but nearly so, they will not intersect on an ordinary size sheet of paper. When the supporting surface underneath the roller is horizontal, the reaction is vertical, and it will not intersect the resultant of a set of gravity loads (except possibly at infinity). The first of these problems, the one of locating the resultant of a group of parallel loads, is discussed in this section. Section 10–11 explains how the reactions of a beam loaded with parallel loads may be determined graphically.

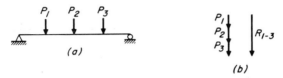

(a)

(b)

Fig. 10–14.

The magnitude and direction of the resultant of the three parallel loads acting on the beam in Fig. 10–14 (a) are determined by drawing a force polygon, shown in (b). The resultant is represented by a line connecting the starting and ending points of the diagram, its direction being parallel to the line.

It is often convenient to resolve a force into two components, an infinite number of pairs of components being available. The forces P_1, P_2, and P_3 of Fig. 10–14 are each resolved into a pair of components making a considerable angle with each other, as shown in Fig. 10–15. This procedure is followed to permit the lines of action of the assumed components to intersect within the extent of an ordinary size sheet of drawing paper.

A convenient method of assuming components is illustrated in Fig. 10–15. The loads are plotted end to end, and an arbitrary point is selected either to the right or to the left of the loads. From this point, labeled 0 in the figure, lines are drawn to the starting and ending points of each of the plotted loads. Examination of the force polygon shows each load has

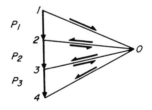

Fig. 10–15.

been broken down into a pair of components. Load P_1 has the components 1-0 and 0-2; load P_2 has the components 2-0 and 0-3; and load P_3 has the components 3-0 and 0-4.

Each of the loads having been replaced with a pair of components, the components may be combined as shown in Fig. 10–16. At an arbitrary point along its line of action, P_1 is replaced with its components *1-0* and *0-2*. The line of action of component *0-2* is extended until it intersects the line of action of P_2. At this point P_2 is replaced with components *2-0* and *0-3*. Finally, the line of action of *0-3* is extended until it intersects the line of action of P_3, at which point P_3 is replaced with components *3-0* and *0-4*.

By examining this diagram, called the *funicular polygon* or *string polygon*, it can be seen that components *2-0* and *0-2* cancel each other (because they are equal and opposite along the same line of action) as do components *3-0* and *0-3*. The entire force system has been reduced to two components *1-0* and *0-4*. On referring to the force polygon of Fig. 10–15, it is obvious that the resultant of the two components is the same as the resultant of the three loads. The direction and magnitude of the resultant can be obtained by drawing a line through the starting and ending points of the polygon. The intersection of the two remaining components, *1-0* and *0-4*, is a point along the line of action of the resultant of the three loads. Any number of loads can be reduced to two components with the string polygon.

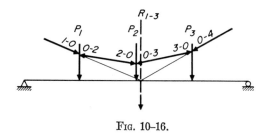

Fɪɢ. 10–16.

10–11. Graphical Determination of Reactions; Parallel Loads

The same general approach is used for determining the reactions of a beam loaded with parallel loads as was used for determining the resultant of a set of parallel loads. The loads P_1 to P_4 applied to the beam of Fig. 10–17 are each resolved into a pair of components. The components reduce to a single pair, *1-0* and *0-5*, as described in Sec. 10–10. The resultant of the two components is the resultant of the four loads and, for equilibrium, is equal and opposite to the resultant of the two reactions. Similarly, the resultant of the left reaction and component *1-0* is equal and opposite to the resultant of the right reaction and component *0-5*.

To handle the problem, each of the loads and reactions will be re-. solved into a pair of components somewhere along its line of action. The lines of action of the loads and the roller reaction are known, but

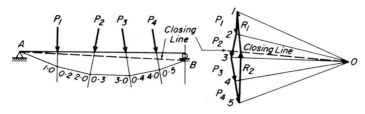

Fig. 10–17.

that of the hinge reaction is unknown. One point along the latter line of action is known: the hinge itself, as indicated by point A in Fig. 10–17. At this point the hinge reaction will be broken down into components.

By drawing the funicular polygon for the loads, P_1 is resolved into two components, $1-0$ and $0-2$. Reaction R_1 is to be resolved into component $1-0$ and some other component, as yet unknown. Because the resolving must be done along the lines of action of each of the forces, $1-0$ is passed through the hinge at point A and continued until it intersects the line of action of P_1. Nothing more is done with R_1 at the present time. Each of the external loads is broken down into its components as its line of action is encountered, until the line of action of component $0-5$ is extended to intersect the line of action of R_2.

The entire force system has now been reduced to four forces: $1-0$, $0-5$, R_1 and R_2. The string polygon shows that forces R_2 and $0-5$ intersect at point B and forces R_1 and $1-0$ intersect at point A. If equilibrium

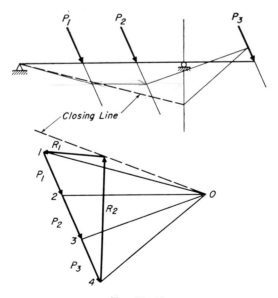

Fig. 10–18.

is present, the resultant of R_1 and $1\text{-}0$ must be equal and opposite to the resultant of R_2 and $0\text{-}5$. A *closing line* is therefore drawn between points A and B, because it must be the line of action of the two resultants.

The values of R_1 and R_2 can now be obtained from the force polygon by drawing a line from point 0 parallel to the closing line. The resultant of $0\text{-}5$ and R_2 must be along the closing line, and R_2 can be drawn from 5 up to the closing line. Since the resultant of R_1, R_2, $1\text{-}0$, and $0\text{-}5$ is zero, R_1 must run from the point where R_2 intersects the closing line to point 1. The values of R_1 and R_2 may be scaled from the polygon.

Two other reaction problems are solved graphically in Figs. 10–18 and 10–19.

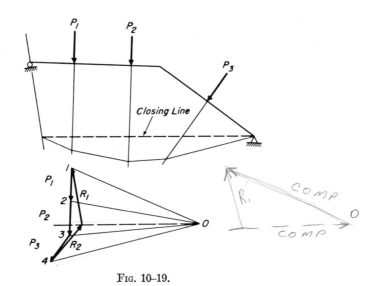

Fig. 10–19.

10–12. Reactions for a Three-hinged Arch

Several methods are available for graphically determining the reactions of a three-hinged arch, but only one is discussed here. At each of the hinges of the arch of Fig. 10–20 (*a*) the point of application of the resultant reaction is known, but the magnitudes and lines of action are not known; therefore, the lines of the string polygon must pass through all of the hinges for a solution to be made. The resultant of all the forces on either side of the crown hinge must pass through that hinge because the moment of those forces about the hinge must be zero.

The arch shown in Fig. 10–20 is loaded only to the left of the crown hinge. The resultant of the loads $R_{1\text{-}2}$ and a point along its line of action x are determined with the force polygon in Fig. 10–20 (*b*) and the string polygon of (a). The sum of the moments of the forces to the right of hinge B is zero, and since the only force to the right of this hinge is the right-hand resultant reaction R_C, its line of action necessarily passes through B.

The line of action R_C is extended until it intersects the line of action of R_{1-2} at y. All of the external forces of the arch have been considered except R_A, and for equilibrium its line of action also passes through y. The resultant of R_A and R_C must be equal and opposite to the resultant of the loads, R_{1-2}, and since their lines of action are now available, their magnitudes may be obtained as shown in Fig. 10–20 (b).

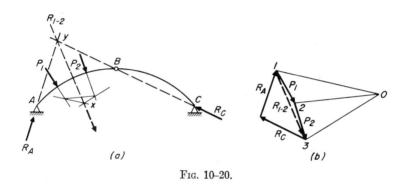

Fig. 10–20.

Should an arch be loaded on both sides of the crown hinge, such as the one of Fig. 10–21 (a), it is possible to handle the problem in exactly the same manner as was used for the arch loaded on one side only. Considering only the loads acting to the left of hinge B, the reaction R_{A_1} and R_{C_1} can be determined. Similarly, their values R_{A_2} and R_{C_2} can be determined for the loads acting to the right of the crown hinge. The total values of the reactions R_A and R_C for all loads can be obtained by combining the two values previously found.

The loads are plotted on the force polygon as shown in Fig. 10–21 (b). Considering only the loads to the left of the hinge, the intersection point of R_{A_1}, R_{C_1}, and R_{1-2} is found at y. In the same manner, considering only the loads on the right side of the structure, the intersection of R_{A_2}, R_{C_2}, and R_{3-4} is found at point z.

Returning to the force polygon, the values of the reactions for loads on the left side only, R_{A_1} and R_{C_1}, are drawn to be equal and opposite to the resultant of R_{1-2}. Similarly, R_{A_2} and R_{C_2} are drawn to be equal and opposite to R_{3-4}. The total values of R_A and R_C can be found, as shown by the dotted lines in the figure. The reaction R_{C_1} is moved down to the upper end of R_{C_2} and R_{A_2} is moved to upper end of R_{C_1}. Then

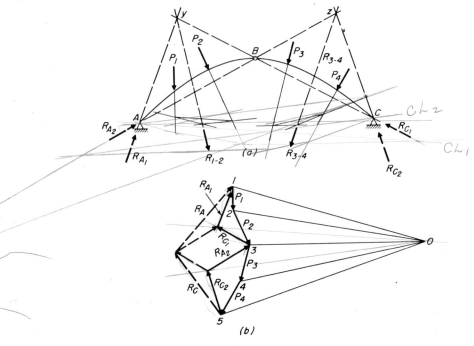

FIG. 10–21.

R_{A_2} will come into the lower end of R_{A_1}. The resultants are found by drawing the lines shown.

Should a three-hinged trussed arch be encountered, the reactions can be determined as described and the stresses determined by the usual Maxwell diagram.

Problems

10–1 to **10–10.** Compute graphically the values of the stresses for all of the members of the trusses. Reactions may be determined algebraically.

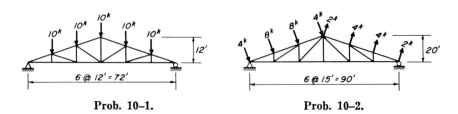

Prob. 10–1.   Prob. 10–2.

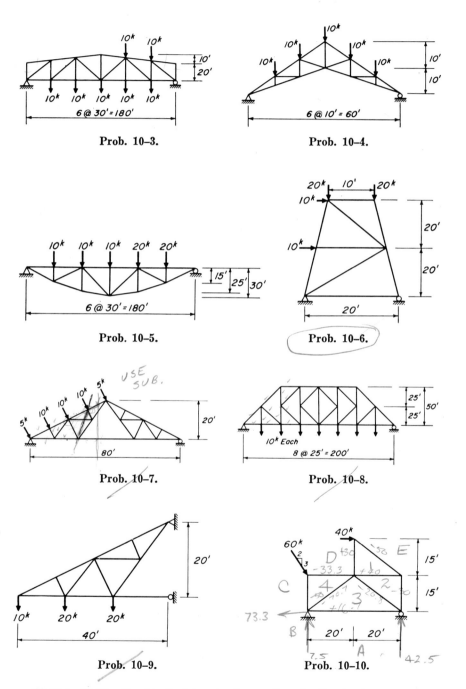

Prob. 10–3.

Prob. 10–4.

Prob. 10–5.

Prob. 10–6.

Prob. 10–7.

Prob. 10–8.

Prob. 10–9.

Prob. 10–10.

10–11 to **10–19.** Graphically determine the reactions for the structures.

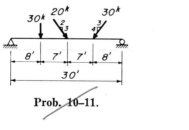

Prob. 10–11.

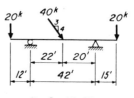

Prob. 10–12.

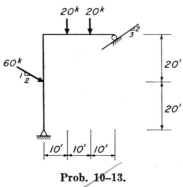

Prob. 10–13.

10–14. The truss of Prob. 10–7.

10–15. The truss of Prob. 10–6.

10–16. The truss of Prob. 10–9.

10–17. The arch of Prob. 3–6.

10–18. The arch of Prob. 3–7.

10–19. The arch of Prob. 3–8.

10–20. Graphically determine the reactions and member stresses for the arch of Prob. 3–10.

10–21. Graphically determine the reactions and member stresses for the arch of Prob. 3–12.

11 | INFLUENCE LINES FOR BEAMS

11-1. Introduction

Structures supporting groups of loads fixed in one position have been discussed in the foregoing chapters. Whether beams, frames, or trusses were being considered and whether the functions sought were shears, reactions, or stresses, the loads were stationary. The engineer in practice, however, rarely deals with structures supporting only fixed loads. Nearly all structures are subject to loads moving back and forth across their spans. Perhaps bridges with their vehicular traffic are the most noticeable examples, but industrial buildings with traveling cranes, office buildings with furniture and human loads, frames supporting conveyor belts, etc. are in the same category.

Each member of a structure must be designed for the most severe stress conditions that can possibly develop in that member. The designer places the live loads at the positions where they will produce these conditions. The critical positions for placing live loads will not be the same for every member. For example, the maximum stress in one member of a bridge truss may occur when there is a line of trucks from end to end of the bridge, while the maximum stress in some other member may occur when the trucks extend only from that member to one end of the bridge. The maximum stresses in certain beams and columns of a building will occur when the live loads are concentrated in certain portions of the building, while the maximum stresses in other beams and columns will occur when the loads are placed elsewhere.

On some occasions it is possible by inspection to determine where to place the loads to give the most critical stresses, but on many other occasions it is necessary to resort to certain criteria or diagrams to find the locations. The most useful of these devices is the influence line.

11-2. The Influence Line Defined

The influence line, which was first used by Professor Winkler, of Berlin, in 1867,[1] shows graphically how the movement of a unit load across a structure influences some function of the structure. The functions which may be represented include reactions, shears, moments, stresses, and deflections.

[1] Kinney, *Indeterminate Structural Analysis* (Reading, Mass.: Addison-Wesley Publishing Company, 1957), Chap. 1.

An influence line may be defined as a curve whose ordinates show the magnitude and character of some function of a structure as a load of unity moves across the structure. Each ordinate of the curve gives the value of the function when the load is at that ordinate.

Influence lines are used primarily for calculating stresses and for determining positions for live loads to cause maximum stresses. The procedure for drawing the diagrams is simply the plotting of values of the function under study as ordinates for various positions of the unit load along the span and the connecting of these ordinates. The student should mentally picture the load moving across the span and try to imagine what is happening to the function in question during the movement. The study of influence lines can immeasurably increase the student's knowledge of what happens to a structure under different loading conditions.

Study of the following sections should fix clearly in his mind what an influence line is. The actual mechanics of developing the diagrams are elementary, once the definition is completely understood. No new fundamentals are introduced here; rather, a method recording information in a convenient and useful form is given.

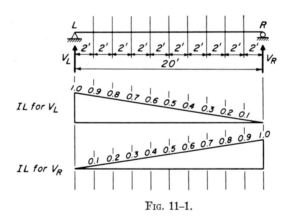

Fig. 11–1.

11–3.   Influence Lines for Simple Beam Reactions

Influence lines for the reactions of a simple beam are given in Fig. 11–1. The variation of the left-hand reaction V_L as a unit load moves from left to right across the beam is considered initially. When the load is directly over the left support, V_L equals 1; when it is 2 ft to the right of the left support, V_L equals 18/20, or 0.9; when it is 4 ft to the right, V_L equals 16/20, or 0.8; etc.

Values of V_L are shown for 2-ft intervals of the unit load across the span. These values lie in a straight line because they change uniformly for equal intervals of the load. For every 2-ft interval the ordinate changes 0.1. The values of V_R, the right-hand reaction, are plotted similarly for successive 2-ft intervals of the unit load. For each position of the unit load the sum of the ordinates of the two diagrams at any point equals (and for equilibrium certainly must equal) the unit load.

11–4. Influence Lines for Simple Beam Shears

Influence lines are plotted in Fig. 11–2 for the shear at two sections in a simple beam. The usual sign convention for shear is used: positive shear occurs when the sum of the transverse forces to the left of a section is up or when the sum of the forces to the right of the section is down.

Placing the unit load over the left support causes no shear at either of the two sections. Moving the unit load 2 ft to the right of the left support results in a left-hand reaction of 0.9 and the sum of the forces to the left of section *1–1* is 0.1 down, or a shear of -0.1. When the load is 4 ft to the right of the left support and an infinitesimal distance to the left of section *1–1*, the shear to the left is -0.2. If the load is moved a very slight distance to the right of section *1–1*, the sum of the forces to the

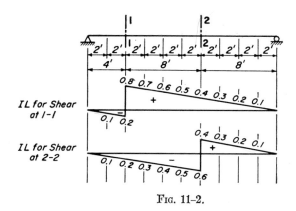

Fig. 11–2.

left of the section becomes 0.8 up, or a $+0.8$ shear. Continuing to move the load across the span toward the right support results in changing values of the shear at section *1–1*. These values are plotted for 2-ft intervals of the unit load. The influence line for shear at section *2–2* is developed in the same manner.

11–5. Influence Lines for Simple Beam Moments

Influence lines are plotted in Fig. 11–3 for the moment at the same sections of the beam used in Fig. 11–2 for the shear illustrations. To review, a positive moment causes tension in the bottom fibers of a beam

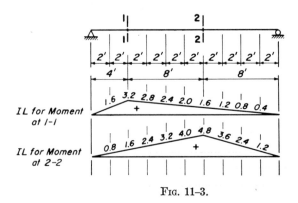

Fig. 11–3.

and occurs at a particular section when the sum of the moments of all the forces to the left is clockwise or when the sum to the right is counter-clockwise. Moments are taken at each of the sections for 2-ft intervals of the unit load.

The major difference between shear and moment diagrams as compared with influence lines should now be clear. A shear or moment diagram shows the variation of shear or moment across an entire structure for loads fixed in one position. An influence line for shear or moment shows the variation of that function at one section in the structure caused

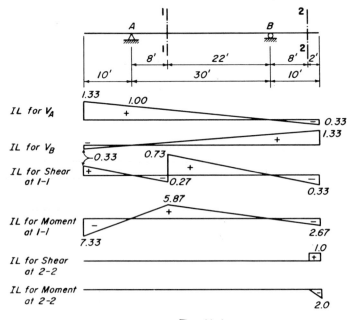

Fig. 11–4.

by the movement of a unit load from one end of the structure to the other.

Influence lines for functions of determinate structures consist of a set of straight lines. An experienced analyst will be able to compute values of the function under study at a few critical positions and connect the plotted values with straight lines. A person beginning his study, however, must be very careful to compute the value of the function for enough positions of the unit load. The shapes of influence lines for stresses in truss members (Chapter 12) are often deceptive in their seeming simplicity. It is obviously better to plot ordinates for several extra positions of the load than to fail to plot one essential value.

Several influence lines for moment, shear, and reactions for an overhanging beam are plotted in Fig. 11–4.

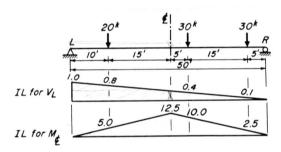

FIG. 11–5.

11–6.   Uses of Influence Lines; Concentrated Loads

Influence lines are the plotted values of functions of structures for various positions of a unit load. Having an influence line for a particular function of a structure makes the value of the function for a concentrated load at any position on the structure immediately available. The beam of Fig. 11–1 and the influence line for the left reaction are used to illustrate this statement. A concentrated 1^k load 4 ft to the right of the left support caused V_L to equal 0.8^k. Should a concentrated load of 175^k be placed in the same position, V_L would be 175 times as great, or 140^k.

The value of a function due to a series of concentrated loads is quickly obtained by multiplying each concentrated load by the corresponding ordinate of the influence line for that function. Loads of 150^k 6 ft to the right of L in Fig. 11–1 and 200^k 16 ft to the right of L would cause V_L to equal $(150)(0.7) + (200)(0.2)$, or 145^k.

Influence lines for the left reaction and the center-line moment are shown for a simple beam in Fig. 11–5, and the values of these functions are calculated for the several loads supported by the beam.

$$V_L = (20)\,(0.8) + (30)\,(0.4) + (30)\,(0.1) = 31^k$$

$$M_{\text{ℂ}} = (20)\,(5.0) + (30)\,(10.0) + (30)\,(2.5) = 475'^k$$

11–7.   Uses of Influence Lines; Uniform Loads

The value of a certain function of a structure may be obtained from the influence line, when the structure is loaded with a uniform load, by multiplying the area of the influence line by the intensity of the uniform load. The following discussion proves this statement to be correct.

A uniform load of intensity w lb/ft (pound per foot) is equivalent to a continuous series of smaller loads of $(w)\,(\frac{1}{10})$ lb on each $\frac{1}{10}$ ft, or $w\,dx$ lb on each dx distance. Considering each dx distance to be loaded with a concentrated load of $w\,dx$, the value of the function under study for one of these small loads is $(w\,dx)\,(y)$, or $wy\,dx$, where y is the ordinate of the influence line at that point. The effect of all of these concentrated loads is equal to $\int wy\,dx$. This expression shows that the effect of a uniform load on some function of a structure equals the intensity of the uniform load times the area of the influence line along the section of the structure covered by the uniform load.

Assuming the beam of Fig. 11–5 to be loaded with a uniform load of 3 klf for the entire span, the values of V_L and $M_{\text{ℂ}}$ would be as follows:

$$V_L = (3)(\tfrac{1}{2} \times 1.0 \times 50) = 75^k \qquad \text{AREA OF INFLUENCE LINE}$$

$$M_{\text{ℂ}} = (3)(\tfrac{1}{2} \times 12.5 \times 50) = 937.5'^k$$

If the uniform load extended only from the left end to the center line of the beam, the values of V_L and $M_{\text{ℂ}}$ would be

$$V_L = (3)\left(\frac{1.0 + .5}{2} \times 25\right) = 56.25^k$$

$$M_{\text{ℂ}} = (3)(\tfrac{1}{2} \times 12.5 \times 25) = 468.75'^k$$

Should a structure support uniform and concentrated loads, the value of the function under study can be found by multiplying each concentrated load by its respective ordinate on the influence line and the uniform load by the area of the influence line opposite the section covered by the uniform load.

11–8.   Common Simple Beam Formulas from Influence Lines

Several useful expressions for moment in simple beams can be determined with influence lines. Formulas are developed for moment at the center line of a simple beam in Fig. 11–6 (a), the beam being loaded first with a uniform load and second with a concentrated load at the center line. In Fig. 11–6 (b), formulas are developed for moment at any point

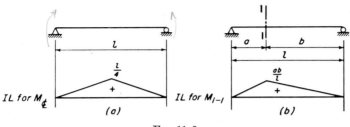

FIG. 11-6.

in a simple beam loaded with a uniform load and for moment at any point where a concentrated load is located.

Loaded with a uniform load:

$$M_{\text{¢}} = (w)\left(\frac{1}{2} \times l \times \frac{l}{4}\right) = \frac{wl^2}{8}$$

Loaded with a uniform load:

$$M_{1-1} = (w)\left(\frac{1}{2} \times \frac{ab}{l} \times l\right) = \frac{wab}{2}$$

Loaded with a concentrated load P at center line:

$$M_{\text{¢}} = \frac{Pl}{4}$$

Loaded with a concentrated load P at center line:

$$M_{1-1} = \frac{P_{ab}}{l}$$

11-9. Influence Lines for Beams with Floor Joists

Frequently the loads supported by a beam are not applied directly to the beam but are transmitted to the beam from a system of other members which are supported by the beam. Perhaps the most obvious cases of this type of framing exist in building floors and bridge floors. A common building floor framing system is shown in Fig. 11-7.

Loads from the floor slab are supported directly by the joists, which are supported at their ends by the floor beams, which are supported at their ends by the girders, which receive their support from the columns. Bridge floor arrangements and building floor arrangements are closely related; a discussion of the former is presented in Sec. 12-2.

Floor beam $A-A$ is removed from the floor system of Fig. 11-7 and considered in Fig. 11-8 for the purpose of preparing influence lines. Live

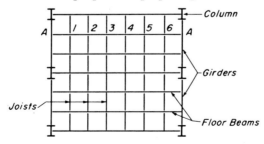

FIG. 11-7.

loads can be applied to this floor beam only at points *1, 2, 3,* etc., where joists frame into it on each side. Influence lines are shown in the figure for moment at point *2* and for shear between points *2* and *3*. Development of the first diagram needs no explanation, but some discussion is necessary for the second.

For each position of the unit load the shear is constant from *2* to *3* because the load can be applied to the beam only through the joists. The ordinates of the influence lines at each of the points can be calculated by the usual methods. As the load moves from *2* to *3*, it is being applied to the beam through the two joists in proportion to its position between them. For instance, if the load is three-fourths of the distance from *2* to *3,*

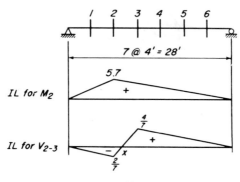

Fig. 11–8.

Fig. 11–8, the effect is $\frac{1}{4}^k$ down at *2* and $\frac{3}{4}^k$ down at *3*. As the load moves from *2* to *3*, the value of the left reaction varies linearly, as does the amount of load actually applied at point *2*. The difference between these two values is the shear between *2* and *3*, and it varies linearly, which permits the construction of a straight line between the two points. This type of influence line is a forerunner of those encountered in trusses in the next chapter. There is a section between the two points where a unit load will cause no shear in the panel; this point is designated with the letter x on the influence line. Points of this type may occur in influence lines drawn from any functions.

Problems

11–1. Prepare influence lines for shears and moments at sections *1–1* and *2–2* and for both reactions as shown in the accompanying illustration.

11–2. By using influence lines, find the shear and moment at section *1–1* in the accompanying illustration if the beam is loaded with a uniform load of 3 klf.

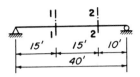

Prob. 11–1.

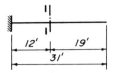

Prob. 11–2.

11–3. Draw influence lines for reactions and for moments at A and B in the accompanying illustration.

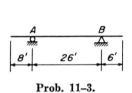

Prob. 11–3.

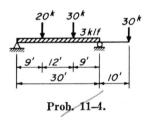

Prob. 11–4.

11–4. Determine the values of shear and moment 10 ft to the right of the left support shown in the accompanying illustration by using influence lines.

11–5. Draw the influence lines for reactions at A, B, and C for a unit load moving across the top beam of the structure shown in the accompanying illustration.

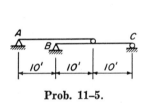

Prob. 11–5.

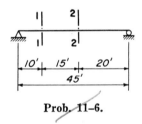

Prob. 11–6.

11–6. In the structure shown in the accompanying illustration place a 50^k concentrated load and a 3^k uniform load to give maximum negative shear at *1–1*. Compute the value of the shear. Answer the same question for maximum positive moment at *2–2*.

11–7. Draw the influence line for moment at section *1–1* as a unit load moves from A to B in the structure shown in the accompanying illustration.

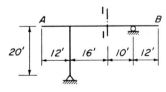

Prob. 11–7.

11-8. Draw influence lines for reactions at supports A and B and for moment at section *1-1* in the accompanying illustration.

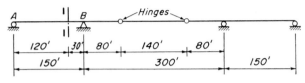

Prob. 11-8.

11-9. Draw influence lines for shear at the hinge and moment at the interior support of the structure shown in the accompanying illustration.

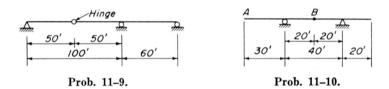

Prob. 11-9.   **Prob. 11-10.**

11-10. By using influence lines, find the maximum positive and negative moments due to a 4-klf uniform load that can occur at A and B in the accompanying illustration.

11-11. Draw influence lines for left reaction and for moment and shear at B that are due to the movement of a unit load from A to B in the structure shown in the accompanying illustration.

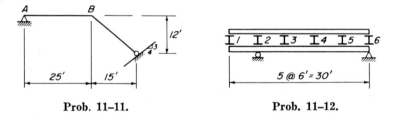

Prob. 11-11.   **Prob. 11-12.**

11-12. For the structure shown in the accompanying illustration prepare influence lines for a) shear in panel *1-2*, b) shear in panel *2-3*, and c) moment at *4*.

12 | INFLUENCE LINES FOR TRUSSES

12–1. General

The variation of stresses in trusses due to moving loads is of great importance. Influence lines may be drawn and used for making stress calculations, or they may be sketched roughly without computing the values of the ordinates and used only for placing the moving loads to cause maximum or minimum stresses.

The procedure used for preparing influence lines for trusses is closely related to the one used for beams, particularly those which have loads applied to them from joists, as described in Sec. 11–9. The exact manner of application of loads to a bridge truss from the bridge floor is described in the following section. A similar discussion could be made for the application of loads to roof trusses.

12–2. Arrangement of Bridge Floor Systems

The arrangement of the members of a bridge floor system should be carefully studied so that the manner of application of loads to the truss will be fully understood. Probably the most common type of floor system

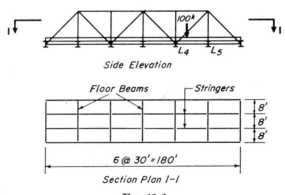

Side Elevation

Section Plan I–I

Fig. 12–1.

consists of a concrete slab supported by steel stringers running parallel to the trusses. The stringers run the length of each panel and are supported at their ends by floor beams that run transverse to the roadway and frame into the panel points or joints of the truss, Fig. 12–1.

The foregoing discussion apparently indicates that the stringers rest on the floor beams and the floor beams on the trusses. This method of explanation has been used to emphasize the manner in which loads are transferred from the pavement to the trusses, but the members are usually riveted directly to each other. Stringers are conservatively assumed to be simply supported, but actually there is some continuity in their construction.

A 100^k load is applied to the floor slab in the fifth panel of the truss of Fig. 12–1. The load is transferred from the floor slab to the stringers, thence to the floor beams, and finally to joints L_4 and L_5 of the supporting trusses. The amount of load going to each stringer depends on the position of the load between the stringers; if halfway, each stringer would carry half. Similarly, the amount of load transferred from the stringers to the floor beams depends on the longitudinal position of the load.

Figure 12–2 illustrates the calculations involved in figuring the transfer of the 100^k load to the trusses. The final reactions shown for the floor beams represent the downward loads applied at the truss panel points. The computation of truss loads is usually a much simpler process than the one described here.

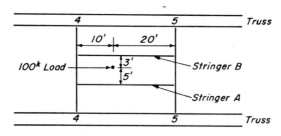

Load transferred to each stringer

$$A = \tfrac{3}{8} \times 100 = 37.5^k$$
$$B = \tfrac{5}{8} \times 100 = 62.5^k$$

Load transferred from stringer A to floor beams

$$4\text{-}4 = \tfrac{20}{30} \times 37.5 = 25^k$$
$$5\text{-}5 = \tfrac{10}{30} \times 37.5 = 12.5^k$$

Load transferred from stringer B to floor beams

$$4\text{-}4 = \tfrac{20}{30} \times 62.5 = 41.67^k$$
$$5\text{-}5 = \tfrac{10}{30} \times 62.5 = 20.83^k$$

Floor beams loaded as follows:

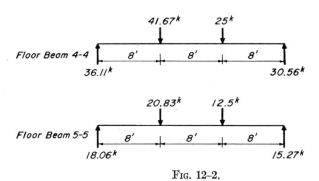

F<small>IG.</small> 12–2.

12–3.   Influence Lines for Truss Reactions

Influence lines for reactions of simply supported trusses are used to determine the maximum loads which may be applied to the supports. Although their preparation is elementary, they offer a good introductory problem in learning the construction of influence lines for truss members.

Influence lines for the reactions at both supports of an overhanging truss are given in Fig. 12–3. Loads can be applied to the truss only by the floor beams at the panel points, and floor beams are assumed to be present at each of the panel points including the end ones. A load applied at the very end of the truss opposite the end panel point will be transferred to that panel point by the end floor beam.

12–4.   Influence Lines for Member Stresses of Parallel-Chord Trusses

Influence lines for stresses in truss members may be constructed in the same manner as those for various beam functions. The unit load moves across the truss, and the ordinates for the stress in the member under

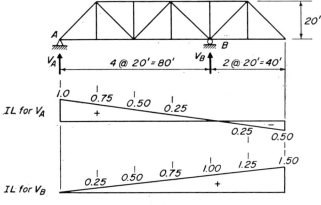

F<small>IG.</small> 12–3.

consideration may be computed for the load at each panel point. In most cases it is unnecessary to place the load at every panel point and calculate the resulting value of the stress, because certain portions of influence lines can readily be seen to consist of straight lines for several panels.

One method used for calculating the stresses in a chord member of a truss consists in passing an imaginary section through the truss cutting the member in question and taking moments at the intersection of the other members cut by the section. The resulting stress in the member is equal to the moment divided by the lever arm; therefore, the influence line for a chord member is the same shape as the influence line for moment at its moment center.

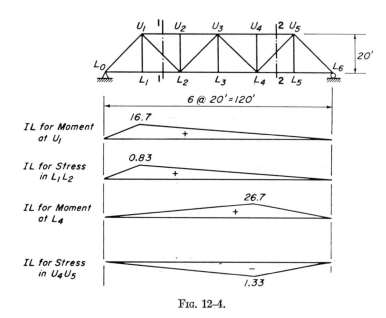

Fig. 12–4.

The truss of Fig. 12–4 is used to illustrate this point. The stress in member L_1L_2 is determined by passing section 1–1 and taking moments at U_1. An influence line is shown for the moment at U_1 and for the stress in L_1L_2, the ordinates of the latter figure being those of the former divided by the lever arm. Similarly, section 2–2 is passed to compute the stress in U_4U_5, and influence lines are shown for the moment at L_4 and for the stress in U_4U_5.

The stresses in the diagonals of parallel-chord trusses may be calculated from the shear in each panel. The influence line for the shear in a panel is of the same shape as the influence line for the stress in the diagonal, because the vertical component of stress in the diagonal is equal numerically to the shear in the panel. Figure 12–5 illustrates this fact for two of the diagonals of the same truss considered in Fig. 12–4. For some positions of the unit loads the diagonals are in compression, and for others they are in tension.

The vertical components of stress in the diagonals can be converted into the actual stresses from their slopes. The sign convention for positive and negative shears is the same as the one used previously.

12–5. Influence Lines for Members of Nonparallel-Chord Trusses

Influence-line ordinates for the stress in a chord member of a curved-chord truss may be determined by passing a vertical section through the

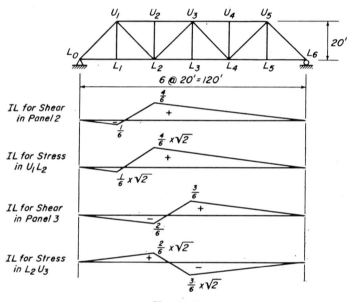

Fig. 12–5.

panel and taking moments at the intersection of the diagonal and the other chord. Several such influence lines are drawn for chords of a Parker truss in Fig. 12–6.

The ordinates for the influence line for stress in a diagonal may be obtained by passing a vertical section through the panel and taking moments at the intersection of the two chord members, as illustrated in Fig. 12–6, where the stress in U_1L_2 is obtained by passing section $1–1$ and taking moments at the intersection of chords U_1U_2 and L_1L_2 at point x. The influence line is drawn for the vertical component of stress in the inclined member. In the following pages many influence lines are drawn for either the vertical or horizontal components of stress for inclined members. Stress components obtained from the diagrams may be quickly adjusted to resultant stresses from slopes of the members.

The influence line for the mid-vertical U_3L_3 is obtained indirectly by computing the vertical components of stress in U_2U_3 and U_3U_4. The ordinates for U_3L_3 are found by summing up these components. The influence lines for the other verticals are more easily drawn. Member U_1L_1 can have a stress only when the unit load lies between L_0 and L_2. It has

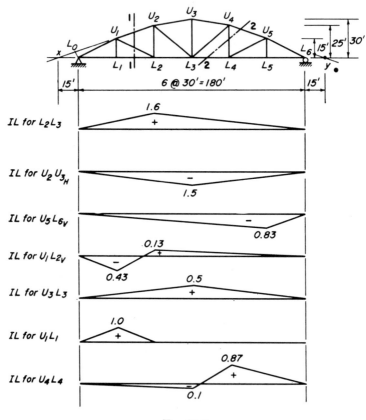

Fig. 12–6.

no stress if the load is at either of these joints, but a tension of unity occurs when the load is at L_1. Influence lines for verticals such as U_4L_4 can be drawn by two methods. A section such as 2–2 may be passed through the truss and moments taken at the intersection of the chords at point y, or if the influence diagram for L_4U_5 is available, its vertical components may be used to calculate the ordinates for U_4L_4.

12–6.   Influence Lines for K Truss

Figure 12–7 shows influence lines for several members of a K truss. The calculations necessary for preparing the diagrams for the chord members are equivalent to those used for the chords of trusses previously considered.   The values needed to plot the diagrams for vertical and diagonal members are slightly more difficult to obtain.

The stresses in the two diagonals of each panel may be obtained from the shear in the panel.   By knowing that the horizontal components are

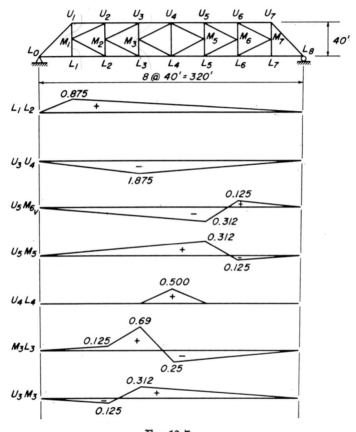

Fig. 12–7.

equal and opposite, the relationship between their vertical components can be found from their slopes.   If the slopes are equal, the shear to be carried divides equally between the two.   The influence lines for the verticals, such as $U_5 M_5$, may be determined from the influence lines for the adjoining diagonals if available.   On the other hand, the ordinates may be computed independently for various positions of the unit load. The student should make a careful comparison of the influence lines for the upper and lower verticals, such as those given for M_3L_3 and U_3M_3 in the figure.

The influence line for the mid-vertical U_4L_4 can be developed by computing the vertical components of stress in M_3L_4 and L_4M_5, or in M_3U_4 and U_4M_5, for each position of the unit load. The vertical components of stress in each of these pairs of members will cancel each other unless the shear in panel *4* is unequal to the shear in panel *5*, which is possible only when the unit load is at L_4.

12–7. Determination of Maximum Stresses

Truss members are designed to resist maximum stresses which may be caused by any combination of the dead, live, and impact loads to which the truss may be subjected. The live load probably consists of a series of moving concentrated loads representing the wheel loads of the vehicles using the structure, but for convenience in stress analysis an approximately equivalent uniform live load with only one or two concentrated loads is often used in their place. Live loads for which highway and railroad bridges are designed and common impact expressions are discussed in detail in Chapter 13.

Two methods are available for calculating the maximum stresses in the members of a truss. These are the exact and panel-load methods.

Exact Method. The exact method, previously illustrated for beams in Secs. 11–6 and 11–7, requires the preparation of an influence line for stress in the member under consideration.

The dead load, representing the weight of the structure, extends for the entire length of the truss, but the uniform and concentrated live loads are placed at the points on the influence line which cause maximum stress of the character being studied. If tension is being studied, the live uniform load is placed along the section of the truss corresponding to the positive or tensile section of the influence line, and the live concentrated loads are placed at the maximum positive tensile ordinates on the diagram.

Members whose influence lines have both positive and negative ordinates may possibly be in tension for one combination of loads and in compression for another. A member subject to *stress reversal* must be designed to resist both the maximum compressive and maximum tensile stresses.

In members U_1U_2, U_1L_2, and U_2L_3 of the truss of Fig. 12–8, the maximum possible stresses due to the following loads are desired.

1) Dead uniform load of 1.5 klf.

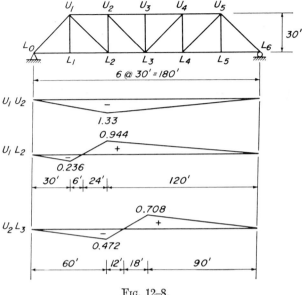

FIG. 12–8.

2) Live uniform load of 2 klf.
3) Moving concentrated load of 20^k.
4) Impact of 24.4 per cent.

The influence lines are drawn, and the stresses are computed by the exact method as described in the following paragraphs:

U_1U_2. The member is in compression for every position of the unit load; therefore, the dead uniform load and the live uniform load are placed over the entire span. The moving concentrated load of 20^k is placed at the maximum compression ordinate on the influence line. The impact factor is multiplied by the live load stresses and added to the total.

$$DL = (1.5) (180) (-1.33) (\tfrac{1}{2}) = -180.0$$
$$LL = (2) (180) (-1.33) (\tfrac{1}{2}) = -240.0$$
$$+ (20) (-1.33) = - 26.7$$
$$I = (0.244) (-240.0 - 26.7) = - 65.1$$

Total stress $= -511.8^k$ compression

U_1L_2. Examination of the influence line for U_1L_2 shows that for some positions of the unit load the member is in compression, while for others it is in tension. The live loads should be placed over the positive portion of the diagram and the dead loads across the entire structure to obtain the largest possible tensile stress. Similarly, the live loads should be placed over the negative portion of the diagram and the dead loads over the entire structure to obtain the largest possible compressive stress.

Maximum Tension

$$DL = (1.5) (144) (+0.944) (\tfrac{1}{2}) = +102.0$$
$$+ (1.5) (36) (-0.236) (\tfrac{1}{2}) = - 6.4$$
$$LL = (2) (144) (+0.944) (\tfrac{1}{2}) = +136.0$$
$$+ (20) (+0.944) = + 18.9$$
$$I = (0.244) (+136.0+18.9) = + 37.8$$

Total stress $ = +288.3^{k}$ tension

Maximum Compression

$$DL = (1.5) (144) (+0.944) (\tfrac{1}{2}) = +102.0$$
$$+ (1.5) (36) (-0.236) (\tfrac{1}{2}) = - 6.4$$
$$LL = (2) (36) (-0.236) (\tfrac{1}{2}) = - 8.4$$
$$+ (20) (-0.236) = - 4.7$$
$$I = (0.244) (-8.4-4.7) = - 3.2$$

Total stress $ = + 79.3^{k}$ tension

U_2L_3. The calculations for U_1L_2 proved it could have only tensile stresses regardless of the positioning of the live loads given. The following calculations show stress reversal may occur in member U_2L_3.

Maximum Tension

$$DL = (1.5) (108) (+0.708) (\tfrac{1}{2}) = + 57.3$$
$$+ (1.5) (72) (-0.472) (\tfrac{1}{2}) = - 25.5$$
$$LL = (2) (108) (+0.708) (\tfrac{1}{2}) = + 76.4$$
$$+ (20) (+0.708) = + 14.2$$
$$I = (0.244) (+76.4+14.2) = + 22.1$$

Total stress $ = +144.5^{k}$ tension

Maximum Compression

$$DL = (1.5) (108) (+0.708) (\tfrac{1}{2}) = +57.3$$
$$+ (1.5) (72) (-0.472) (\tfrac{1}{2}) = -25.5$$
$$LL = (2.0) (72) (-0.472) (\tfrac{1}{2}) = -34.0$$
$$+ (20) (-0.472) = - 9.4$$
$$I = (0.244) (-34.0-9.4) = -10.6$$

Total stress $ = -22.2^{k}$ compression

Panel-Load Method. The first part of this section considered the exact method of calculating maximum tensile and compressive stresses due to a set of moving loads. For maximum tension the load was placed on the exact portion of the truss corresponding to the positive section of the influence line, and the tension caused equaled the intensity of the uniform load times the positive area of the diagram. The results were exact or mathematically correct, but an approximate method called the panel-load method is sometimes more convenient to use.

One basis for using an approximate method can be found in Sec. 13–4, where common empirical formulas for impact are presented. The values obtained from such expressions are only estimates of the effect of impact and are given as percentages of the live-load stresses. Since the total stress in a truss member is the sum of the dead load plus live load plus impact stresses and since the impact is only approximately correct, it seems unnecessary to use great precision in computing the live-load stresses. It is therefore satisfactory to use a reasonable estimate for the live-load portion, if the calculations are appreciably expedited thereby. It will be seen that the panel-load method cannot give stresses smaller than those obtained by the exact method and will give the same values in some cases.

For this discussion the influence line for member U_2L_3 of the truss of Fig. 12–9 and a moving uniform load of 2 klf are used. By the exact method the largest possible tension in U_2L_3 occurs when the uniform load is placed along the positive portion of the diagram, as shown in Fig. 12–9 (a). The stress would be as follows: (2) (171.43) (+0.884) (½) =151.5^k tension. In the panel-load method, full panel loads are assumed to be placed at each of the panel points on the side of the influence line being loaded. This placement makes it unnecessary to compute the

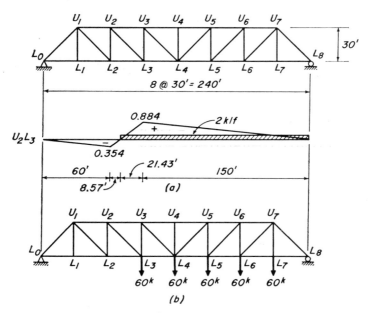

Fig. 12–9.

numerical values of the ordinates for the influence line, because a rough sketch of the diagram will reveal which panel points should be loaded for maximum tension and which ones should be loaded for maximum compression. The stress in the member may be computed by some other method.

For maximum tension in U_2L_3, full panel loads ($2 \times 30 = 60^k$) are placed at each panel point inside the positive section of the influence line. To have full panel loads, the uniform load must extend from L_2 to the right end, whereas the positive section of the influence line extends only from the zero point between L_2 and L_3 to the right end. A larger panel load is caused at L_3 than is used by the exact method, and since the effect of the half panel load at L_2 having a negative influence-line ordinate is neglected, the resulting positive stress will be larger than the value obtained by the exact method. For the full panel loads, the stress in U_2L_3 obtained by statics is $+159.0^k$, or 5 per cent higher than the exact value.

The results cannot possibly be smaller than the exact values because the panel load next to the point where the influence line changes from tension to compression is made larger. Should the influence line consist of a single triangle, identical results will be obtained by the two methods because the uniform load will be assumed to extend over the same length in both cases, i.e., the entire span.

12–8. Counters in Bridge Trusses

The fact that a member in compression is in danger of bending or buckling reduces its strength and makes its design something of a problem. The design of a 20-ft member for a tensile stress of 100^k will result in a much smaller section than is required for a member of the same length subject to a compressive load of the same magnitude. The ability of a member to resist compressive loads depends upon its stiffness, which is measured by the *slenderness ratio*. The slenderness ratio is the ratio of the length of a member to its least radius of gyration. As a section becomes longer, or as its slenderness ratio increases, the danger of buckling increases, and a larger section is required to withstand the same load.

This discussion shows there is a considerable advantage in keeping the diagonals of a truss in tension if possible. If a truss supported only dead load, it would be a simple matter to arrange the diagonals so that they were all in tension. All of the diagonals of the Pratt truss of Fig. 12–10 (a) would be in tension for a uniform dead load. The calculations in Sec. 12–7, however, have shown that live loads may cause the stresses in some of the diagonals of a bridge truss to alternate between tension and compression. The constant passage of trains or trucks back and forth across a bridge will probably cause the stresses in some of the diagonals to continually change from tension to compression and back to tension.

The possibilities of stress reversal are much greater in the diagonals near the center of a truss. The reason for this situation can be seen by referring to the truss of Fig. 12–9, where a positive shear obviously causes tension in members U_1L_2 and U_2L_3. The positive dead-load shear is much smaller in panel 3 than in panel 2, and it is more likely for the live load to be in a position to cause a negative shear large enough to overcome the positive shear and produce compression in the diagonal.

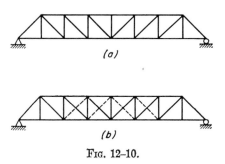

(a)

(b)

Fig. 12–10.

A few decades ago, when it was common for truss members to be pin-connected, the diagonals were actually eyebars which were capable of resisting little compression. The same stress condition exists in trusses erected today with diagonals consisting of a pair of small steel angles or other shapes of little stiffness. It was formerly common to add another tension-resisting diagonal to the panels where stress reversal could occur, the new diagonal running across the first one and into the previously unconnected corners of the panel. These members, called *counters* or *counter diagonals*, can be seen in hundreds of older bridges across the country but rarely in new ones.

Figure 12–10 (b) shows a Pratt truss to which counters have been added in the middle four panels, the counters being represented by dotted lines. When counters have been added in a panel, both diagonals may consist of relatively slender and light members, neither being able to resist appreciable compression. With light and slender diagonals the entire shear in the panel is assumed to be resisted by the diagonal which would be in tension for that type of shear, while the other diagonal is relaxed or without stress. The two diagonals in a panel may be thought of as cables which can resist no compression whatsoever. If compression were applied to one of the cables, it would become limp, while the other one would be stretched. A truss with counters is actually statically indeterminate unless the counter is adjusted to have zero stress under dead load.

Today's bridges are designed with diagonals capable of withstanding stress reversal. The constant change in character of stress in a member, as vehicles move back and forth across the structure, places the member in danger of a fatigue failure unless it is designed with an extra-large safety factor. The AREA and AASHO specifications require the compressive and tensile stresses used in the design of members subject to reversal to be increased by 50 per cent of the smaller. For illustration, a member having a maximum tension of 120^k and a maximum compression of 60^k would be designed for those stresses plus 50 per cent of 60^k, or 30^k; i.e., the tensile design stress would be 150^k and the compressive design stress 90^k. It is important to realize that the verticals in some trusses, those of the Pratt being one example, are also subject to possible stress reversal.

Problems

12–1 to 12–5. Draw influence lines for the members indicated.

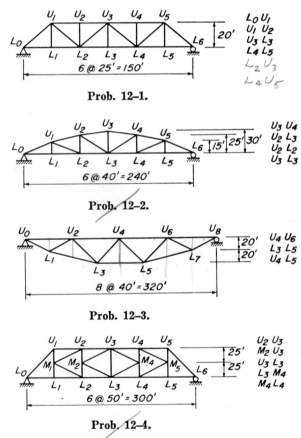

Prob. 12–1.

Prob. 12–2.

Prob. 12–3.

Prob. 12–4.

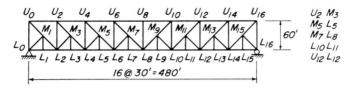

Prob. 12–5.

12–6. By the exact method, compute the maximum and minimum stresses in U_1L_2 and L_2U_3 of the truss of Prob. 12–1 for a uniform dead load of 1.2 klf, a moving uniform load of 2.4 klf, a moving concentrated load of 20^k, and an impact factor of 22 per cent.

12–7. By the exact method, determine if stress reversal is possible in U_2L_3 and U_2L_3 of the truss of Prob. 12–2 for the loads used in Prob. 12–6.

12–8. Solve Prob. 12–6 by using the panel-load method.

12–9. Solve Prob. 12–7 by using the panel-load method.

12–10. Compute by the panel-load method the maximum and minimum stresses in members M_7L_8, $U_{10}L_{10}$, and M_9L_{10} of the truss of Prob. 12–5 for a moving uniform load of 1800 lb/ft.

12–11. Draw influence lines for the stresses in members U_2L_3, L_3U_4, and L_5U_6 of the structure shown in the accompanying illustration. Assume the members are incapable of resisting compressive stresses, as are the other diagonals in those panels.

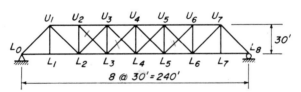

Prob. 12–11.

12–12. Draw influence lines for members a, b, and c of the structure shown in the accompanying illustration.

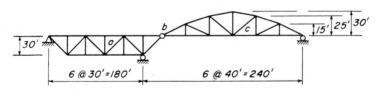

Prob. 12–12.

13 |

MOVING LOADS

13–1. General

Chapters 11 and 12 have repeatedly indicated that, to design a beam, girder, truss, or any other structure supporting moving loads, the designer must be able to determine which positions of these loads cause maximum shear, moment, etc. at various points in the structure. If he can place the loads at the positions causing maximums, he need not worry about any other positions the loads might take on the structure. Should a structure be loaded with a uniform live load and not more than one or two moving concentrated loads, the critical positions for placing the loads will be obvious from the influence lines.

If, however, the structure is to support a series of concentrated loads of varying magnitudes, such as groups of truck or train wheels, the problem is not as simple. The influence line will, of course, indicate the approximate positions for placing the loads, because it is reasonable to assume that the heaviest loads should be grouped in the vicinity of the largest ordinates of the diagram. The procedure for finding exactly the critical positions of the loads is substantially a trial-and-error method for which the influence line will provide a good initial estimate.

13–2. Live Loads for Highway Bridges

Although highway bridges must support several different types of vehicles, the heaviest possible loads are caused by a series of trucks. The AASHO specifies that highway bridges shall be designed for a continual line of motor trucks. The truck loads specified are designated with an H prefix followed by a number indicating the total weight of the truck, in tons. The weight may be followed by another number indicating the year of the specifications. For example, an H20–44 loading indicates a 20-ton truck and the 1944 specifications. A sketch of the truck and the distances between axle centers, wheel centers, etc. is shown in Fig. 13–1.

The selection of the particular truck loading to be used in design depends upon the bridge location, anticipated traffic, etc. These loadings may be broken down into three groups as follows.

Two-Axle Trucks; H20, H15, and H10. The weight of an H truck is assumed to be distributed two-tenths to the front axle (e.g., 4 tons, or 8^k, for an H20 loading) and eight-tenths to the rear axle. The axles are spaced 14′-0″ on center, while the center-to-center lateral spacing of the wheels is 6′-0″. Should a truck loading varying in weight from these be desired,

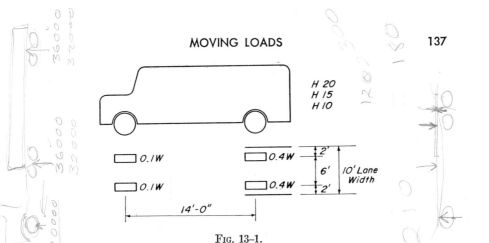

Fig. 13–1.

one that has axle loads in direct proportion to the standard ones listed here may be used. A loading as small as the H10 may be used only for bridges supporting the lightest traffic.

Two-Axle Trucks Plus One-Axle Semi-Trailer; H20–S16 and H15–S12. For today's highway bridges carrying a great amount of truck traffic, the two-axle truck loading with a one-axle semi-trailer weighing 80 per cent of the main truck load is commonly specified for design. The H20–S16 truck has 4 tons on the front axle, 16 tons on the rear axle, and 16 tons on the trailer axle. The distance from the rear truck axle to the semi-trailer axle is varied from 14 to 30 ft, depending on which spacing will cause the most critical conditions.

Uniform Lane Loadings. Computation of stresses caused by a series of concentrated loads, whether they represent two-axle trucks or two-axle trucks with semi-trailers, is a tedious job; therefore, a lane loading which will produce approximately the same stresses is frequently used. The lane loading consists of a uniform load plus a single moving concentrated load. This load system represents a line of medium-weight traffic with a heavy truck somewhere in the line. The uniform load per foot is equal to 0.016 times the total weight of the truck to which the load is to be roughly equivalent. The concentrated load equals 0.45 times the truck weight for moment calculations and 0.65 times the truck weight for shear calculations. These values for an H20 loading would be as follows: 0.016×20 tons equals 640 lb/ft of lane; concentrated load for moment 0.45×20 tons equals 18^k; and concentrated load for shear 0.65×20 tons equals 26^k.

The lane loading is more convenient to handle, but it may not be used unless it produces stresses equal to or greater than those produced by the corresponding H loading. Lane loadings can be shown to cause larger moments for spans above 56 ft and larger shears for spans above 33 ft. By noting the large percentage of highway bridges having spans greater than 56 ft, the frequency of application of lane loadings can be understood. The possibility of having a continuous series of heavily loaded trucks in every lane of a bridge having more than two lanes does not seem as great as that for a bridge having only two lanes. The AASHO, therefore, permits the stresses caused by full loads in every lane to be reduced by a certain factor if the bridge has more than two lanes.

John F. Fitzgerald Expressway, Mystic River Bridge to Haymarket Square, Boston, Massachusetts. (Courtesy of American Institute of Steel Construction, Inc.)

13-3. Live Loads for Railway Bridges

Railway bridges are commonly analyzed for a series of loads devised by Theodore Cooper. His loads, referred to as E loadings, represent two locomotives followed by a line of freight cars. A series of concentrated loads is used for the locomotives, while a uniform load represents the freight cars. Mr. Cooper introduced his loading system in 1894; it was the so-called E-40 load, which is pictured in Fig. 13-2. The train is assumed to have a 40^k load on the driving axle of the engine. Since his system was introduced, the weights of trains have been increased considerably, until at the present time bridges are designed on the basis of loads in the vicinity of an E–72 loading, and the use of E–80 and E–90 loadings is not uncommon.

Various tables that are obtainable present detailed information pertaining to Cooper's loadings such as axle loads, moments, and shears. If information is available for one E loading, the information for any other E loading can be obtained by direct proportion. The axle loads of an E–75 are 75/40 those for an E–40; those for an E–60 are 60/72 of those for an E–72; etc. Tables used in conjunction with the maximum criteria presented later in this chapter greatly reduce the computations.

Cooper's loadings do not accurately picture today's trains, but they are still in general use despite the availability of several more modern and more realistic loadings such as Dr. D. B. Steinman's M–60 loading.[1]

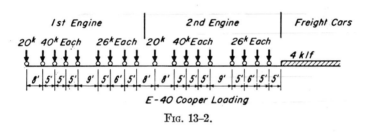

E–40 Cooper Loading

Fig. 13–2.

13–4. Impact Loadings

The truck and train loads applied to highway and railroad bridges are applied not gently and gradually but rather violently, which causes stresses to increase. Additional loads, called impact loads, must be considered, and they are taken into account by increasing the live-load stresses by some percentage, the percentage being obtained from purely empirical expressions. Numerous formulas have been presented for estimating impact. One example is the following 1949 AASHO formula for highway bridges, in which I is the per cent of impact and L is the length of the span, in feet, over which live load is placed to obtain a maximum stress. The AASHO says that it is unnecessary to use an impact percentage greater than 30 per cent, regardless of the value given by the formula. Notice that the longer the span length becomes the smaller becomes the impact.

$$I = \frac{50}{L + 25}$$

[1] *Transactions of the American Society of Civil Engineers,* vol. 86.

Impact factors or percentages for railroad bridges are higher than those for highway bridges because of the much greater vibrations caused by the wheels of a train as compared to the relatively soft rubber-tired vehicles on a highway bridge. A person need only stand near a railroad bridge for a few seconds while a fast-moving and heavily loaded freight train passes over to see the difference. Tests have shown the impact on railroad bridges will often run as high as 100 per cent or more. Not only does a train have a direct vertical impact, or bouncing up and down, but it also has a lurching or swaying back-and-forth type of motion. Some AREA impact formulas are as follows:

Direct Vertical Effect for Beams, Girders, Floor Beams, etc.

$$I = 60 - \frac{L^2}{500} \qquad \text{for } L < 100 \text{ ft}$$

$$I = \frac{1800}{L-40} + 10 \qquad \text{for } L = 100 \text{ ft or more}$$

Direct Vertical Effect for Trusses

$$I = \frac{4000}{L+25} + 15$$

Lurching Effect of Locomotive

$$\text{Lurching} = \frac{100}{S}$$

where S is the center-to-center distance between trusses, longitudinal girders, or stringers.

13–5. Maximum Shear in a Beam Supporting Uniform Live Loads

The simple beam of Fig. 13–3 and the influence lines for shear at section *1–1* and at the beam ends are considered here. It is apparent from these diagrams that maximum shear is caused when the moving uniform load completely covers the beam. Under this loading condition, the reactions are at their maximums, as are the shears an infinitesimal distance from the supports. A uniform load of 6 klf would cause shears at each end of the beam equal to $6 \times \frac{1}{2} \times 20 \times 1.0 = 60^k$.

Examination of the influence line for shear at section *1–1* shows that maximum shear at the section would be developed if the uniform load were placed over the positive or negative portion of the diagram having the largest area. For section *1–1* the load is placed across the beam from the section to the right support, which causes a positive shear of $6 \times \frac{1}{2} \times 14 \times 0.7 = +29.4^k$. The maximum negative shear at the section is developed when the uniform load extends from the left support to the section and equals $6 \times \frac{1}{2} \times 6 \times 0.3 = -5.4^{k}$.

To review, the problem of determining the maximum shear in a simple beam loaded with a moving uniform load is elementary. The beam is loaded for the entire span, and the reactions equal the maximum shear that can occur. If the maximum shear is desired at a certain section in the beam, the uniform load is so placed that it extends from the section

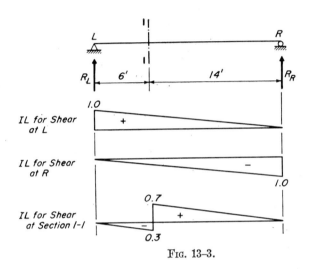

FIG. 13–3.

to the support which is the greatest distance away. The value of the shear so developed is computed from the area of the influence line corresponding to the portion of the beam along which the load is placed. The maximum shears at points in beams other than simple ones due to a moving uniform load can be determined from the influence lines in a similar manner.

13–6. Maximum Bending Moments at Points in Beams Supporting Uniform Live Loads

Influence lines for bending moment at two sections in a simple beam are presented in Fig. 13–4. Since these influence lines have positive ordinates for their entire lengths, it is readily apparent that maximum moments will occur at both sections when the uniform load extends across the entire span. For a uniform load of 4 klf the maximum moments at sections $1-1$ and $2-2$ are as follows:

$$M_{1-1} = 4 \times \frac{1}{2} \times 30 \times 6.67 = 400'^{k}$$
$$M_{2-2} = 4 \times \frac{1}{2} \times 30 \times 4.17 = 250'^{k}$$

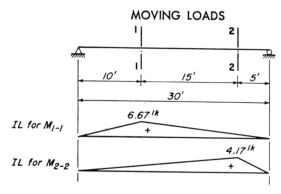

FIG. 13-4.

The ordinates of the influence lines for moments at sections in other types of beams will rarely be all positive or all negative. Maximum positive moment for a moving uniform load can be found by placing the load over the positive portion of the diagram and maximum negative moment by placing the load over the negative portion. The intensity of the load is multiplied by the corresponding influence-line area.

13–7.   Maximum End Shear in a Beam Supporting Moving Concentrated Loads

The largest shear which can be developed in a simple beam has been shown to occur an infinitesimal distance from one of the supports. At this point the shear equals the reaction, and the influence line for the reaction is the same as the influence line for the shear next to it. Influence lines are plotted for the left reaction and the shear an infinitesimal distance to the right of the reaction for a simple beam in Fig. 13–5.

If a simple beam is loaded with a series of moving concentrated loads, the maximum shear occurs at the supports, and the problem becomes a question of which position of the loads will cause the greatest end reaction

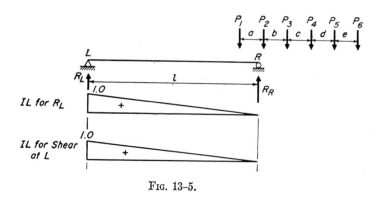

FIG. 13-5.

and thus the greatest shear. For example, the beam of Fig. 13–5 is to be loaded with the series of loads shown, and it is desired to find the maximum shear which can occur at the left support. As the series of loads moves onto the span from the right side, the left reaction begins to build up from zero to a maximum when P_1 comes over the support. Immediately after P_1 leaves the span, the reaction decreases by the amount of the load. As the loads continue to the left, the left reaction begins to increase again until it reaches another maximum when P_2 is over the support. This process is repeated as each of the loads moves toward the left support. The left reaction reaches a maximum for each and then falls off as the load moves off the span.

One method of determining the maximum value of the left reaction is trial and error. The reaction may be computed when P_1 is over the support, when P_2 is over the support, and so forth for all of the loads. The largest value of the left reaction obtained is the largest shear possible in the beam for that loading condition. The method is tedious, and a simpler procedure based on a consideration of the change in the reaction as each load passes off the span is available.

For the following discussion ΣP is considered to be the sum of the loads remaining on the beam at any time. As P_1 passes off the span and P_2 moves over the support, the shear changes as follows:

$$dV = \frac{\Sigma P a}{l} - P_1$$

As P_2 passes off the span and P_3 moves over the left support, the shear change is

$$dV = \frac{\Sigma P b}{l} - P_2$$

If the resulting change is positive, the shear has increased; if negative, it has decreased. The loads may be considered one by one as they leave the span and the next load moves over the support. The first load leaving the span which causes a decrease should be the one placed over the support for computation of maximum shear. For normal loading conditions, one of the first two or three loads will be found to be the critical one.

Should another load come onto the span from the right end, as the loads are moved successively over the left support, its increasing effect on the left reaction, and thus the shear, must be included in the calculations. The shear increase equals the magnitude of the load times the distance moved onto the span divided by the span length, or simply the magnitude times the ordinate of the influence line opposite the position of the load. Example 13–1 illustrates the application of this method of determining maximum end shear in a simple beam caused by a series of moving concentrated loads.

EXAMPLE 13-1. Determine the maximum shear developed at the left end of the beam shown in Fig. 13-6 as the concentrated loads shown move across the span from right to left.

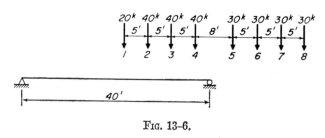

FIG. 13-6.

Solution: Move load *1* off span to left and load *2* over support:

$$dV = \frac{(240)(5)}{40} - 20 = +10 \qquad \text{an increase}$$

Move load *3* over support:

$$dV = \frac{(200)(5)}{40} - 40 = -15 \qquad \text{a decrease}$$

Place load *2* over left support for maximum end shear:

$$V = \frac{(30)(7+12+17+22) + (40)(30+35+40)}{40} = 148.5^{\text{k}}$$

13-8. Maximum Shear at Interior Points of Beams Supporting Moving Concentrated Loads

The maximum possible shear in a beam at some point away from the supports caused by the passage of a series of concentrated loads is often needed for design. Its value may be determined by a method closely related to the one used for computing maximum end shears. The beam and loads of Fig. 13-7 will be used in the following discussion.

The problem may be solved by trial and error, as could the end shear problem. The loads may be moved across the span from right to left, and the shear then computed when the first load is over the section, when the second load is over the section, etc. Eventually the maximum shear will be determined. The work is not as lengthy as this discussion may seem to indicate, because the maximum will probably occur when one of the first two or three loads is above the section. The influence line for shear at section *1-1* in the beam of Fig. 13-7 shows that a good estimate for positioning the loads can be made by placing as many loads as possible over the positive portion of the influence line and as few as possible over the negative portion. If the loads are moved onto the span from the right side until the first 20^{k} load is at the section, the shear developed is probably close to the absolute maximum possible.

A consideration of the shear change as each load passes over the section presents a much quicker solution than the trial-and-error method discussed in the preceding paragraph. As the loads move across the span, the shear builds up as each load approaches the section. When the 10^k load is at the section, a maximum shear occurs, but after it moves an infinitesimal distance to the left, the shear falls off 10^k. Continuing to move the loads to the left causes the shear to gradually increase until the first 20^k load reaches the section. At that time another maximum occurs, but as soon as the load moves slightly beyond the section, the shear is reduced by the amount of the load. The absolute maximum shear occurs when one of the concentrated loads is at the section.

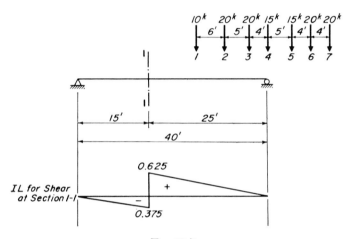

Fig. 13–7.

As the loads move across the span, the maximum shears that occur for each load as it passes over the section will increase until the load causing the absolute maximum reaches the section. After it passes the section, the maximums occurring for the successive loads will decrease. If it were possible to find which load caused the absolute maximum, it would be necessary to compute the shear for only one position of the loads. This load can be determined from a consideration of the changes in shear as each of the loads passes the section.

The shear change, as the loads are moved one after another to the section, equals the increase in the left reaction due to the movement of the loads to the left plus the increase in the left reaction due to any additional loads which have come onto the span from the right, less the load which has just passed over the section. Should the sum of these values be positive, the shear has increased. The first load which in moving past the section causes a decrease is the one which will cause absolute maximum shear, and the computations are made with that load over the section. Example 13–2 illustrates the computation of maximum shear at an interior point of a beam.

EXAMPLE 13–2. Compute the maximum shear at section *1–1* in the beam of Fig. 13–7 for the loads given in the figure.

Solution: Move load *1* past section and load *2* up to section, noting that load *7* moves onto span:

$$dV = \frac{(100)(6)}{40} + \frac{(20)(3)}{40} - 10 = +6.5 \quad \text{an increase}$$

Move load *3* to section:

$$dV = \frac{(120)(5)}{40} - 20 = -5 \quad \text{a decrease}$$

By using load *2* to compute maximum shear:

$$R_L = \frac{(20)(3+7+20+25)+(15)(11+16)+(10)(31)}{40} = 45.4^k$$

$$V = 45.4 - 10 = 35.4^k$$

13–9. Maximum Moment at a Point in a Beam Supporting Concentrated Live Loads

The design of a beam may require the calculation of maximum moments at several points in the beam caused by the movement of a series of concentrated loads across the span. The trial-and-error method of moving one load after another up to the point in question and computing the moment in each case is one way of handling the problem. The influence

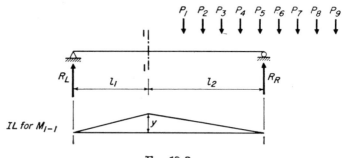

FIG. 13–8.

line presents a method of estimating the value of the maximum moment. Examination of the simple beam of Fig. 13–8 and the influence line for moment at section *1–1* indicates that maximum moment will occur when as many of the large loads as possible are located near the peak ordinates of the diagram. The loads could be positioned on the diagram in this manner and the moment calculated. The result should be a fairly good estimate of the maximum possible moment at the point.

A study of the moment change as each load moves up to and past the section provides a method of quickly obtaining the exact maximum moment. As the group of loads in Fig. 13–8 is moved onto the span and up to the section, the moment at section *1–1* equals $R_L \times l_1$ minus any loads that move past the section times their lever arms back to the section. As a load moves toward the section from the right, the moment increases until the load is at the section, because its movement to the left causes an increase in R_L and a corresponding increase in $R_L \times l_1$. When the load passes the section, the moment begins to decrease, because the increase in $R_L \times l_1$ is not as great as the increase in the load times the distance back to the section. A maximum moment occurs when each load is at the section, and the problem is to determine which load causes the absolute maximum.

The movement of the loads from right to left on the beam of Fig. 13–8 or up the influence line causes a moment increase. The movement of the first loads past the section or down the influence line may cause a decrease in total moment. The change that occurs in the moment is equal to the increase due to the loads on the right of the section times their increase in influence-line ordinates less the loads on the left of the section times their ordinate decrease.

The total moment at section *1–1* is greater if the increases to the right are greater than the decreases to the left. A movement of the loads on the right of the section to the left a distance of 1 ft causes each of the ordinates of the loads to increase by $1 \times y/l_2$. The total increase in moment would be as follows:

$$\text{Moment increase} = \text{total load to right} \times \frac{y}{l_2}$$

The movement of the loads on the left of the section to the left a distance of 1 ft causes each of the ordinates of the loads to decrease by $1 \times y/l_1$. The total decrease in moment may be written as

$$\text{Moment decrease} = \text{total load to left} \times \frac{y}{l_1}$$

The rate of change of moment at the section is constant until one of the loads passes the section. The new rate of change of moment will remain constant until another load passes the section. Although the rate of change of moment changes as each load passes the section, it will be positive until the load causing absolute maximum moment reaches the section; thereafter, the moment will decrease. As this particular load reaches the section, the rate of change of moment at the section becomes zero, because the rate of increase equals the rate of decrease.

Moment decrease = moment increase

$$\text{Total load to left} \times \frac{y}{l_1} = \text{total load to right} \times \frac{y}{l_2}$$

By canceling y from the equation,

$$\frac{\text{Total load to left}}{l_1} = \frac{\text{total load to right}}{l_2}$$

Absolute maximum moment at any point in a beam due to a moving series of concentrated loads occurs when the average load to the left of the point is equal to the average load to the right of the point. To determine the absolute maximum moment at a point in a beam, each load is moved up until it is an infinitesimal distance to the right of the point, and the average load on each side of the point is determined. The load is moved just to the left of the point, and the averages are computed again. If the movement of the load from the right of the point to the left of the point causes the average load to the right to change from larger than the average load to the left to smaller, the critical load has been found. The moment is computed with that load over the point because during its passage the criterion is satisfied. Example 13–3 illustrates the application of the average-load method. A convenient table is given in Fig. 13–9 for recording the average-load calculations.

	Try Load 6	
	Average Load to Left	*Average Load to Right*
With Load to Right of Point		
With Load to Left of Point		

Fɪɢ. 13–9.

Exᴀᴍᴘʟᴇ 13–3. Calculate the absolute maximum moment at a point 25 ft from the left end of the simple beam shown in Fig. 13–10 as the series of concentrated loads shown moves across the span.

Solution: The influence line indicates that maximum moment will occur when as many loads as possible are on the span.

Try 3		Try 4	
$\frac{35}{25}=1.40$	$\frac{105}{30}=3.50$	$\frac{60}{25}=2.40$	$\frac{100}{30}=3.33$
$\frac{60}{25}=2.40$	$\frac{80}{30}=2.67$	$\frac{85}{25}=3.40$	$\frac{75}{30}=2.50$

By using load 4 at section 1–1,

$$R_L = \frac{(20)(6+14)+(10)(18)+(25)(24+30+36+42)+(10)(46)}{55} = 78.9^k$$

$$M = (78.9)(25) - (25)(6+12) - (10)(16) = 1362'^k$$

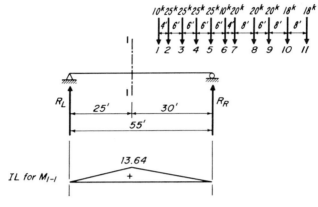

FIG. 13-10.

13-10. Absolute Maximum Moment Developed by a Series of Concentrated Live Loads

The absolute maximum moment in a simple beam is thought of as occurring at the beam center line. Maximum moment does occur at the center line if the beam is loaded with a uniform load or a single concentrated load. A beam, however, may be required to support a moving series of varying concentrated loads such as the wheels of a train, and the absolute maximum moment will in all probability occur at some position other than the center line.

The largest possible moment should be determined, because the beam must be capable of withstanding the worst possible conditions. To calculate the moment, it is necessary to find the point where it occurs and the position of the loads causing it. Assuming the largest moment to be developed at the center line of long span beams is reasonable, but for short-span beams this assumption may be considerably in error. It is, therefore, necessary to have a definite procedure for determining absolute maximum moment.

The moment diagram for a simple beam loaded with a group of concentrated loads will consist of a set of straight lines regardless of the

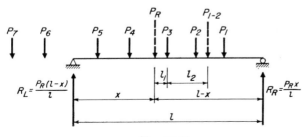

FIG. 13-11.

position of the loads; therefore, the absolute maximum moment occurring during the movement of these loads across the span will occur at one of the loads, usually the one nearest the center of gravity of the group. The beam of Fig. 13–11 and the series of loads, P_1, P_2, P_3, etc. are studied in the following paragraphs. The load P_3 is assumed to be the one nearest the center of gravity of the loads on the span, and it is located a distance l_1 from P_R (the resultant of all the loads on the span) and a distance l_2 from P_{1-2} (the resultant of loads P_1 and P_2). The left reaction R_L is located a distance x from P_R. In the following paragraphs, maximum moment is assumed to occur at P_3, and a definite method is developed for placing this load to cause the maximum.

The moment at P_3 may be written as follows:

$$M = R_R(l - x - l_1) - (P_{1-2})(l_2)$$

Substituting the value of R_R, $P_R x/l$, gives

$$M = \left(\frac{P_R x}{l}\right)(l - x - l_1) - (P_{1-2})(l_2)$$

It is desired to find the value of x for which the moment at P_3 will be a maximum. Maximum moment at P_3, which occurs when the shear is zero, may be found by differentiating the moment expression with respect to x, equating the result to zero, and solving for x.

$$\frac{dM}{dx} = l - 2x - l_1 = 0$$

$$x = \frac{l}{2} - \frac{l_1}{2}$$

A general rule for absolute maximum moment may be stated as follows: *Maximum moment in a beam loaded with a moving series of concentrated loads will occur at the load nearest the center of gravity of the loads on the beam when the center of gravity is the same distance on one side of the center line of the beam as the load nearest the center of gravity of the loads is on the other side.*

Should the load nearest the center of gravity of the loads be a relatively small one, the absolute maximum moment may occur at some other load nearby. Occasionally two or three loads have to be considered to find the greatest value; however, the problem is not a difficult one because the other moment criteria—average load to left equals average load to right—must be satisfied, and there will be little trouble in determining which of the nearby loads will govern.

Example 13–4 illustrates the calculation of absolute maximum moment in a beam.

EXAMPLE 13–4. Determine the absolute maximum moment in the 50-ft simple beam of Fig. 13–12 caused by the moving concentrated load system shown.

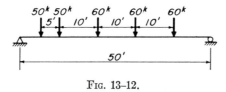

FIG. 13–12.

Solution: Center of gravity of loads:

$$\frac{(50)(5) + (60)(15 + 25 + 35)}{280} = 16.96'$$

Place loads as follows:

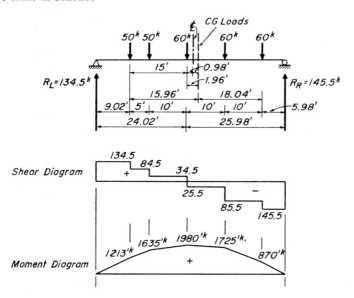

13–11. Discussion of Methods

Two methods were introduced for determining maximum shears and moments at special points in a beam. These methods are the so-called increase-decrease method and the average-load criterion method. The first of the two is the process of determining if the function increases or decreases as the loads are successively moved up to the point, and the second consists in computing the average load to the left and to the right of the point for each position of the loads. It is important to realize that the increase-decrease method is perfectly applicable for all types of influence lines, while the average-load criterion was derived only for a trian-

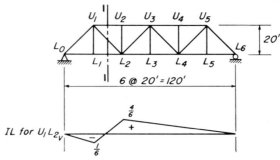

Fig. 13–13.

gular-shaped influence line. For another type of influence line another criterion would have to be developed; however, once developed it would be more easily applied than the first method.

The chapter has included methods for calculating maximum shears and moments in simple beams only. The discussion was not expanded to include trusses and other types of beams because it was felt that, if the student could handle the simple-beam problems, he could handle the others, since their solutions are so closely related to the simple-beam solutions. Several nonsimple-beam problems are included in the problem section at the end of the chapter.

As an illustration of the relationship between simple-beam problems and truss problems, the truss of Fig. 13–13 is considered. For a set of loads in a given position, the stress in member U_1U_2 may be found by passing section 1–1 and taking moments at L_2. To determine the maximum stress in U_1U_2 for a series of moving loads, the first part of the problem is the positioning of the loads to cause maximum moment at L_2 in the truss. An identical problem is the positioning of loads on a 120-ft simple beam to cause maximum moment 40 ft from the left end. Similarly, to find maximum stress in L_3L_4, the loads would be placed to cause maximum moment at U_3, or at the center line of a 120-ft simple beam.

The stress in member U_1L_2 can be calculated from the shear in panel 2. The influence line shows the member to be subject to stress reversal for live loads; therefore, maximum tension would be developed when the loads were placed to cause maximum positive shear at L_2, or 40 ft from the left end of a simple beam, and maximum compression is developed when maximum negative shear is developed at L_1.

Problems

13–1. Compute the maximum possible shear at the following points on the 50-ft simple beam caused by the right-to-left movement of the loads shown in the accompanying illustration. a) Left end. b) Ten feet from left end. c) Center line.

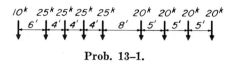

Prob. 13–1.

13–2. Compute the maximum possible moments at points 10, 20, and 25 ft from the left end of the beam of Prob. 13–1.

13–3. What is the absolute maximum moment that can occur in the beam of Prob. 13–1?

13–4. A simple beam of 30-ft span supports a pair of 20^k moving concentrated loads 10 ft apart. Compute the maximum possible moment at the center line of the beam and the absolute maximum moment in the beam.

13–5. Compute the maximum shear that can occur at the left support of the beam shown in the accompanying illustration for the load system of Prob. 13–1.

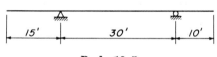

Prob. 13–5.

13–6. For a 60-ft simple beam supporting a uniform dead load of 2 klf, a 3-klf uniform live load, and the moving concentrated load system of Example 13–1, find the maximum shear at the left support and at a section 15 ft from the left support.

13–7. Find the maximum possible moment at the center line of the beam of Prob. 13–6.

13–8. Calculate the maximum possible moment at joints L_2 and L_3 of the Pratt truss shown in the accompanying illustration for the load system of Prob. 13–1.

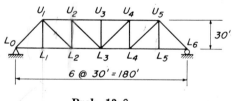

Prob. 13–8.

13–9. Determine the maximum possible shears in panels *1* and *2* of the truss of Prob. 13–8.

13–10. For the truss of Prob. 13–8 determine the maximum possible stresses in members U_1U_2, L_2L_3, L_0U_1, and U_2L_3.

13–11. By using the load system of Example 13–3 compute the maximum possible stresses in members L_1L_2, U_2U_3, U_1L_2, and U_2L_2 of the Parker truss shown in the accompanying illustration.

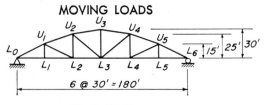

Prob. 13–11.

13–12. Compute the maximum stresses in members L_0L_1, L_1U_2, and U_2U_3 as the load system of Example 13–3 moves across the deck truss shown in the accompanying illustration.

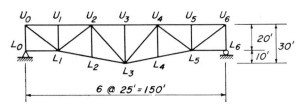

Prob. 13–12.

14 |

SPACE FRAMES

14–1. General

A structure whose members do not all lie in the same plane is a space frame. Nearly all engineering structures fall into this classification. Bridges and buildings are two leading examples. They, however, may usually be broken down into separate truss systems, each lying in a single plane at right angles to the other. Figure 14–1 (a) shows that an independent analysis of each of the systems is permissible. Two members, AB and BC, at right angles to each other, are shown in the figure. It is evident that a stress in AB has no effect on the stress in BC, because the component of a force at 90° is zero. Similarly, the stresses in one truss have no effect on the stresses in another truss framed into it at a right angle.

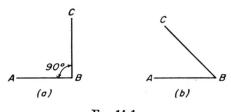

(a)   (b)

Fig. 14–1.

The members joining two systems together serve as members of both systems, and their total stress is obtained by combining the stresses developed as a part of each of the systems. The end posts of bridge trusses having end portals (see Figs. 16–7 and 16–8) are one illustration. They serve as the end posts of the bridge trusses and as the columns of the portal.

Many towers, domes, derricks, etc. are three-dimensional structures made up of members so arranged that it is impossible to divide them into different systems, each lying in a single plane, which may be handled individually. The difference is that the truss systems lie in planes which are not at right angles to each other. The stresses in one truss framed into another at an angle other than 90° affect the stresses in that truss, just as a stress in member AB of Fig. 14–1 (b) causes a stress in member BC. For trusses of this type it is necessary to analyze the whole structure as a unit, rather than consider the systems in various planes individually. This chapter is devoted to these types of space frames.

Transmission towers for the country's first 345,000 volt transmission line, Chief Joseph-Snohomish Dam, Washington State. (Courtesy of Bethlehem Steel Company)

The average structural engineer is so accustomed to visualizing structures in one plane that, when he encounters space frames, he frequently makes mistakes because his mind is still operating on a single-plane basis. If the layout of a space frame is not completely clear, the construction of a small model will probably clarify the situation. Even the most simple models of paper, cardboard, or wire are helpful.

14–2. Basic Principles

Prior to introducing the method of analyzing space frames, a few of the basic principles pertaining to such structures need to be considered. Three-dimensional structures, as were two-dimensional structures, are assumed to be made up of members subject to axial stress only. In other words, the frames are assumed to have members which are straight between joints, to have loads applied at joints only, to have members whose ends are free to rotate (note that for this situation to be true the members would have to be connected with universal joints or at least with several frictionless pins), etc. Analyses based on these assumptions are quite satisfactory despite the welded, bolted, and riveted connections used in actual practice.

A system of forces coming together at a single point, though not all in the same plane, may be combined into one resultant force. Similarly, it can be seen that an inclined force may have three coordinate components, and three reference planes will be used in handling them. The three planes used here are one horizontal and two verticals, each being perpendicular to the other. The intersections of these planes form the three coordinate axes used, X, Y, and Z. The stress in any member inclined to the axes may be broken down into components along them, their magnitudes being proportional to their length projections on the axes. The inclined stress S in Fig. 14–2 is graphically broken down into components S_x, S_y, and S_z.

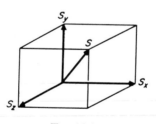

Fig. 14–2.

The same values may be computed algebraically from the following relationship: The stress in a member is to the length of the member as the X, Y, or Z component of stress is to the corresponding X, Y, or Z component of length.

$$\frac{S}{l} = \frac{S_x}{l_x} = \frac{S_y}{l_y} = \frac{S_z}{l_z}$$

$$l^2 = l_x{}^2 + l_y{}^2 + l_z{}^2$$

$$S^2 = S_x{}^2 + S_y{}^2 + S_z{}^2$$

Space frames may be either statically determinate or statically indeterminate; consideration is given here only to those which are determinate. The methods developed in later chapters for indeterminate structures apply equally to three-dimensional and two-dimensional structures.

14–3.   Statics Equations

There are more statics equations available for determining the reactions of three-dimensional structures because there are two more axes to take moments about and one new axis along which to sum up forces. For equilibrium the sum of the forces along each of the three reference axes equal zero, as does the sum of the moments of all the forces about each of the axes. A total of six equations is available ($\Sigma X=0$, $\Sigma Y=0$, $\Sigma Z=0$, $\Sigma M_x=0$, $\Sigma M_y=0$, and $\Sigma M_z=0$), and six reaction components may be determined directly from them.

Should a structure have more than six reaction components, it is statically indeterminate externally; if less than six, it is unstable; and if equal to six, it is statically determinate externally. Many space frames, however, have more than six reaction components and yet are statically determinate internally. Example 14–2 shows that reactions for this type of structure may be determined by solving them concurrently with the member stresses.

The basic figure of the space frame is the triangle. A triangle can be extended into a space frame by adding three members and one joint. Each of the new members frames into one of the joints of the basic triangle, the other ends coming together to form a new joint. The elementary space frame formed has six members and four joints. It may be enlarged by the addition of three members and one joint. For each of the joints of a space frame three equations ($\Sigma X=0$, $\Sigma Y=0$, and $\Sigma Z=0$) are available to calculate the unknowns. Letting $j=$ number of joints, $m=$ number of members, and $r=$ number of reaction components, it can be seen that for a space frame to be statically determinate the following relation must hold:

$$3j = m + r$$

Should there be joints in the frame where the members are all in one plane, only two equations are available at each, and it is necessary to subtract one from the left-hand side of the equation for each such joint. The omission of one member for each reaction component in excess of six will cause this equation to be satisfied, and the structure will be statically determinate internally. When this situation occurs, it is possible to compute by three-dimensional statics the stresses and reactions for the frame, although it is statically indeterminate externally.

The general rule for stability as regards outer forces is that the projection of the structure on any one of the three planes must itself be stable;

therefore, as with two-dimensional structures, there must be at least three nonconcurrent reaction components in any one plane. The results of reaction computations will be inconsistent for any other case.

In the preceding paragraphs external stability and determinateness and internal stability and determinateness have been treated as though they were completely independent subjects. The two have been divorced for clarity for the reader who has not previously encountered space frames. He will learn, however, as he solves the problems in the pages that follow, that it is impossible in a majority of cases to consider the two separately. For instance, many frames are statically indeterminate externally and statically determinate internally and can be completely analyzed by statics. Few two-dimensional structures fall into this class.

14–4. Special Theorems Applying to Space Frames

From the principles of elementary statics there may be developed two theorems which are useful in analyzing space frames. These are discussed in the following paragraphs.

a) The component of a force at 90° is zero, because no matter how large the force may be it equals zero when multiplied by the cosine of 90°. A force in one plane cannot have components in a plane normal to the original plane. Furthermore, a force in one plane cannot cause moment about any axis in its plane, because it will either intersect the axis or be parallel to it.

From the foregoing it is evident that if several members of a frame come together at a joint, all but one lying in the same plane, the component of stress in the member normal to the plane of the other members must equal the sum of the components of the external forces at the joint normal to the same plane. If no external forces are present, the member has a stress of zero.

b) The equations of statics clearly show that, if there is a joint in a truss where no external loads are applied and where it has been proved that all but two of the members coming into the joint have no stress, these two members must have zero stress unless they happen to lie in a straight line.

14–5. Types of Support

Trusses in one plane have been assumed to be supported with rollers or hinges which could supply one or two reaction components. For three-dimensional structures the same types of support are used, but the number of reaction components may vary from one to three.

1) The *hinge* may have three reaction components because it can resist forces in X, Y, and Z directions.

2) The *slotted roller* is free to move in one direction parallel to the supporting surface. Movement is prevented in the other direction parallel to the surface as well as perpendicular to it, giving a total of two reaction components.

3) *Plane rollers, flat plates, or steel balls* have resistance only to movement perpendicular to the supporting surface, or one reaction component.

This discussion indicates it is possible to select a type of support having three reaction components or one which may have one or two of the components eliminated. A little thought on the subject shows that the possibility of limiting the number of reaction components of a space frame is very advantageous. A frame which is indeterminate externally may have its total reaction components limited to six, making it determinate. (Advantages of statically determinate and statically indeterminate structures are discussed in Chapter 15.) For some structures it is desirable to eliminate the reaction components in certain directions. The most obvious example occurs when a space frame is supported on walls where a reaction or thrust perpendicular to the wall is undesirable.

The directions in which reaction components are possible are indicated by dark heavy lines at the support points, as shown in the diagrams of the frames analyzed in Examples 14–1 to 14–3.

14–6. Illustrative Examples

Examples 14–1 and 14–2 illustrate the application of the foregoing principles to elementary space frames. Example 14–1 considers a structure supported at three points with six reaction components, which can be computed directly. The second example presents a space frame supported at four points with seven reaction components, which cannot be solved directly.

EXAMPLE 14–1. Determine the reactions and member stresses in the structure shown in Fig. 14–3.

Solution: The frame is statically determinate and stable externally because there is a total of six reaction components, three nonconcurrent ones in each plane. Internally it is statically determinate as proved with the joint equation.

$$3j = m + r$$
$$12 = 6 + 6$$
$$12 = 12$$

For a frame with three vertical reaction components, moments may be taken about an axis through any two of them to find the third.

$$\Sigma M_x = 0 \text{ about } ac$$
$$(40)(30) - (20)(20) + 30Z_b = 0$$
$$Z_b = -26.7^k \downarrow$$

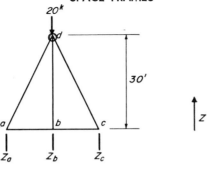

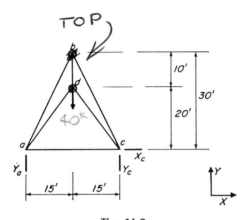

Fig. 14-3.

$\Sigma M_y = 0$ about line of action of Y_a
$$(20)(15) + (26.7)(15) - 30Z_c = 0$$
$$Z_c = +23.3^k \uparrow$$

$\Sigma Z = 0$
$$-20 - 26.7 + 23.3 + Z_a = 0$$
$$Z_a = +23.4^k \uparrow$$

Similarly, where there are three unknown horizontal components, moments may be taken about a vertical axis passing through the point of intersection of two of the components.

$\Sigma M_z = 0$ about line of action of Z_c
$$-(40)(15) + 30Y_a = 0$$
$$Y_a = +20^k \uparrow$$

$\Sigma Y = 0$
$$20 - 40 + Y_c = 0$$
$$Y_c = +20^k \uparrow$$

$\Sigma X = 0$
$$0 + X_c = 0$$
$$X_c = 0$$

When the reactions have been found, the member stresses can readily be computed by the method of joints. At joint a, member ad is the only member having a Z component of length; therefore, its component must be equal and opposite to Z_a, or 23.4^k compression. The X and Y components of ad are proportional to its components of length in those directions. Setting up a table similar to the one shown simplifies the computation of components and resultant stresses.

Considering joint a, the Y component of stress in member ab can be determined by joints now that the Y component of ad is known.

$$\Sigma Y \text{ at joint } a = 0$$
$$20 - 15.6 - Y_{ab} = 0$$
$$Y_{ab} = -4.4 \text{ compression}$$

The other member stresses are computed by joints and shown in the table.

MEMBER	PROJECTION			LENGTH	COMPONENT OF STRESS			STRESS
	X	Y	Z		X	Y	Z	
ab	15	30	0	33.5	− 2.2	− 4.4	0	− 4.92
ad	15	20	30	39.1	− 11.7	− 15.6	− 23.4	− 30.5
ac	30	0	0	30.0	+ 13.9	0	0	+ 13.9
bc	15	30	0	33.5	− 2.2	− 4.5	0	− 5.02
bd	0	10	30	31.6	0	+ 8.9	+ 26.7	+ 28.2
cd	15	20	30	39.1	− 11.7	− 15.5	− 23.3	− 30.4

EXAMPLE 14–2. Find all reactions and member stresses in Fig. 14–4.

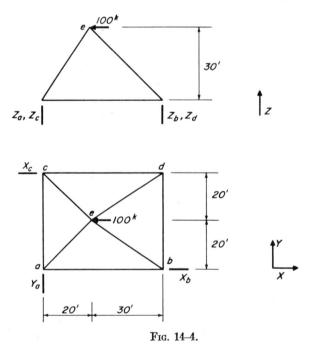

FIG. 14–4.

Solution: Examination of the frame shows it to be statically indeterminate externally because there are seven definite reaction components and only six equations of statics. Internally, however, it is statically determinate as shown, and the analysis may be handled by statics.

$$3j = m + r$$
$$15 = 8 + 7$$
$$15 = 15$$

Although the frame is statically indeterminate externally, there are only three unknown reaction components in the XY plane, and these may be determined immediately. The other four components will be solved in conjunction with the member stresses.

$\Sigma M_z = 0$ about line of action of Z_a
$$-(100)(20) + 40X_c = 0$$
$$X_c = +50^k \rightarrow$$

$\Sigma X = 0$
$$+50 - 100 + X_b = 0$$
$$X_b = +50^k \rightarrow$$

$\Sigma Y = 0$
$$0 + Y_a = 0$$
$$Y_a = 0$$

If the value of one of the Z reaction components should be known, the values of the other three could be determined by statics. It is assumed that Z_d has a value of S downward, and the reaction components are computed in terms of S.

$\Sigma M_y = 0$ about ac
$$-(100)(30) + 50S + 50Z_b = 0$$
$$Z_b = 60 - S$$

$\Sigma M_x = 0$ about ab
$$+40S - 40Z_c = 0$$
$$Z_c = +S$$

$\Sigma Z = 0$
$$+S - S - (60 - S) + Z_a = 0$$
$$Z_a = 60 - S$$

checking by $\Sigma M_x = 0$ about cd
$$(60 - S)(40) - 40Z_a = 0$$
$$Z_a = 60 - S$$

The calculation of member stresses may now be started from the reaction components in terms of S. These computations are continued until the stresses at both ends of one bar are determined in terms of S. The two values must be equal, and they are equated to give the correct value of S.

The Z component of stress in de equals S and is in tension, while the Z component of stress in be equals 60-S and is also in tension. The Y component of stress in de equals $(^{20}\!/_{30})(S) = \frac{2}{3} S$, and the Y component of stress in be is $(^{20}\!/_{30})(60 - S) = 40 - \frac{2}{3} S$. By $\Sigma Y = 0$ at joint d, member bd is in compression with a stress of $\frac{2}{3} S$. Similarly, by $\Sigma Y = 0$ at joint b, member bd is seen to have a compressive stress of $40 - \frac{2}{3} S$. Equating the two expressions yields the value of S.

$$\tfrac{2}{3}S = 40 - \tfrac{2}{3}S$$
$$\tfrac{4}{3}S = 40$$
$$S = 30^k$$

The numerical values of the Z reaction components can now be found from S, and the stresses in the frame can be determined by joints. The use of a table to work with length and stress components is again convenient. The results are as follows:

MEMBER	PROJECTION			LENGTH	COMPONENT OF STRESS			STRESS
	X	Y	Z		X	Y	Z	
ab	50	0	0	50	+20	0	0	+20
ae	20	20	30	41.2	−20	−20	−30	−41.2
ac	0	40	0	40	0	+20	0	+20
be	30	20	30	46.9	+30	+20	+30	+46.9
bd	0	40	0	40	0	−20	0	−20
de	30	20	30	46.9	+30	+20	+30	+46.9
cd	50	0	0	50	−30	0	0	−30
ce	20	20	30	41.2	−20	−20	−30	−41.2

14–7. More Complicated Frames

The method of joints was used to determine the stresses in the elementary space frames analyzed in Sec. 14–6. For more complicated space frames, even if the reactions are available, the computer may find he has

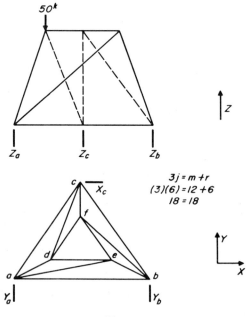

FIG. 14–5.

Field House, University of Wichita, Wichita, Kansas. (Courtesy of American Institute of Steel Construction, Inc.)

difficulty calculating any of the stresses by the method of joints. The frame of Fig. 14–5 falls into this class.

It is possible to compute all reaction components immediately, but no stresses may be determined by the method of joints as presented in Examples 14–1 and 14–2. The application of the zero-member principle of paragraph *a* of Sec. 14–4, however, will quickly prove that several members have no stress. For example, at joint *f* members *fc*, *fb*, and *fe* lie in the same plane. Member *fd* does not, and it has a component of stress perpendicular to the plane of the other three members. This component must be equal and opposite to all components perpendicular to the plane from external loads applied at the joint. Since there are no loads present, member *fd* has no stress. A similar analysis can be made at joint *e* to show the stress in member *fe* is zero.

Two of the four members meeting at joint *f* have been proved to have no stress. The remaining two members are not in a straight line and must have zero stresses, since there are no external loads applied at the joint (paragraph *b* of Sec. 14–4). It is now possible to compute the stresses in the remaining members by joints for this particular truss.

For other structures the use of the zero-member principle will not be sufficient (if it is of any value at all) in determining stresses. In this latter type of frame the use of moments will probably enable the computer to make the analysis. The frame of Fig. 14–5 could be analyzed by taking moments. If an imaginary section were passed completely around joint *e* isolating it as a free body, moments could be taken about line *ab* to find the stress in member *ef*. Stresses in *ae* and *eb* intersect line *ab*, and the line of action of *de* is parallel to *ab*. Several moment equations of this type are used in Example 14–3.

As the space frames become more complicated, it may not be possible to find a single stress by the methods introduced to this point. If a member is arbitrarily given a stress, say *S*, it may be possible to compute the stresses in several members in terms of *S*. Once the stress at both ends of a member is known in terms of *S*, the two values may be equated to find *S*, and the stress analysis for the frame may be carried out.

EXAMPLE 14–3. Analyze the space frame of Fig. 14–6.

Solution: Although there are eight reaction components, the structure is statically determinate:

$$3j = m + r$$
$$(3)(8) = 16 + 8$$
$$24 = 24$$

A brief examination of the structure will reveal four zero members. At joint *h* member *eh* has no stress, and at joint *g* the same can be said for member *gh*; therefore, members *hd* and *hc* meeting at joint *h* have zero stresses.

By removing joint *e* as a free body and taking moments about line *ad*, the stress in *ef* is determined, and by taking moments about line *ab*, stress *de* is found. The method of joints is then used to find the stresses in *ae* and *da*.

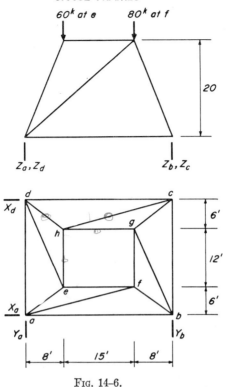

$$\text{Fig. 14–6.}$$

$\Sigma M_y = 0$ about line ad

$(60)(8) - 20S_{ef} = 0$

$S_{ef} = 24^k$ compression

$\Sigma M_x = 0$ about line ab

$(60)(6) - 20Y_{de} - 6Z_{de} = 0$

$360 - 20Y_{de} - (6)(^{20}\!/_{18})(Y_{de}) = 0$

$Y_{de} = 13.5^k$ compression

$\Sigma Y = 0$ at joint e

$Y_{ae} = 13.5^k$ compression

$\Sigma Y = 0$ at joint d

$Y_{da} = 13.5^k$ tension

An imaginary section is passed around joint f and moments are taken about line ab to find the stress in fg. By using the same free body, moments are taken about line bc to find the stress in af.

$\Sigma M_x = 0$ about line ab

$(80)(6) - 20S_{fg} = 0$

$S_{fg} = 24^k$ compression

$\Sigma M_y = 0$ about line bc

$-(80)(8) + (24)(20) + 20X_{af} + 8Z_{af} = 0$

$X_{af} = 5.9^k$ compression

A similar moment procedure may be used, with joint g as the free body, to determine the stress in member bg, and the values of all remaining stresses and reactions can be determined by joints. A summation of the results is as follows:

MEMBER	PROJECTION			LENGTH	COMPONENT OF STRESS			STRESS
	X	Y	Z		X	Y	Z	
ab	31	0	0	31	$+22$	0	0	$+22$
bc	0	24	0	24	0	$+6$	0	$+6$
cd	31	0	0	31	$+8$	0	0	$+8$
da	0	24	0	24	0	$+13.5$	0	$+13.5$
ae	8	6	20	22.4	-18	-13.5	-45	-50.4
af	23	6	20	31.1	-5.9	-1.5	-5.1	-7.9
bf	8	6	20	22.4	-30	-22.5	-75	-84
bg	8	18	20	28.1	$+8$	$+18$	$+20$	$+28.1$
cg	8	6	20	22.4	-8	-6	-20	-22.4
ch	23	6	20	31.1	0	0	0	0
dh	8	6	20	22.4	0	0	0	0
de	8	18	20	28.1	-6	-13.5	-15	-21.1
ef	15	0	0	15	-24	0	0	-24
fg	0	12	0	12	0	-24	0	-24
gh	15	0	0	15	0	0	0	0
he	0	12	0	12	0	0	0	0

Reactions:

$Za = 50 \uparrow$ $X_a = 2 \rightarrow$
$Zb = 55 \uparrow$ $X_d = 2 \leftarrow$
$Zc = 20 \uparrow$ $Y_a = 1.5 \uparrow$
$Zd = 15 \uparrow$ $Y_b = 1.5 \downarrow$

Problems

Prob. 14–1 to 14–5. Compute the reaction components and the member stresses for the space frames.

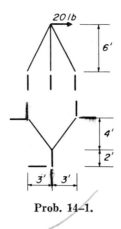

Prob. 14–1.

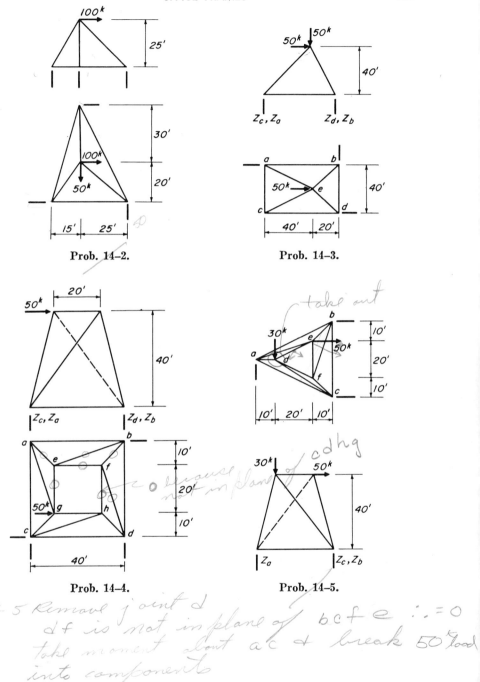

Prob. 14–2.   Prob. 14–3.

Prob. 14–4.   Prob. 14–5.

14 5 Remove joint d
df is not in plane of bcfe ∴ = 0
take moment about ac & break 50 load
into components

15 | DISCUSSION OF INDETERMINATE STRUCTURES

15–1. Introduction

The use of indeterminate structures is becoming more extensive each year; in the past the use has been more common in Europe, where the resulting savings in material are of primary importance. Up until the past few decades indeterminate structures were avoided by most American engineers, if possible, but three great developments have completely changed the picture. These are 1) monolithic reinforced concrete structures, 2) arc welding of steel structures, and 3) modern methods of analysis (primarily the Hardy-Cross method discussed in Chapter 23).

The preceding chapters may have led the reader to believe that statically determinate beams and trusses are the rule in modern structures. The truth is that it is a difficult task to find an ideal simply supported beam. Probably the best place to look for one would be in a structures textbook; for beams which are riveted or welded to columns are not simply supported.

The same situation holds for statically determinate trusses. Those rare trusses which are pin-connected are not blessed with frictionless pins, and if pins are used, they frequently rust in place and then permit little rotation. The other assumptions made about trusses in the earlier chapters are not altogether true, and in a strict sense all trusses are statically indeterminate because they have bending and secondary stresses.

15–2. Continuous Structures

As the spans of simple structures become longer, their bending moments increase rapidly. If the weight of a structure per foot remained constant, regardless of the span, the dead-load moment would vary in proportion to the square of the span length $(M = wl^2/8)$. This proportion, however, is not correct, because the weight of structures must increase with longer spans to be strong enough to resist the increased bending moments; therefore, the dead-load moment increases at a greater rate than does the square of the span.

For economy, it pays in long spans to introduce types of structure which have smaller moments than the tremendous ones which occur in long-span, simply supported structures. Chapter 3 introduced one type of structure which considerably reduced bending moments: the cantilever-type construction. Two other moment-reducing structures are discussed in the following paragraphs.

In some locations, it may be possible to have a beam with fixed ends, rather than one with simple supports. A comparison of the moments developed in a uniformly loaded simple beam with those in a uniformly loaded fixed-ended beam is made in Fig. 15–1.

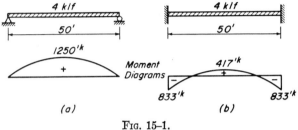

FIG. 15–1.

The maximum bending moment for the fixed-ended beam is only two-thirds of that for the simply supported beam. Usually it is difficult to fix the ends, particularly in the case of bridges; for this reason flanking spans are often used, as illustrated in Fig. 15–2. These spans will partially fix the interior supports, thus tending to reduce the moment in the center span. This figure presents a comparison of the bending moments that occur in three uniformly loaded simple beams (spans 100, 300, and 100 ft with the moments of a uniformly loaded beam continuous over the same three spans.

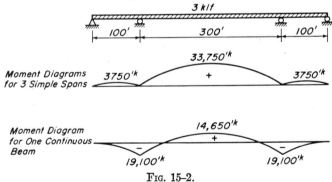

FIG. 15–2.

The maximum bending moment for the continuous beam is approximately 43 per cent less than that for the simple beams. Unfortunately, there will not be a corresponding 43 per cent reduction in total cost. The cost-reduction figure probably is only 2 or 3 per cent of the total structure cost because such items as foundations, connections, and floor system are not reduced a great deal by the moment reductions.

In the foregoing discussion, the moments developed in beams have been shown to be reduced appreciably by continuity. This reduction occurs where beams are rigidly fastened to each other or where beams and columns are rigidly connected. There is a continuity of action in resisting a load applied to any part of a continuous structure because the load is resisted by the combined efforts of all of the members of the frame.

15–3. Advantages of Indeterminate Structures

In comparing indeterminate structures with determinate structures, the first consideration, to most, would pertain to cost. It is, however, impossible to make a statement favoring one type, economically, without reservation. Each structure presents a different situation, and all factors must be considered, economic or otherwise. In general, indeterminate structures have the advantages discussed in the following paragraphs.

Savings in Materials. 1) The smaller moments developed permit the use of smaller members, the material saving possibly running as high as 10 to 20 per cent of the steel used in bridges. The large number of stress reversals occurring in railroad bridges keeps their maximum saving nearer the 10 per cent value.

2) A structural member of a given size can support more load if it is part of a continuous structure than if it is simply supported. The continuity permits the use of smaller members for the same loads and spans or increased spacing of supports for the same size members. The possibility of fewer columns in buildings or piers in bridges may permit a reduction in over-all costs.

3) Continuous structures of concrete or steel are cheaper without the joints, pins, etc. required to make them statically determinate, as was frequently the practice in past years. Monolithic reinforced-concrete structures are erected so that they are naturally continuous and indeterminate. To install the hinges and other devices necessary to make them determinate would not only be a difficult construction problem but also be very expensive. Furthermore, if a building frame consisted of columns and simple beams, it would be necessary to have objectionable diagonal bracing between the joints to make the frame stable and rigid.

More Rigid Structures. A rigid structure is of particular importance where there are many moving loads and considerable vibration.

More Attractive Structures. It is difficult to imagine determinate structures having the gracefulness and beauty of many indeterminate arches and rigid frames being erected today.

Adaptation to Cantilever Erection. The cantilever method of erecting bridges is of particular value where conditions underneath (probably

Broadway Street Bridge, Kansas City, Missouri. (American Bridge)

naval traffic or deep water) hinder the erection of falsework. Continuous indeterminate bridges and cantilever-type bridges are conveniently erected by the cantilever method.

15–4. Disadvantages of Indeterminate Structures

A comparison of determinate and indeterminate structures shows the latter have several disadvantages which may make their use undesirable on many occasions. They are discussed in the following paragraphs.

Support Settlement. Indeterminate structures are not desirable where foundation conditions are poor, because seemingly minor support settlements or rotations may cause major changes in the moments, shears, reactions, and stresses. Where indeterminate bridges are used despite the presence of poor foundation conditions, it is often felt necessary to weigh the dead-load reactions. The supports of the bridge are jacked up or down until the calculated reaction is obtained, after which the support is built to that elevation.

Development of Other Stresses. Support settlements are not the only condition that causes stress variations in indeterminate structures. Variation in the relative positions of members caused by temperature changes, poor fabrication, or internal deformation of members of the structure under load may cause serious stress changes throughout the structure.

Difficulty of Analysis and Design. The stresses of indeterminate structures depend not only upon their dimensions but also upon their elastic properties (moduli of elasticity, moments of inertia, and cross-sectional areas). This situation presents a major design difficulty: the stresses cannot be determined until the member sizes are known, and the member sizes cannot be determined until their stresses are known. The problem is handled by assuming member sizes and computing the stresses, designing the members for these stresses and computing the stresses for the new sizes, etc. until the final design is obtained. Design by this method—the method of successive approximations—takes more time than the design of a comparable determinate structure, but the extra cost is only a small part of the total structure cost.

Stress Reversals. Generally, more stress reversals occur in indeterminate structures than in determinate structures. Additional material may be required at certain sections to resist the different stress conditions.

15–5. The Wichert Truss

Continuous trusses are thought of as being statically indeterminate, but there are a few exceptions. Two of these have been discussed in preceding chapters: the cantilever-type trusses and trusses with certain members omitted, shown in Fig. 8–9. Mr. E. M. Wichert patented another type of statically determinate continuous truss in 1932. His truss falls into the omitted-member class, because the verticals over interior supports are left out. (Müller-Breslau, a professor in Berlin, had discussed this form of truss as early as 1887.[1]) The Wichert truss of Fig. 15–3, which has 32 members, 18 joints, and 4 reaction components, is shown to be statically determinate as follows:

$$m = 2j - r$$
$$32 = 36 - 4$$
$$32 = 32$$

A Wichert truss has all of the advantages but none of the disadvantages of continuity. Being determinate, it is easy to analyze and design and is not appreciably affected by support settlements, minor fabrication errors, etc. The method of analysis is based on the conditions at the interior support. The support at L_5 in the truss of Fig. 15–3 is a roller, and the reaction there is vertical with no horizontal components; therefore, the horizontal components of stress in the members L_4L_5 and L_5L_6 must be equal and opposite for equilibrium (i.e., both tension or both compression). Members having the same slope and the same horizontal stress components must have the same stresses and the same vertical components of stress. Assuming the reaction V_B at the roller to be up,

---

[1] Sutherland and Bowman, *Structural Theory* (New York: John Wiley & Sons, Inc. 1954), Chap. 5.

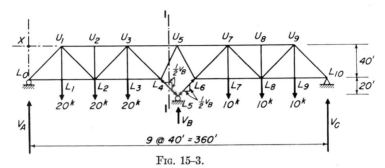

FIG. 15–3.

the two stresses are in compression, and the sum of their vertical components is equal and opposite to the reaction. This relation may be stated as follows:

$$V_{L_4L_5} = V_{L_5L_6} = \tfrac{1}{2}V_B$$

The horizontal components of the two stresses can be expressed in terms of the vertical components, which are in terms of V_B. The members have an inclination of 45°, and the vertical and horizontal components are equal, as shown on the members in the figure. Moments may be taken about joint U_5 of all the forces to the left of section *1–1*. Since the components of stress in L_4L_5 are expressed in terms of V_B, the equation will contain two unknowns, V_A and V_B. Moments may then be taken about L_{10} of all the external forces acting on the truss. The resulting equation has the same two unknowns, V_A and V_B, and their values may be determined by solving the two equations simultaneously. When two of the reactions are had, a complete analysis can be made by the usual method of statics. Example 15–1 presents a complete analysis of this truss.

Analysis of several Wichert trusses of different arrangements will show that instability is possible under some circumstances. This situation will occur when the lower-chord members meeting at the interior supports become very flat, and instability will be indicated by the tremendous values of those reactions. There is a definite slope of the bottom-chord members at which the truss becomes unstable, and this slope can be seen for the truss in Fig. 15–3. Should L_4L_5 be so flat that its line of action intersects the line of action of the top chord as far to the left as point X in the figure, the truss will be unstable.

Wichert trusses of more than two spans are quite tedious to analyze, although they are statically determinate. Dr. D. B. Steinman, in his book *The Wichert Truss,* published in 1932, presents a detailed discussion of the various types, including methods of analysis for multispan trusses, design, and economy.

EXAMPLE 15–1.   Calculate the reactions and member stresses of the Wichert truss of Fig. 15–3.

Solution: $\Sigma M_{U_5}=0$ (to left of section *1–1*)

$180V_A-(20)(60+100+140)+60H_{L_4L_5}=0$

$180V_A-6000+(60)(\tfrac{1}{2}V_B)=0$

$180V_A+30V_B=6000 \qquad\qquad (1)$

$\Sigma M_{L_{10}}=0$ (entire structure)

$-(10)(40+80+120)-(20)(240+280+320)+360V_A+180V_B=0$

$360V_A+180V_B=19{,}200 \qquad\qquad (2)$

Solving Eqs. 1 and 2 simultaneously gives:

$V_A=23.3^k$

$V_B=60.0^k$

By $\Sigma V=0$

$V_C=6.7^k$

By statics the following stresses are obtained:

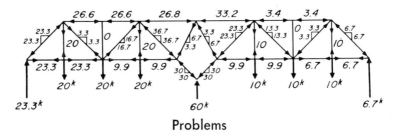

Problems

15–1. Determine the member stresses in the truss shown in the accompanying illustration.

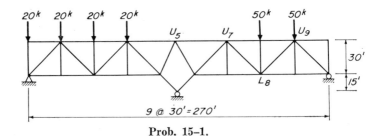

Prob. 15–1.

15–2. Draw an influence line for V_A in the truss of Fig. 15–3. (Notice that V_A will have a value when the unit load is over the center support.)

15–3. Compute the stresses in all of the members of the truss of Fig. 15–3 for a vertical load of 50^k acting at joint L_8.

15–4. Draw influence lines for members U_5U_7 and L_8U_9 of the truss of Prob. 15–1.

16

APPROXIMATE ANALYSIS OF INDETERMINATE STRUCTURES

16–1. General

Statically indeterminate structures may be analyzed "exactly" or "approximately." Several exact methods, which are based on elastic distortions, are discussed in Chapters 19 to 24. Approximate methods, involving the use of simplifying assumptions, are presented in this chapter. These latter methods have many practical applications such as the following:

1) An exact analysis may be so tedious and cumbersome that time is not available to perform the necessary computations.

2) The structure may be so complicated that no one who has the knowledge to make an exact analysis is available.

3) For some structures either method may be subject to so many errors and imperfections that approximate methods may yield stresses as accurate as an exact analysis. A specific example is the analysis of a building frame for wind loads where the walls, partitions, and floors contribute an indeterminate amount to wind resistance. Wind stresses calculated in the frame by either method are not accurate.

4) To design the members of an indeterminate structure, it is necessary to make an estimate of their sizes before stress analysis can begin by an exact method. Approximate analysis of the structure will yield stresses from which reasonably good initial estimates can be made as to member sizes.

5) Approximate analyses are quite useful in rough checking exact solutions.

Many different methods are available for making approximate analyses. A few of the more common ones are presented here, with consideration being given to trusses and building frames.

To be able to analyze a structure by statics, there must be no more unknowns than there are equations of statics available. If a truss or frame has 10 more unknowns than equations, it is indeterminate to the tenth degree. To analyze it by an approximate method, one assumption must be made for each degree of indeterminancy, or a total of ten assumptions. It will be seen that each assumption presents another equation to use in the calculations.

16–2.   Trusses with Two Diagonals in Each Panel

Diagonals Having Little Stiffness. The truss of Fig. 16–1 has two diagonals in each panel. If one of these diagonals were to be removed from each of the six panels, the truss would become statically determinate. The structure is statically indeterminate to the sixth degree.

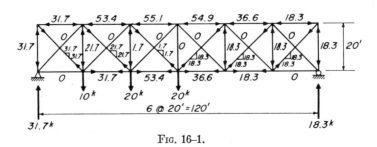

Fig. 16–1.

If the diagonals are relatively long and slender, such as those made of a pair of small steel angles, they will be able to carry reasonably large tensile stresses but negligible compression. For this situation it is logical to assume that the shear in each panel is carried entirely by the diagonal that would be in tension for that type of shear. The other diagonal has no stress. Making this assumption in each panel makes a total six assumptions for six redundants, and the equations of statics may be used to complete the analysis. The stresses in Fig. 16–1 were obtained on this basis.

Diagonals Having Considerable Stiffness. In some trusses the diagonals are constructed of sufficient stiffness to resist compressive loads. For panels having two diagonals the shear may be considered to be taken

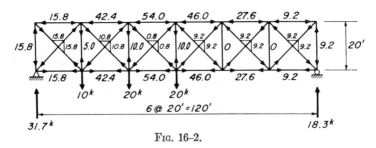

Fig. 16–2.

by both of them. The division of shear causes one diagonal to be in tension and the other to be in compression. The usual approximation made is that each diagonal takes 50 per cent of the shear. It is possible to to assume some other division, such as one-third of shear to compression diagonal and two-thirds to tension diagonal.

The stresses calculated for the truss in Fig. 16–2 are based on a 50 per cent division of the shear in each panel.

16–3.   Analysis of Mill Buildings

The building trusses analyzed in previous chapters have been assumed to rest on top of masonry walls or on top of columns on the sides of buildings.   A different, but common, type of industrial construction is the mill bent or mill building the trusses of which are rigidly fastened to the columns so that they act together.   Figure 16–3 shows two types of framing commonly used for mill buildings.

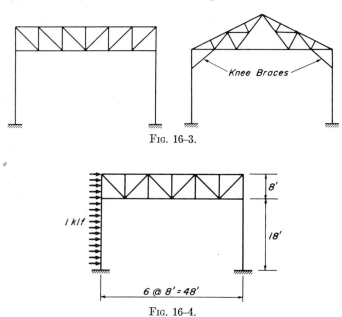

FIG. 16–3.

FIG. 16–4.

For gravity loads these trusses are analyzed as though they were simply supported on walls instead of being rigidly fastened to the columns, but for lateral loads the columns and trusses should be analyzed as a unit. In office buildings of corresponding heights, the inside walls and partitions offer considerable resistance to wind, in many cases supplying sufficient resistance.   Mill bents, however, must be analyzed and designed for wind loads, because there are no interior walls to help resist the wind forces. These buildings may have traveling cranes whose operation will cause additional lateral loads which need to be considered in design.   The mill building of Fig. 16–4 is analyzed for a wind load of 1^k per foot of height. Should there be cranes loads, they would be handled in exactly the same manner.

If the column bases are fixed, there will be three unknown reactions at each support, giving a total of six unknowns. The structure is statically indeterminate to the third degree, and to analyze it by an approximate method, three assumptions must be made.

When a column is rigidly attached to the foundation, there can be no column rotation at the base. Even though the building is subjected to wind loads causing the columns to bend laterally, a tangent to the column at the base will remain vertical. If the truss at the tops of the columns is very stiff and rigidly fastened to them, a tangent to the column at the junction will remain vertical. A column rigidly fixed top and bottom will assume the shape of an S curve when it is subjected to lateral loads, Fig. 16–5.

At a point midway from the column base to the bottom of the truss or knee brace the moment is zero because it changes from a moment causing tension on one side of the column to a moment causing tension on the other side. The point of zero moment is commonly called a point of inflection or a point of contraflexture. If points of inflection are assumed in each of the columns, two of the necessary three assumptions have been made (two $\Sigma M = 0$ equations are made available).

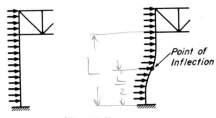

Fig. 16–5.

The discussion of the location of points of inflection has been based on the assumption that the column bases are completely fixed. If the columns are anchored in a deep concrete foundation or a concrete foundation wall, the assumption is good. Frequently, though, the columns are supported by small concrete footings which offer little resistance to rotation, and the column bases act as hinges, in which case the points of inflection are at the bases. The usual situation probably lies in between the two extremes, with the column bases only partially fixed. The points of inflection are commonly assumed to lie about one-fourth to one-third of the distance from the base up to the bottom of the truss, or to the knee brace if one is used.

The third assumption made is that the horizontal shear divides equally between the two columns at the plane of contraflexure. An exact analysis proves this to be a very reasonable assumption if the columns are approximately the same size. If they are not similar in size, an assumption may be made that the shear splits between them in a little different proportion, the stiffest column carrying the largest amount of shear. The methods of analysis discussed in later chapters show that distributing the shear in proportion to the I/l^3 values of the columns is a very good assumption.

The mill building of Fig. 16–4 is analyzed in Fig. 16–6 on the basis of the following assumptions: the plane of contraflexure is assumed to be at the one-third point, or 6 ft above the column bases, and the total shear above the plane of contraflexure of 20^k divides equally between the columns.

Moments are taken of the forces above the plane of. contraflexure about the point of inflection in the left column to find the vertical force in the right-hand column. By $\Sigma V = 0$ the vertical force in the left-hand column is obtained. With the wind blowing from left to right, the right-hand (or leeward) column is in compression and the left-hand (or windward) column is in tension.

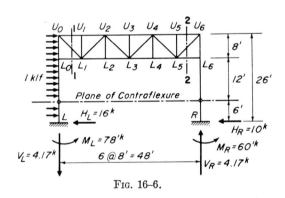

FIG. 16–6.

Moments at each column base are determined by taking moments about the base of the forces applied to the column at and below the point of inflection.

Finally, stresses in the truss are computed by statics. In computing the stresses of members of this truss which are connected to a column, all of the forces acting on the column must be taken into account because the columns are subject to both axial stress and bending moment. Section 1–1 is passed through the truss, and moments are taken about joint U_0 to obtain the stress in L_0L_1. By using the same section, moments are taken about joint L_1 to find the stress in U_0U_1. Similarly, section 2–2 is passed through the truss and moments are taken about U_6 to find stress in L_5L_6 and about L_5 to obtain stress in U_5U_6. The remaining stresses can be obtained by the method of joints.

$\Sigma M_{\text{left PI}} = 0$ of forces above plane of contraflexure

(1) (20) (10) $-48V_R = 0$
$$V_R = 4.17^k \uparrow = \text{axial stress in right column}$$

By $\Sigma V = 0$,

$$V_L = 4.17^k \downarrow = \text{axial stress in left column}$$

Assuming total horizontal shear above plane of contraflexure of (1) (20) divides equally between the two columns (10^k each),

$$H_L = 10 + (1) (6) = 16^k \leftarrow$$
$$H_R = 10^k \leftarrow$$

Moment reactions for each column found by taking moments at base of forces on column up to PI:

$$M_L = (10) (6) + (1) (6) (3) = 78'^k \;\rotatebox[origin=c]{-90}{\curvearrowleft}$$
$$M_R = (10) (6) = 60'^k \;\rotatebox[origin=c]{-90}{\curvearrowleft}$$

Stress in L_0L_1

$\Sigma M_{U_0} = 0$

(10) (20) $-$ (20) (1) (10) $+8L_0L_1 = 0$
$$L_0L_1 = 0$$

Stress in U_0U_1

$\Sigma M_{L_1} = 0$

(10) (12) $-$ (20) (1) (2) $-$ (4.17) (8) $-8U_0U_1 = 0$
$$U_0U_1 = 5.83^k$$

16–4. Lateral Bracing for Bridges

Bridge trusses may be braced laterally by bracing systems in the planes of the top and bottom chords as well as by vertical or inclined planes of bracing. The planes of bracing tie the main trusses together and cause the

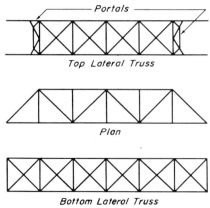

Portals

Top Lateral Truss

Plan

Bottom Lateral Truss

Fig. 16–7.

Bowaters Southern Corporation Plant, Calhoun, Tennessee. (Courtesy of
American Institute of Steel Construction, Inc.)

entire structure to act as a rigid framework. They prevent excessive
vibrations and resist the lateral loads of wind, earthquake, nosing of
locomotives, and the centrifugal effect of traffic on curved bridges. Figure 16–7 shows a Warren bridge truss with the bracing systems which
might be used in the plane of the top and bottom chords.

The loads are applied as concentrated loads at the joints of the lateral
trusses, which permits analysis by the approximate methods discussed in
Sec. 16–2. The top lateral bracing is usually subject to light loads, and
the diagonals will probably be slender and able to resist only tensile loads.
The design lateral loads are probably larger on the bottom of the truss,
and the diagonals of the bottom-chord lateral system may be large enough

End Posts of Truss

Fig. 16–8.

to carry some compressive stresses. The chord members of the lateral trusses are the chord members of the main trusses, but the AASHO specifications do not require a strengthening of these members unless their stresses, as a part of the lateral system, are greater than 25 per cent of their normal stresses as parts of the main trusses.

A system of bracing is frequently used in the plane of the end posts, similar to the one shown in Figs. 16–7 and 16–8. This type of bracing is commonly referred to as portal bracing. The portal has the purpose of furnishing the end reaction to the top lateral system and transferring it down to the supports. The arrangement of the members of portals is quite similar to that of mill buildings, and the portals may be analyzed exactly as were the mill buildings.

Portals for girder bridges may be of the types shown in Fig. 16–9, where the horizontal beam is rigidly connected to the columns (actually the girders). Similar structures are an essential part of steel building frames,

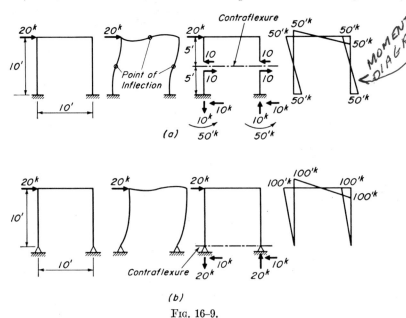

Fig. 16–9.

and they also may be analyzed on the basis of the same assumptions used for mill buildings. A portal or bent which is fixed at the column bases is analyzed in Fig. 16–9 (a). Figure 16–9 (b) shows the analysis of a portal which is hinged at the column bases. In each case the deformed shape of the bent, the reactions, and the moment diagrams are shown.

16–5.   Analysis of Building Frames for Vertical Loads

An approximate method of analyzing building frames for vertical loads is to assume that the girders in the frame have points of inflection at approximately the one-tenth-points from each end and that the axial stresses in the girders are zero.[1]

The assumptions have the effect of creating a simple beam between the points of inflection, and the positive moments in the beam can be determined by statics. Negative moments occur in the girders between their ends and the points of inflection. They may be computed by considering the portion of the beam out to the point of inflection to be a cantilever.

The shear at the end of each of the girders contributes to the axial stresses in the columns. Similarly, the negative moments at the ends of the girders are transferred to the columns. For interior columns, the girder moments on each side oppose each other and may cancel. Exterior columns have moments on only one side, caused by the girders framing into them, and these need to be considered in design.

In Fig. 16–10, beam AB of the building frame shown is analyzed by assuming points of inflection at one-tenth-points and fixed supports at beam ends.

16–6.   Analysis of Building Frames for Horizontal Loads

Rigid frame buildings are highly indeterminate, and their analysis by the usual exact methods is so lengthy as to make the approximate methods very popular. The total degree of indeterminacy of a building frame (internal and external) can be determined by considering it to consist of separate portals. One level of the rigid frame of Fig. 16–11 is broken down into a set of portals in Fig. 16–12. Each of the portals is indeterminate to the third degree, and the total degree of indeterminacy of a building equals 3 times the number of individual portals in the frame.

Another method of obtaining the degree of indeterminacy is to assume that each of the girders is cut by an imaginary section. If these values—shear, axial force, and moment—are known in each girder, the free bodies produced can be analyzed by statics. The total degree of indeterminacy equals 3 times the number of girders.

[1] Wilbur and Norris, *Elementary Structural Analysis* (New York: McGraw-Hill Book Company, Inc., 1948), p. 273.

Multi-story steel frame building, showing structural skeleton; new Hotel Sheraton, Philadelphia, Pennsylvania. (Courtesy of Bethlehem Steel Company)

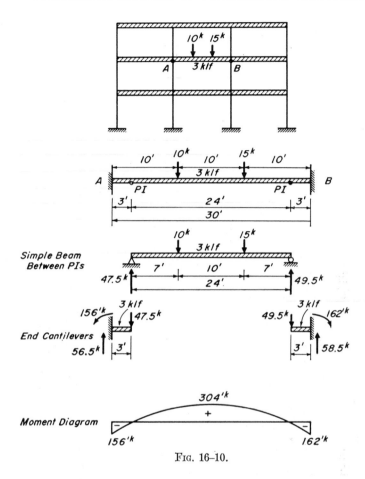

FIG. 16–10.

The building frame of Fig. 16–11 is analyzed by two approximate methods in the pages to follow, and the results are compared with those obtained by one of the exact methods considered in a later chapter. The dimensions and loading of the frame are selected to illustrate the methods involved while keeping the computations as simple as possible. There are 9 girders in the frame, giving a total degree of indeterminancy of 27, and at least 27 assumptions will be needed to permit an approximate solution.

The two methods considered are the portal method and the cantilever method. Neither of these takes into account the relative stiffnesses or the elastic properties of the members of the frame. These omissions are of particular importance in unsymmetrical or unusual frames and in very tall buildings where the relative stiffnesses of members vary greatly. The columns in the lower floors of tall buildings are much larger and stiffer than the girders which are framed into them.

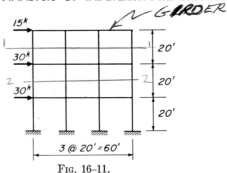

Fɪɢ. 16–11.

In both the portal and cantilever methods, the entire wind loads are assumed to be resisted by the building frames, with no stiffening assistance from the floors, walls, and partitions. Changes in length of girders and columns are assumed to be negligible. They, however, are not negligible in tall slender buildings the height of which is five or more times the least horizontal dimension.

The Portal Method. A well-known method of estimating moments, shears, and axial stresses in building frames subjected to lateral loads is the portal method. Because of its simplicity, it has probably been used more than any other approximate method for determining wind stresses in building frames. The method was presented by Albert Smith in the *Journal of the Western Society of Engineers* in April, 1915.

At least three assumptions must be made for each individual portal or for each girder. In the portal method, the frame is theoretically divided into independent portals, Fig. 16–12, and the following three assumptions are made:

1) The columns bend in such a manner that there is a point of inflection at mid-depth, Fig. 16–9 (*a*).

2) The girders bend in such a manner that there is a point of inflection at their center lines.

3) The horizontal shear on any level divides among the columns in the ratio of one part to exterior columns and two parts to interior columns. The reason for this ratio can be seen in Fig. 16–12. Each of the interior columns is serving two bents, while the exterior columns are serving only one.

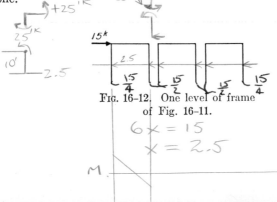

Fɪɢ. 16–12. One level of frame of Fig. 16–11.

For this frame there are 27 redundants; to obtain their values, one assumption as to the location of the point of inflection has been made for each of the 21 columns and girders. Three assumptions are made on each level as to the shear split in each individual portal, or the number of shear assumptions equals one less than the number of columns on each level. For the frame, 9 shear assumptions are made, giving a total of 30 assumptions and only 27 redundants. More assumptions are made than necessary, but they are consistent with the solution (i.e., if only 27 of the assumptions were used and the remaining values were obtained by statics, the results would be identical).

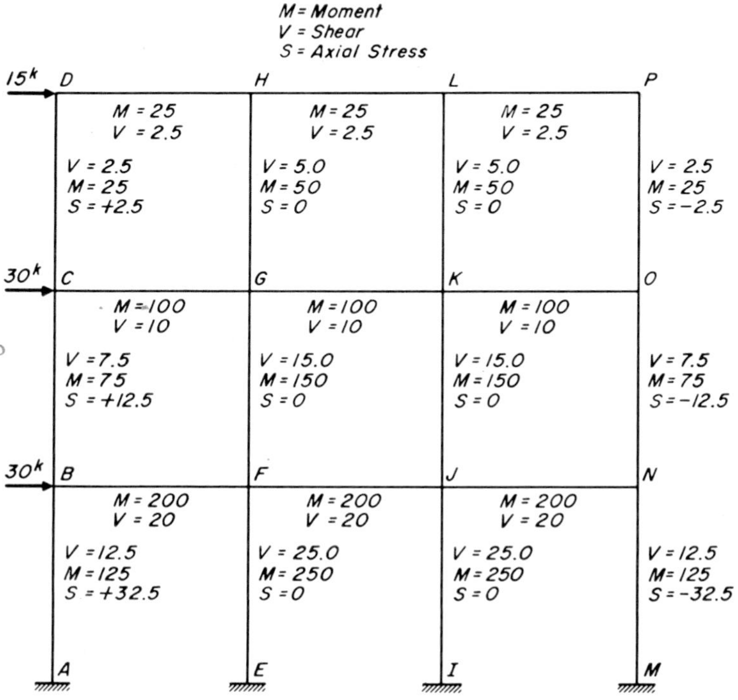

Fig. 16–13. Portal Method.

Frame Analysis. The frame is analyzed in Fig. 16–13 on the basis of these assumptions. Briefly the calculations were made as follows:

1) Column shears. The shears in each column on the various levels were first obtained. The total shear on the top level is 15^k. Because there are two exterior and two interior columns, the following expression may be written:

$$x + 2x + 2x + x = 15^k$$
$$x = 2.5^k$$
$$2x = 5.0^k$$

The shear in column CD is 2.5^k; in GH it is 5.0^k; etc. Similarly, the shears were determined for the columns on the first and second levels, where the total shears are 75^k and 45^k, respectively.

2) Column moments. The columns are assumed to have points of inflection at their mid-depths; therefore, their moments, top and bottom, equal the column shear times half the column heights.

3) Girder moments and shears. At any joint in the frame the sum of the moments in the girders equals the sum of the moments in the columns. The column moments have been previously determined. By beginning at the upper left-hand corner of the frame and working across from left to right, adding or subtracting the moments as the case may be, the girder moments were found in this order: DH, HL, LP, CG, GK, etc. It follows that with points of inflection at girder center lines, the girder shears equal the girder moments divided by half-girder lengths.

4) Column axial stresses. The axial stresses in the columns may be directly obtained from the girder shears. Starting at the upper left-hand corner, the column axial stress in CD is equal to the shear in girder DH. The axial stress in column GH is equal to the difference between the two girder shears DH and HL, which equals zero in this case. (If the width of each of the portals is the same, the shears in the girder on one level will

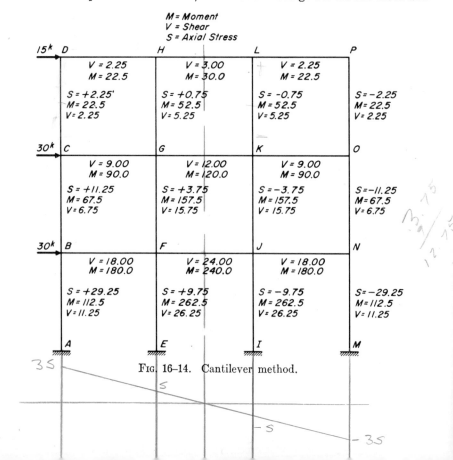

Fig. 16–14. Cantilever method.

be equal, and the interior columns will have no axial stress, since only lateral loads are considered.)

The Cantilever Method. A method similar to the portal method and also easily applied is the cantilever method presented by A. C. Wilson in *Engineering Record*, September 5, 1908. Mr. Wilson's method makes use of the assumptions which the portal method uses as to locations of points of inflection in columns and girders, but the third assumption differs somewhat. Rather than assume the shear on a particular level to divide between the columns in some ratio, the axial stress in each column is considered to be proportional to its distance from the center of gravity of all the columns on that level. The wind loads are tending to overturn the building, and the columns on the leeward side will be compressed, while those on the windward side will be put in tension. The greater the distance a column is from the center of gravity of its group of columns the greater will be its axial stress.

The new assumption is equivalent to making a number of axial-stress assumptions equal to one less than the number of columns on each level. Again, the structure has 27 redundants and 30 assumptions are made (21 columns and girder point-of-inflection assumptions and 9 column axial-stress assumptions), but the extra assumptions are consistent with the solution.

Frame Analysis. The frame previously analyzed by the portal method is analyzed by the cantilever method in Fig. 16–14. Briefly the calculations are made as follows:

1) Column axial stresses. Considering first the top level, moments are taken about the point of contraflexure in column CD of the forces above the plane of contraflexure through the columns on that level. According to the third assumption, the axial stress in GH will only be one-third of that in CD, and these stresses in GH and CD will be tensile, while those in KL and OP will be compressive. The following expression is written, with respect to Fig. 16–15, to determine the values of the column axial stresses on the top level.

$$(15)\,(10) + (1S)\,(20) - (1S)\,(40) - (3S)\,(60) = 0$$
$$S = 0.75^{k}$$
$$3S = 2.25^{k}$$

The axial stress in CD is 2.25^{k} and that in GH is 0.75^{k}, etc. Similar calculations are made for each level to obtain the column axial stresses.

2) Girder shears. The next step is to obtain the girder shears from the column axial stresses. These shears are obtained by starting at the top left-hand corner and working across the top level and adding or subtracting the axial stresses in the columns according to their signs. This procedure is similar to the method of joints used for finding truss stresses.

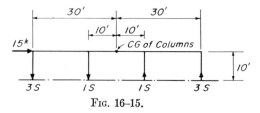

FIG. 16–15.

3) Column and girder moments and column shears. The final steps can be quickly summarized. The girder moments, as before, are equal to the girder shears times the girder half lengths. The column moments are obtained by starting at the top left-hand corner and working across each level in succession, adding or subtracting the previously obtained column and girder moments as indicated. The column shears are equal to the column moments divided by half the column heights.

Table 16–1 compares the moments in the members of this frame as determined by the two approximate methods and by the moment-distribution method described in Chapter 23. It is noted that for several members the approximate results vary considerably from the results obtained by the

TABLE 16–1

MEMBER MOMENTS

Member	Portal	Cantilever	Moment Distribution	Member	Portal	Cantilever	Moment Distribution
AB	125	112.5	199	IJ	250	262.5	224
BA	125	112.5	127	JI	250	262.5	177
BC	75	67.5	62	JF	200	240	139
BF	200	180	189	JK	150	157.5	122
CB	75	67.5	92	JN	200	180	161
CD	25	22.5	10	KJ	150	157.5	141
CG	100	90	102	KG	100	120	83
DC	25	22.5	36	KL	50	52.5	34
DH	25	22.5	36	KO	100	90	93
EF	250	262.5	224	LK	50	52.5	56
FE	250	262.5	177	LH	25	30	26
FB	200	180	161	LP	25	22.5	30
FG	150	157.5	122	MN	125	112.5	199
FJ	200	240	139	NM	125	112.5	127
GF	150	157.5	141	NJ	200	180	189
GC	100	90	93	NO	75	67.5	62
GH	50	52.5	34	ON	75	67.5	92
GK	100	120	83	OK	100	90	102
HG	50	52.5	56	OP	25	22.5	10
HD	25	22.5	30	PO	25	22.5	36
HL	25	30	26	PL	25	22.5	36

exact method. Experience with the exact methods for handling indeterminate building frames will show that the points of inflection will not occur exactly at the mid-points. Using more realistic locations for the assumed inflection points will greatly improve results. (If the points of inflection in the columns are taken as being a little above mid-depth and for exterior girders as being a little more than halfway from the outside, considerable improvement will be made.)

Problems

16–1. Compute the stresses in the members of the truss shown in the accompanying illustration for each of the following conditions: (a) Diagonals unable to carry compression. (b) Diagonal that would be in compression can resist half of shear in panel. (c) Diagonal that would be in compression can resist one-third of shear in panel.

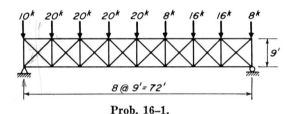

10^k 20^k 20^k 20^k 20^k 8^k 16^k 16^k 8^k

$9'$

$8 @ 9' = 72'$

Prob. 16–1.

16–2. Determine the stresses for all of the members of the truss of the mill building shown in the accompanying illustration. Assume PI's to be 12 ft above column bases.

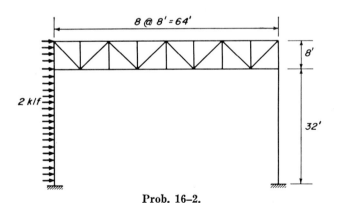

$8 @ 8' = 64'$

$8'$

$2 \, k/f$

$32'$

Prob. 16–2.

16–3. Work Prob. 16–2 by assuming PI's to be 16 ft above column bases.

16–4. Compute moments, shears, and axial stresses for all of the members of the frame shown in the accompanying illustration (a) by using portal method; (b) by using cantilever method.

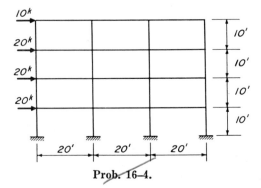

Prob. 16–4.

16–5. Compute moments, shears, and axial stresses for all of the members of the frame shown in the accompanying illustration (a) by using portal method; (b) by using cantilever method.

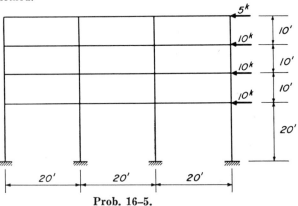

Prob. 16–5.

16–6. Assuming PI's to be 8 ft from the column bases, determine the stresses in all members of the structure shown in the accompanying illustration.

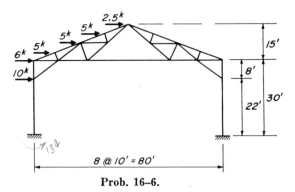

Prob. 16–6.

16–7. Draw shear and moment diagrams for the columns of Prob. 16–6.

17 | DEFLECTIONS

17-1. Reasons for Computing Deflections

The members of all structures are made up of elastic materials; such materials deflect when loaded. If deflections exceed allowable values, they may detract from the appearance of the structures and the materials attached to the members may be damaged. For example, a floor joist which deflects too much may cause cracks in the ceiling below, or if it supports concrete or tile floors, it may cause cracks in the floors. In addition, the use of a floor supported by beams which "give" appreciably does not inspire confidence, although the beams may be perfectly safe. Excessive vibration may occur in a floor of this type, particularly if it supports machinery.

Standard American practice is to limit deflections caused by live load to $\frac{1}{360}$ of the spans. This figure was probably originated for beams supporting plastered ceilings and was thought to be sufficient to prevent plaster cracks. (Although most of the deflections in a building are due to dead load, they will have substantially taken place before plaster is applied.)

The deflections of members may be controlled by cambering. The members are constructed of such a shape that they will assume their theoretical shape under some loading condition (usually dead load). A simple beam would be constructed with a slight convex bend so that under gravity loads it would become straight as assumed in the calculations. Some designers take into account both dead and live loads in figuring the amount of camber.

Deflection computations may be used for computing the reactions for indeterminate beams and trusses as well as the stresses in the members of redundant trusses. In fact, the importance of deflections in the analysis of statically indeterminate structures is nearly as great as the importance of the equations of statics is in the analysis of statically determinate structures.

Despite the importance of deflections, it is rarely necessary, even for indeterminate structures, to compute structure deformations for the purpose of correcting the original structure dimensions on which computations are based. The deformations of the materials used in ordinary work are quite small as compared to the over-all dimensions. For example, the strain that occurs in a steel section that has a modulus of elasticity of 30×10^6 psi (pounds per square inch) when the stress is 20,000 psi is only

$$\epsilon = \frac{f}{E} = \frac{20 \times 10^3}{30 \times 10^6} = 0.000667, \text{ or } 0.0667 \text{ per cent}$$

17–2. The Moment-Area Theorems

The first method presented for the calculation of deflections is the very interesting and valuable moment-area method presented by Prof. Charles E. Greene of the University of Michigan in about 1873. Under changing loads the neutral axis of a member changes in shape according to the positions and magnitudes of the loads. The elastic curve of a member is the shape the neutral axis takes under temporary loads. Professor Greene's theorems are based on the shape of the elastic curve of a member and the relationship between bending moment and the rate of change of slope at a point on the curve.

To develop the theorems, the simple beam of Fig. 17–1 is considered. Under the loads P_1 to P_4 it deflects downward as indicated in the figure.

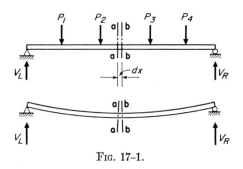

Fig. 17–1.

The dx section bounded on its ends by sections a–a and b–b is shown in Fig. 17–2. The size, degree of curvature, and distortion of the segment are tremendously exaggerated so that the slopes and deflections to be discussed can be seen easily. Line ac lies along the neutral axis of the beam and is unchanged in length. Line ce is drawn parallel to ab; therefore, be equals ac and de represents the lengthening of the bottom fiber of the dx section. Figure 17–2 (b) shows an enlarged view of triangle cde and the angle $d\theta$, which is the change in slope of the tangent to the elastic curve at the left end of the section from the tangent at the right end. Sufficient information is now available to determine $d\theta$. In the derivation to follow, it is to be remembered that the $d\theta$ angle being considered is minute, and for a very small angle the sine, tangent, and the angle in radians are identical, which permits their values to be used interchangeably. It is worthwhile to check a set of natural trigonometry tables to see the range of angles for which the functions coincide.

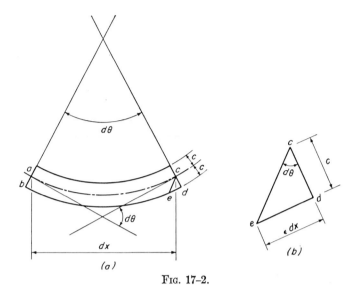

FIG. 17-2.

The bending moments developed by the external loads are positive and cause shortening of the upper beam fibers and lengthening of the lower fibers. The changes in fiber dimensions have cause the change in slope $d\theta$. The modulus of elasticity is known, and the stress at any point can be determined by the flexure formula; therefore, the strain in any fiber can be found, because it equals the stress divided by the modulus of elasticity. The value of $d\theta$ may be expressed as follows:

$$\tan d\theta = d\theta \text{ in radians} = \frac{\text{strain}}{c}$$

$$d\theta = \frac{\epsilon \, dx}{c}$$

By substituting the value of ϵ,

$$d\theta = \frac{(f/E)(dx)}{c}$$

But f is equal to Mc/I, and

$$d\theta = \frac{(Mc/EI) \, dx}{c} = \frac{M \, dx}{EI}$$

The change in slope in a dx distance is equal to $M \, dx/EI$, and the total change in slope from one point A in the beam to another point B can be expressed as the summation of all the $d\theta$ changes in the dx distances between the two points.

$$\theta_{AB} = \int_A^B \frac{M\,dx}{EI}$$

If the M/EI diagram is drawn for the beam, the above expression will be seen to equal each dx distance, from A to B, multiplied by its respective M/EI ordinate. The summation of these multiplications is the area of the diagram between the two points. From this discussion the first moment-area theorem may be expressed as follows: *The change in slope between the tangents to the elastic curve at two points is equal to the area of the M/EI diagram between the two points.*

Once we have a method by which changes in slopes between tangents to the elastic curve at various points may be determined, it is only a brief step to a method for computing deflections between the tangents. In a dx distance the neutral axis changes in direction by an amount $d\theta$. The deflection of one point on the beam with respect to the tangent at another point due to this angle change is equal to x (the distance from the point at which deflection is desired to the particular differential distance) times $d\theta$.

$$\delta = x\,d\theta$$

The value of $d\theta$ from the first theorem is substituted in this expression:

$$\delta = x\,\frac{M\,dx}{EI} = \frac{Mx\,dx}{EI}$$

To determine the total deflection from the tangent at one point A to the tangent at another point B on the beam, it is necessary to obtain a summation of the products of each $d\theta$ angle (from A to B) times the distance to the point where deflection is desired. The preceding sentence is a statement of the second moment-area theorem.

$$\delta_{AB} = \int_A^B \frac{Mx\,dx}{EI}$$

The deflection of a tangent to the elastic curve of a beam with respect to a tangent at another point is equal to the moment of the M/EI diagram between the two points, taken about the point at which deflection is desired.

17–3. Application of the Moment-Area Theorems

Moment-area is most conveniently used for beams in which the direction of the tangent to the elastic curve at one or more points is known, such as cantilever beams where the tangent at the fixed end does not change in slope. The method is applied quite easily to beams loaded with concentrated loads, because the moment diagrams consist of straight lines.

These diagrams can be broken down into single triangles and rectangles, which facilitates the mathematics. Beams supporting uniform loads or uniformly varying loads may be handled, but the mathematics is slightly more difficult.

The properties of several figures given in Fig. 17–3 are useful in handling the M/EI diagrams.

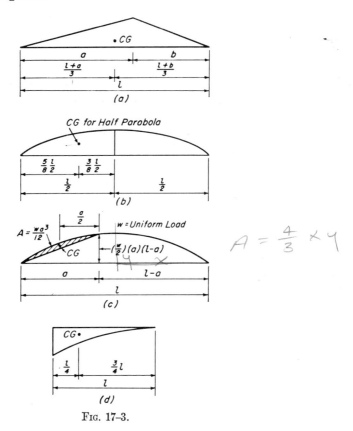

FIG. 17–3.

Examples 17–1 to 17–6 illustrate the application of the moment-area theorems. It may occasionally be possible to simplify the mathematics by drawing the moment diagram and making the calculations in terms of symbols, such as P for a concentrated load, w for a uniform load, or l for span length, as illustrated by Examples 17–1 and 17–3. The numerical values of each of the symbols are substituted in the final step to obtain the slope or deflection desired.

Care must be taken to use consistent units in the calculations. The procedure here is to use all of the distances in feet and all of the loads and reactions in kilopounds. At the end of each problem the kilopounds are changed to pounds and the feet to inches. The resulting deflections will be in inches and the slopes in radians. (There are 2π radians in 360°.)

To prevent mistakes in the application of moment-area theory, it is emphasized that the slopes and deflections which are obtained are with respect to tangents to the elastic curve at the points being considered. The theorems do not directly give the slope or deflection at a point in the beam as compared to the horizontal (except in one or two special cases), they give the change in slope of the elastic curve from one point to another or the deflection of the tangent at one point with respect to the tangent at another point.

If a beam or frame has several loads applied, the M/EI diagram may be inconvenient to handle. The calculations may be simplified by drawing a separate diagram for each of the loads and determining the slopes and deflections for each diagram separately. The final results for a particular point can be found by adding the results for all of the loads. The principle of superposition applies to area moment and to any of the other methods of determining slopes and deflections discussed in subsequent pages.

Example 17–6 shows that moment-area is one method which may be used to determine the moments at the ends of a fixed-ended beam, which is statically indeterminate to the third degree.

Example 17–1. Determine the slope and deflection of the right end of the cantilever beam shown in Fig. 17–4.

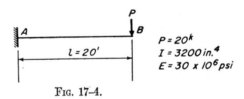

Fig. 17–4.

Solution: A tangent to the elastic curve at the fixed end is horizontal; therefore, the changes in slope and deflection of a tangent at the free end with respect to a tangent a the fixed end are the slope and deflection of that point.

Slope at B=area of M/EI diagram from A to B

$$\theta_B = \left(\frac{1}{2}\right)(l)\left(\frac{Pl}{EI}\right) = \frac{Pl^2}{2EI} \quad = AREA \; OF \; \frac{M}{EI}$$

$$= \frac{(20 \times 1000)(20 \times 12)^2}{(2)(30 \times 10^6)(3200)} = 0.00599 \text{ radian} = 0.34°$$

Deflection at B=moment of M/EI diagram from A to B about B

Moment of $\frac{M}{EI}$ about B

$$\delta_B = \left(\frac{1}{2}\right)(l)\left(\frac{Pl}{EI}\right)\left(\frac{2}{3}l\right) = \frac{Pl^3}{3EI}$$

$$= \frac{(20 \times 1000)(20 \times 12)^3}{(3)(30 \times 10^6)(3200)} = 0.96 \text{ in.}$$

EXAMPLE 17–2. Determine the slope and deflection of the beam at point B, 10 ft from the left end of the structure shown in Fig. 17–5.

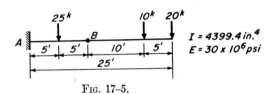

FIG. 17–5.

Solution: The left end is again fixed; the slope at B equals the area of the M/EI diagram from A to B; and the deflection at B equals the moment of the M/EI diagram from A to B taken about B. The diagram is broken down into convenient triangles as shown for making the calculations.

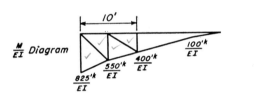

Slope

$$\theta_B = \frac{(\frac{1}{2})(825)(5) + (\frac{1}{2})(550)(5) + (\frac{1}{2})(550)(5) + (\frac{1}{2})(400)(5)}{EI} = \frac{5812.5 \text{ ft}^2\text{-k}}{EI}$$

$$= \frac{(5812.5)(12 \times 12)(1000)}{(30 \times 10^6)(4399.4)} = 0.00634 \text{ radian} = 0.36°$$

Deflection

$$\delta_B = \frac{(\frac{1}{2})(825)(5)(8.33) + (\frac{1}{2})(550)(5)(6.67) + (\frac{1}{2})(550)(5)(3.33) + (\frac{1}{2})(400)(5)(1.67)}{EI}$$

$$= \frac{32,600 \text{ ft}^3\text{-k}}{EI} = \frac{(32,600)(12 \times 12 \times 12)(1000)}{(30 \times 10^6)(4399.4)} = 0.427 \text{ in.}$$

EXAMPLE 17–3. Determine the slope and deflection at the free end of the cantilever beam shown in Fig. 17–6.

FIG. 17–6.

Solution:

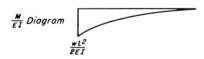

$\frac{M}{EI}$ *Diagram*

$\frac{wl^2}{2EI}$

Slope

$$\theta_A = \left(\frac{1}{3}\right)(l)\left(\frac{wl^2}{2EI}\right) = \frac{wl^3}{6EI}$$

$$= \frac{(4000/12)(20 \times 12)^3}{(6)(30 \times 10^6)(9000)} = 0.00283 \text{ radian} = 0.16°$$

Deflection

$$\delta_A = \left(\frac{1}{3}\right)(l)\left(\frac{wl^2}{2EI}\right)\left(\frac{3}{4}l\right) = \frac{wl^4}{8EI}$$

$$= \frac{(4000/12)(20 \times 12)^4}{(8)(30 \times 10^6)(9000)} = 0.512 \text{ in.}$$

EXAMPLE 17–4. Compute the slope and deflection at the free end of the cantilever beam shown in Fig. 17–7.

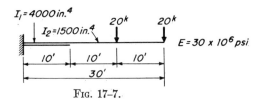

$I_1 = 4000 in.^4$

$I_2 = 1500 in.^4$

20^k 20^k

$E = 30 \times 10^6 psi$

10'   10'   10'

30'

FIG. 17–7.

Solution: The moment of inertia of the beam has been increased near the support where bending moment is greatest. The M/EI diagram is drawn by keeping the constant E as a symbol but dividing the ordinates by the proper moments of inertia. The resulting figure is conveniently divided into triangles and the computations made as before.

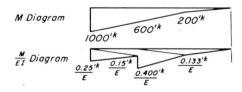

M Diagram

1000'ᵏ   600'ᵏ   200'ᵏ

$\frac{M}{EI}$ *Diagram* $\frac{0.25'^k}{E}$ $\frac{0.15'^k}{E}$ $\frac{0.133'^k}{E}$ $\frac{0.400'^k}{E}$

Slope

$$\theta_A = \frac{(\frac{1}{2})(10)(0.25) + (\frac{1}{2})(10)(0.15) + (\frac{1}{2})(10)(0.400) + (\frac{1}{2})(10)(0.133)(2)}{E}$$

$$= \frac{5.333 \text{ ft}^2\text{-k}}{E} = \frac{(5.333)(144)(1000)}{30 \times 10^6} = 0.0256 \text{ radian} = 1.47°$$

Deflection

$$\delta_A = [(\tfrac{1}{2})(10)(0.25)(26.67) + (\tfrac{1}{2})(10)(0.15)(23.33) + (\tfrac{1}{2})(10)(0.400)(16.67)$$
$$+ (\tfrac{1}{2})(10)(0.133)(13.33) + (\tfrac{1}{2})(10)(0.133)(6.67)]/E$$

$$= \frac{97.46 \text{ ft}^3\text{-k}}{E} = \frac{(97.46)(1728)(1000)}{30 \times 10^6} = 5.61 \text{ in.}$$

EXAMPLE 17–5. Compute the deflection at the center line of the uniformly loaded simple beam shown in Fig. 17–8.

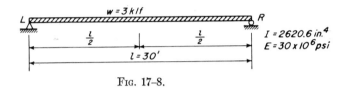

FIG. 17–8.

Solution: The tangents to the elastic curve at each end of the beam are inclined. It is a simple matter to determine the deflection between a tangent at the center line and one of the end tangents, but the result is not the actual deflection at the center line of the beam. To obtain the correct deflection, it is necessary to work in a somewhat roundabout manner as follows:

1. The deflection δ_1 of the tangent at the right end R from the tangent at the left end L is found.

2. The deflection of a tangent at the center line from a tangent at L, δ_2, is found.

3. By proportions the distance from the original chord between L and R and the tangent at L, δ_3, can be computed. The difference between δ_3 and δ_2 is the center-line deflection.

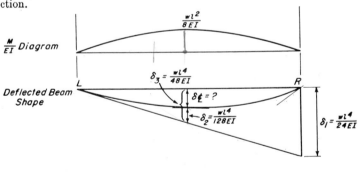

$$\delta_1 = \left(\frac{2}{3}\right)(l)\left(\frac{wl^2}{8EI}\right)\left(\frac{l}{2}\right) = \frac{wl^4}{24EI}$$

$$\delta_2 = \left(\frac{2}{3}\right)\left(\frac{l}{2}\right)\left(\frac{wl^2}{8EI}\right)\left(\frac{3}{8}\right)\left(\frac{l}{2}\right) = \frac{wl^4}{128EI}$$

$$\delta_3 = \frac{1}{2} \times \delta_1 = \frac{1}{2} \times \frac{wl^4}{24EI} = \frac{wl^4}{48EI}$$

$$\delta_{\cancel{C}} = \frac{wl^4}{48EI} - \frac{wl^4}{128EI} = \frac{5wl^4}{384EI}$$

$$\delta_{\mathbb{C}} = \frac{(5)(3000/12)(30 \times 12)^4}{(384)(30 \times 10^6)(2620.6)} = 0.694 \text{ in.}$$

EXAMPLE 17-6. Determine the moments at the ends of the fixed-ended beam shown in Fig. 17-9 for which E and I are constant.

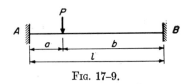

FIG. 17-9.

Solution: Examination of the beam reveals no change of slope and no deflection of the tangent at A from the tangent at B; therefore, the total area of the M/EI diagram from A to B is zero, and the moment of the M/EI diagram about either end is zero.

The M/EI diagram may be drawn in two parts: the simple beam moment diagram the ordinates of which are known, and the moment diagram due to the unknown end moments, M_A and M_B. For each of the latter moments, a triangular-shaped diagram may be drawn and the two combined into one trapezoid. The moment-area theorems are written to express the change in slope and deflection from B to A. Each of the two equations contains the two unknowns M_A and M_B, and the equations are solved simultaneously.

Simple Beam $\frac{M}{EI}$ Diagram

End Moment $\frac{M}{EI}$ Diagram

Theorem 1

$$\left(\frac{1}{2}\right)\left(\frac{Pab}{EIl}\right)(l) + \left(\frac{1}{2}\right)\left(\frac{M_A}{EI}\right)(l) + \left(\frac{1}{2}\right)\left(\frac{M_B}{EI}\right)(l) = 0$$

$$\frac{Pab}{2EI} + \frac{M_A l}{2EI} + \frac{M_B l}{2EI} = 0 \qquad (1)$$

Theorem 2

$$\left(\frac{Pab}{2EI}\right)\left(\frac{l+a}{3}\right) + \left(\frac{M_A l}{2EI}\right)\left(\frac{1}{3}l\right) + \left(\frac{M_B l}{2EI}\right)\left(\frac{2}{3}l\right) = 0$$

$$\frac{Pabl + Pa^2 b}{6EI} + \frac{M_A l^2}{6EI} + \frac{M_B l^2}{3EI} = 0 \qquad (2)$$

By solving Eqs. 1 and 2 simultaneously for M_A and M_B,

$$M_A = -\frac{Pab^2}{l^2} \qquad M_B = -\frac{Pa^2 b}{l^2}$$

17-4. Method of Elastic Weights

A careful study of the procedure used in applying the area-moment theorems will reveal a simpler and more practical method of computing

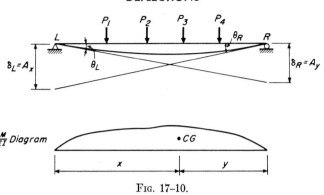

Fig. 17–10.

slopes and deflections for most beams. In reviewing this procedure, the beam and M/EI diagram of Fig. 17–10 are considered.

By letting A equal the area of the M/EI diagram, the deflection of the tangent at R from the tangent at L equals Ay, and the change in slope between the two tangents is A. An imaginary beam is loaded with the M/EI diagram, as shown in Fig. 17–11, and the reactions R_L and R_R are determined. They equal Ay/l and Ax/l, respectively.

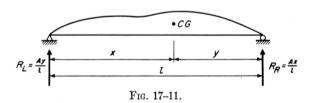

Fig. 17–11.

In Fig. 17–10 the slopes of the tangents to the elastic curve at each end of the beam (θ_L and θ_R) are equal to the deflections between the tangents at each end divided by the span length, as follows:

$$\theta_L = \frac{\delta_R}{l} \qquad \theta_R = \frac{\delta_L}{l}$$

The values of δ_L and δ_R have previously been found to equal Ax and Ay, respectively, and may be substituted in these expressions.

$$\theta_L = \frac{Ay}{l} \qquad \theta_R = \frac{Ax}{l}$$

The end slopes are exactly the same as the reactions for the beam in Fig. 17–11. At either end of the fictitious beam the shear equals the reaction and thus the slope in the actual beam. Further experiments will show that the shear at any point in the beam loaded with the M/EI diagram equals the slope at that point in the actual beam.

A similar argument can be made concerning the computation of deflections, and it will be found that the deflection in the actual beam equals the moment in the fictitious beam. In detail, the two theorems of elastic weights may be stated as follows:

> *1) The slope of the elastic curve of a beam at a point, measured with respect to a chord between the supports, equals the shear at that point if the beam is loaded with the M/EI diagram.*
>
> *2) The deflection of the elastic curve of a beam at a point, measured with respect to a chord between the supports, equals the moment at that point if the beam is loaded with the M/EI diagram.*

17–5. Application of the Method of Elastic Weights

Elastic weights in its present form is applicable only to beams simply supported at each end. It will be found in using the method that maximum deflections in the actual beam occur at points of zero shear in the imaginary beam. The reasoning is the same as that presented for shear and moment diagrams in Sec. 4–5, where maximum moments were found to occur at points of zero shear.

Consideration has not been given to the subject of sign conventions for either the area-moment or the elastic-weight methods. With little difficulty the student can see the directions of slopes and deflections by study of the shears and moments on the fictitious beam. A positive shear in the fictitious beam shows the left side is being pushed up with respect to the right side, or the beam is sloping downward from left to right. Similarly, a positive moment (see Fig. 4–7) indicates downward deflection.

Examples 17–7 to 17–10 illustrate the application of elastic weights.

EXAMPLE 17–7. Determine the deflection at the center line of the beam shown in Fig. 17–12.

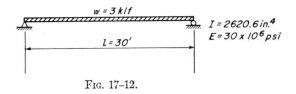

$w = 3\,k/f$

$I = 2620.6\,in.^4$

$E = 30 \times 10^6\,psi$

$l = 30'$

FIG. 17–12.

Solution:

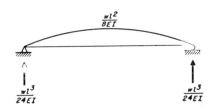

$\frac{wl^2}{8EI}$

$\frac{wl^3}{24EI}$

$\frac{wl^3}{24EI}$

Deflection at center line:

$$\delta_{\mathbb{C}} = \text{moment}_{\mathbb{C}} = \left(\frac{wl^3}{24EI}\right)\left(\frac{l}{2}\right) - \left(\frac{2}{3}\right)\left(\frac{l}{2}\right)\left(\frac{wl^2}{8EI}\right)\left(\frac{3}{8}\frac{l}{2}\right)$$

$$= \frac{5wl^4}{384EI} = \frac{(5)(3000/12)(30 \times 12)^4}{(384)(30 \times 10^6)(2620.6)} = 0.694 \text{ in.}$$

EXAMPLE 17–8. Determine the slope and deflection at the center line of the beam shown in Fig. 17–13.

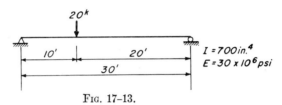

FIG. 17–13.

Solution:

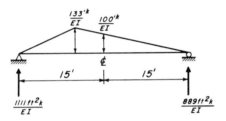

Deflection:

$$\delta_{\mathbb{C}} = \frac{(889)(15) - (\frac{1}{2})(100)(15)(5)}{EI} = \frac{9585 \text{ ft}^3\text{-k}}{EI}$$

$$= \frac{(9585)(1728)(1000)}{(30 \times 10^6)(700)} = 0.792 \text{ in.}$$

Slope:

$$\theta_{\mathbb{C}} = \frac{-889 + (\frac{1}{2})(100)(15)}{EI} = -\frac{139 \text{ ft}^2\text{-k}}{EI}$$

$$= -\frac{(139)(144)(1000)}{(30 \times 10^6)(700)} = -0.00952 \text{ radian}$$

$$= -0.55° \quad \text{(negative slope} \diagup)$$

EXAMPLE 17–9. Compute the maximum deflection for the beam shown in Fig. 17–14.

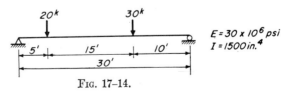

FIG. 17–14.

Solution:

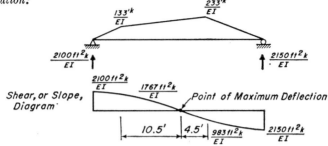

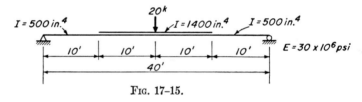

$$\delta_{\max} = \frac{(2100)(15.5) - (\tfrac{1}{2})(5)(133)(12.17) - (10.5)(133)(5.25) - (\tfrac{1}{2})(10.5)(70)(3.5)}{EI}$$

$$= \frac{18,650 \ \text{ft}^3\text{-k}}{EI} = \frac{(19,900)(1728)(1000)}{(30 \times 10^6)(1500)} = 0.764 \ \text{in.}$$

EXAMPLE 17–10. Compute the center-line deflection for the simple beam shown in Fig. 17–15.

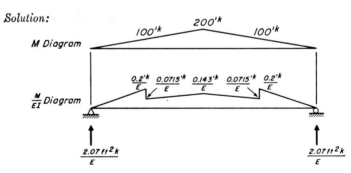

FIG. 17–15.

Solution:

M Diagram

$\frac{M}{EI}$ Diagram

$$\delta_{\mathcal{C}} = \left(\frac{2.07}{E}\right)(20) - \left(\frac{1}{2}\right)(10)\left(\frac{0.2}{E}\right)(13.33) - (10)\left(\frac{0.0715}{E}\right)(5) - \left(\frac{1}{2}\right)(10)\left(\frac{0.0715}{E}\right)(3.33)$$

$$= \frac{23.3}{E} = \frac{(23.3)(1728)(1000)}{30 \times 10^6} = 1.34 \ \text{in.}$$

17–6. Limitations of Elastic-Weight Method

The method of elastic weights was developed for simple beams and in its present form will not work for cantilever beams, overhanging beams,

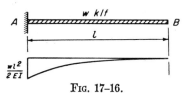

Fig. 17-16.

fixed-ended beams, and continuous beams. The moment-area theorems are used to determine the correct slope and deflection at the free end of the uniformly loaded cantilever beam of Fig. 17-16.

$$\theta_B = \left(\frac{1}{3}\right)(l)\left(\frac{wl^2}{2EI}\right) = \frac{wl^3}{6EI}$$

$$\delta_B = \left(\frac{1}{3}\right)(l)\left(\frac{wl^2}{2EI}\right)\left(\frac{3}{4}l\right) = \frac{wl^4}{8EI}$$

If the elastic-weight method were used in an attempt to find the slope and deflection at the ends of the same beam, the result would be slopes and deflections of zero at the free end and $wl^3/6EI$ and $wl^4/24EI$ at the fixed end, as shown in Figure 17-17.

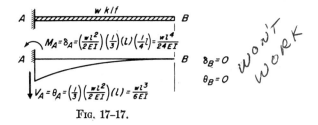

Fig. 17-17.

The slope and deflection at the fixed end A must be zero; but application of elastic weights to the beam results in both shear and moment, falsely indicating slope and deflection.

If the fixed end of the beam were moved to the free end and the resulting beam loaded with the M/EI diagram, the shears and moments would correspond exactly to the slopes and deflections on the actual beam as found by the moment-area method.

17-7. Conjugate-Beam Method

The conjugate-beam method makes use of an "analogous" or "conjugate" beam to be handled by elastic weights in place of the actual beam to which it cannot be correctly applied. The shear and moment in the imaginary beam, loaded with the M/EI diagram, must correspond exactly with the slope and deflection of the actual beam.

The correct mathematical relationship is obtained for a beam simply end-supported, if it is loaded "as is" with the M/EI diagram. If the elastic-weight method is applied to other types of beams, the largest moments due to the M/EI loading occur at the supports, incorrectly indicating that the largest deflections occur at those points. For elastic weights to be applied correctly, use must be made of substitute beams or conjugate beams which have the supports changed so that the correct relationships are obtained.

The loads and properties of the true beam have no effect on the manner in which the conjugate beam is supported. The only factors affecting the supports of the imaginary beam are the supports of the actual beam. The lengths of the two beams are equal. In the following paragraphs is a discussion of the various types of beam support as to what they must become in the conjugate beam so that the elastic-weight method will apply. The mathematical proof of these relationships is explained in detail in texts on strength of materials.

Free End. The free end of a beam slopes and deflects when the beam is loaded. The conjugate beam must have both shear and moment at that end when it is loaded with the M/EI diagram. The only type of end support having both shear and moment is the fixed end. *A free end in the actual beam becomes a fixed end in the conjugate beam.*

Fixed End. A similar discussion in reverse order can be made for a fixed end. No slope or deflection can occur at a fixed end, and there must not be any shear or moment in the conjugate beam at that point. *A fixed end in the actual beam becomes a free end in the conjugate beam.*

Simple End Support. A simple end slopes but does not deflect when the beam is loaded. The imaginary beam will have shear but no moment at that point, a situation which can occur only at a simple support. *A simple end support in the actual beam remains a simple end support in the conjugate beam.*

Simple Interior Support. There is no deflection at either a simple interior or a simple end support. Both types may slope when the beam

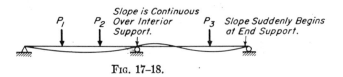

P_1 P_2 Slope is Continuous
Over Interior
Support. P_3 Slope Suddenly Begins
at End Support.

Fig. 17–18.

is loaded, but the situations are somewhat different. The slope at a simple interior support is continuous across the support; that is, no sudden change of slope occurs. This condition is not present at a simple end support where the slope suddenly begins. (See the deflection curve for the beam of Fig. 17–18.) If there is no change of slope at a simple interior support, there can be no change of shear at the corresponding support in the conjugate beam. Any type of external support at this point would cause a change in the shear; therefore, an internal pin (or unsupported hinge) is required. *A simple interior support in the actual beam becomes an unsupported internal hinge in the conjugate beam.*

Internal Hinge. At an unsupported internal hinge, there is both slope and deflection, which means that the corresponding support in the conjugate beam must have shear and moment. *An internal hinge in the actual beam becomes a simple support in the conjugate beam.*

Summary. Figure 17–19 shows several types of common beams and their corresponding conjugates.

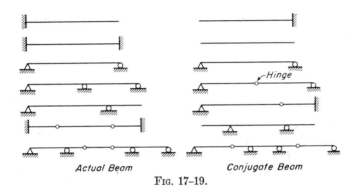

Actual Beam   Conjugate Beam

Fɪɢ. 17–19.

Equilibrium. The reactions, moments, and shears of the conjugate beam are easily computed by statics because the congujate beam is always statically determinate even though the real beam may be statically indeterminate. Sometimes the congujate beam may appear to be completely unstable. The most conspicuous example is the conjugate for the fixed-ended beam (Fig. 17–20), which has no supports whatsoever. On second glance the areas of the M/EI diagram are seen to be so precisely balanced

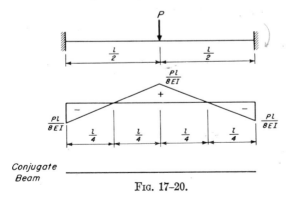

Conjugate Beam

Fɪɢ. 17–20.

between downward and upward loads (positive and negative areas of the diagram, respectively) as to require no supports. Any supports, seemingly required, would have zero reactions, and the proper shears and moments are supplied to coincide with the true slopes and deflections. Even a real beam continuous over several simple supports has a conjugate which is simply end-supported.

17–8. Summary of Beam Relations

A brief summary of the relations that exist between loads, shears, moments, slope changes, slopes, and deflections is presented in Fig. 17–21. The relations are shown for a uniformly loaded beam but are applicable to any type of loading. For the two sets of curves shown, the ordinate on one curve equals the slope at that point on the following curve. It is obvious from these figures that the same mathematical relations that exist between load, shear, and moment hold for M/EI loading, slope, and deflection.

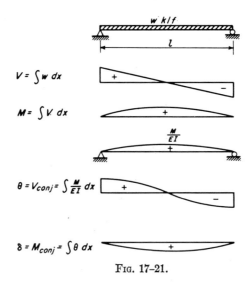

FIG. 17–21.

17–9. Application of Conjugate Method to Beams

Examples 17–11 and 17–12 illustrate the conjugate method of calculating slopes and deflections for beams. The procedure as to symbols and units used in applying the method is in general the same as that used for the moment-area and elastic-weight methods. Maximum deflections occur at points of zero shear on the conjugate structure. For example, the point of zero shear in the beam of Fig. 17–20 is the center line. The deflection is as follows:

$$\delta_{\mathbb{C}} = \text{Mom } \mathbb{C}$$

$$= \left(\frac{1}{2}\right)\left(\frac{l}{4}\right)\left(\frac{Pl}{8EI}\right)\left(\frac{5}{12}l\right) - \left(\frac{1}{2}\right)\left(\frac{l}{4}\right)\left(\frac{Pl}{8EI}\right)\left(\frac{l}{12}\right)$$

$$= \frac{Pl^3}{192EI}$$

EXAMPLE 17-11. Determine the slope and deflection of point A, Fig. 17-22.

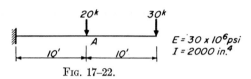

FIG. 17-22.

Solution:

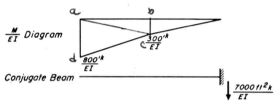

Slope

$$\theta_A = \frac{(\frac{1}{2})(300)(10) + (\frac{1}{2})(800)(10)}{EI} = \frac{5500 \text{ ft}^2\text{-k}}{EI}$$

$$= \frac{(5500)(144)(1000)}{(30 \times 10^6)(2000)} = 0.0132 \text{ radian} = 0.756°$$

Deflection

$$\delta_A = \frac{(\frac{1}{2})(300)(10)(3.33) + (\frac{1}{2})(800)(10)(6.67)}{EI} = \frac{31,667 \text{ ft}^3\text{-k}}{EI}$$

$$= \frac{(31,667)(1728)(1000)}{(30 \times 10^6)(2000)} = 0.913 \text{ in.}$$

EXAMPLE 17-12. Determine deflections at points A and B in the overhanging beam of Fig. 17-23.

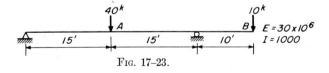

FIG. 17-23.

Solution: The M/EI diagram is drawn and placed on the conjugate beam, which has an interior hinge. The reactions are determined as they were for the cantilever-type structures of Chapter 3. The portion of the beam to the left of the hinge is considered as a simple beam, and its reactions are determined. The reaction at the hinge is applied as a concentrated load acting at the end of the cantilever to the right of the hinge in the opposite direction, and the reactions at the fixed end are determined. To simplify the mathematics, a separate moment diagram is drawn for each of the concentrated loads.

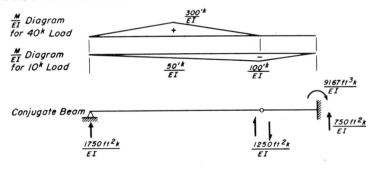

$$\delta_A = \frac{(1750)(15) - (\frac{1}{2})(15)(300)(5) + (\frac{1}{2})(15)(50)(5)}{EI} = \frac{16{,}875 \text{ ft}^3\text{-k}}{EI} = 0.973 \text{ in.} \quad \downarrow$$

$$\delta_B = \frac{(1250)(10) - (\frac{1}{2})(10)(100)(6.67)}{EI} = \frac{9167 \text{ ft}^3\text{-k}}{EI} = 0.528 \text{ in.} \quad \uparrow$$

17–10. Application of Conjugate Method to Frames

The rigid frames of Fig. 17–24 consist of members rigidly connected at their joints. The joints are moment-resisting and prevent the frame members from having freedom of rotation.

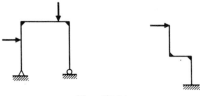

Fig. 17–24.

The slopes and deflections of frames may be determined by the conjugate method as they were for beams, but there are additional factors that may enter the calculations. Consider the frame and loads of Fig. 17–25 (a) and let the deflection of point E be desired. Figure 17–25 (b) shows a sketch of the estimated deformed shape of the frame. It is seen that there are two factors affecting the total deflection at E, these being the deflection at E if joint B were prevented from moving laterally plus the effect of the actual movement to the right of joint B. The frame sways to the right, which causes E to deflect an additional amount. Similarly, to find the total change in slope or the rotation of a particular joint in a complicated frame, it may be necessary to consider the rotations of several joints.

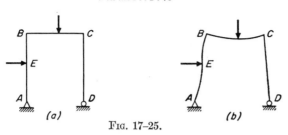

FIG. 17–25.

The foregoing discussion has shown that the calculation of deflections for a rigid frame by the usual conjugate-beam procedure may involve the taking of moments, the structure being loaded with the M/EI diagram, plus a complicated consideration of joint rotations. Slope and deflection are determined for an elementary frame in Example 17–13 in this manner.

EXAMPLE 17–13. Determine the deflections at points B and D of the frame shown in Fig. 17–26.

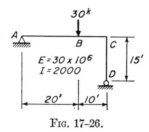

FIG. 17–26.

Solution: A sketch of the estimated deflected shape of the structure and the M/EI diagram are drawn. The deflection of point B is easily determined by the usual procedure. The deflected shape of the structure shows that member CD remains straight, because it has no moment, and it inclines outward at an angle equal to θ_C. The deflection at D equals the length of CD times θ_C.

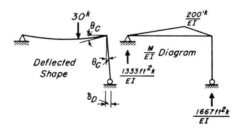

$$\delta_B = \frac{(1333)(20) - (\frac{1}{2})(20)(200)(6.67)}{EI} = \frac{13,333 \text{ ft}^3\text{-k}}{EI} = 0.384 \text{ in.}$$

$$\theta_C = \frac{1667 \text{ ft}^2\text{-k}}{EI} = 0.004 \text{ radian}$$

$$\delta_D = (15 \times 12)(0.004) = 0.72 \text{ in.} \rightarrow$$

Examination of the functions and behavior of the joints of a rigid frame reveals a simpler method of making the calculations. The joints B and C of the frame of Fig. 17–25 may be considered to be interior supports in a beam continuous from A to D. They are definitely support points because at B member AB supports the left end of member BC and at C member CD supports the right end of member BC. Neglecting the small axial deformations of the member joints, B and C cannot deflect vertically, although they may be displaced laterally. There may also be rotation of these points.

An interior support having no vertical deflection but having slope becomes a hinge in the conjugate structure. End supports follow the usual conjugate rules: a simple support remains a simple support, a fixed end becomes a free end, etc. In actuality a roller type of end support is an exception to the rule because it may deflect parallel to its supporting surface and must be fixed in the conjugate structure. Two frames are shown in Fig. 17–27, together with their continuous-beam type of conjugate

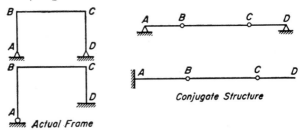

Conjugate Structure

Actual Frame

Fig. 17–27.

structures. The procedure is to draw the M/EI diagram for the entire frame in its original shape, place it on the conjugate structure, and proceed as before for beams as illustrated by Example 17–14 to 17–16. In these solutions it is noted that a deflection which is found to be perpendicular to a member of the conjugate structure is perpendicular to the member in its true position in the real frame.

EXAMPLE 17–14. Determine the deflections of points B and D and the joint rotation of C in the frame of Example 17–13, which is reproduced in Fig. 17–28.

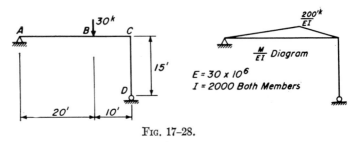

$\frac{M}{EI}$ Diagram

$E = 30 \times 10^6$
$I = 2000$ Both Members

Fig. 17–28.

Solution: The M/EI diagram is drawn and placed on the conjugate structure. The reactions on the beam to the left of the hinge are determined, the one at C being applied as a downward load on the cantilever CD. The reactions at the fixed end of the cantilever are determined, and moments and shears are found to obtain the deflections and slopes desired on the actual frame.

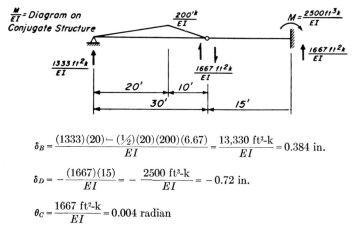

$$\delta_B = \frac{(1333)(20) - (\frac{1}{2})(20)(200)(6.67)}{EI} = \frac{13,330 \text{ ft}^3\text{-k}}{EI} = 0.384 \text{ in.}$$

$$\delta_D = -\frac{(1667)(15)}{EI} = -\frac{2500 \text{ ft}^3\text{-k}}{EI} = -0.72 \text{ in.}$$

$$\theta_C = \frac{1667 \text{ ft}^2\text{-k}}{EI} = 0.004 \text{ radian}$$

EXAMPLE 17–15. Determine the horizontal deflections at points A and B, Fig. 17–29.

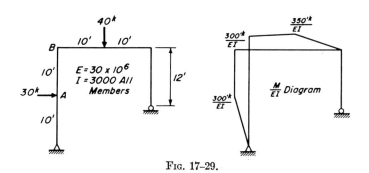

FIG. 17–29.

Solution:

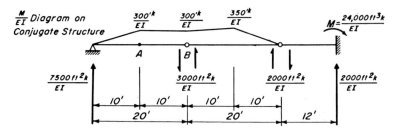

$$\delta_A = \frac{(7500)(10) - (\frac{1}{2})(300)(10)(3.33)}{EI} = \frac{70,000 \text{ ft}^3\text{-k}}{EI} = 1.34 \text{ in.}$$

$$\delta_B = \frac{(7500)(20) - (10)(300)(5) - (\frac{1}{2})(300)(10)(13.33)}{EI} = \frac{115,000 \text{ ft}^3\text{-k}}{EI} = 2.21 \text{ in.}$$

EXAMPLE 17–16. Determine the deflections at points A and B in the frame shown in Fig. 17–30, for which the members do not have the same moments of inertia.

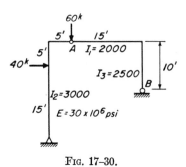

FIG. 17–30.

Solution: It is necessary to divide the moments by the respective moments of inertia or by their relative values in preparing the M/EI diagram. The moment of inertia of the beam of 2000 in.^{4} is used as the base to which the others are referred.

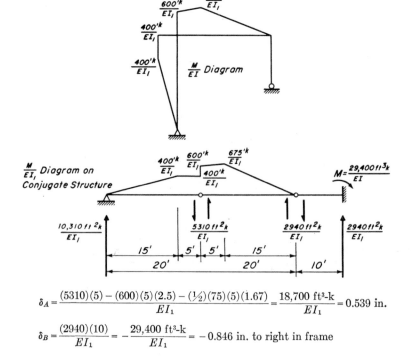

$$\delta_A = \frac{(5310)(5) - (600)(5)(2.5) - (\frac{1}{2})(75)(5)(1.67)}{EI_1} = \frac{18,700 \text{ ft}^3\text{-k}}{EI_1} = 0.539 \text{ in.}$$

$$\delta_B = \frac{(2940)(10)}{EI_1} = -\frac{29,400 \text{ ft}^3\text{-k}}{EI_1} = -0.846 \text{ in. to right in frame}$$

Problems

Use the moment-area method for solving Probs. 17–1 to 17–6.

17–1. Determine the slope and deflection at point A of the cantilever beam shown in the accompanying illustration.

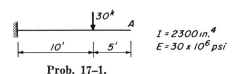

$I = 2300\,in.^4$
$E = 30 \times 10^6\,psi$

Prob. 17–1.

17–2. Compute the values of slope and deflection 10 ft from the fixed end for the cantilever beam shown in the accompanying illustration.

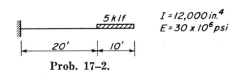

$I = 12,000\,in.^4$
$E = 30 \times 10^6\,psi$

Prob. 17–2.

17–3. Find the slope and deflection at points A and B for the beam shown in the accompanying illustration.

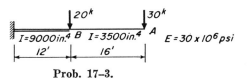

$E = 30 \times 10^6\,psi$

Prob. 17–3.

17–4. Find the slope and deflection at point A of the simple beam shown in the accompanying illustration.

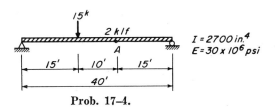

$I = 2700\,in.^4$
$E = 30 \times 10^6\,psi$

Prob. 17–4.

17–5. Determine an expression for the fixed end moments of the beam shown in the accompanying illustration.

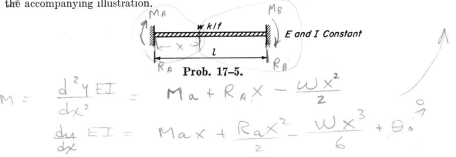

E and I Constant

Prob. 17–5.

17–6. Determine the fixed end moments for the beam shown in the accompanying illustration.

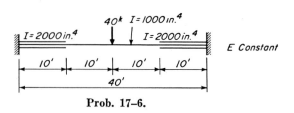

Prob. 17–6.

Use the elastic-weight method for solving Probs. 17–7 to 17–10.

17–7. Determine the deflection at point A of the structure shown in the accompanying illustration.

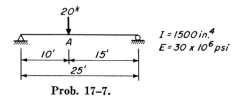

Prob. 17–7.

17–8. Determine the slope and deflection at the center line of the simple beam shown in the accompanying illustration.

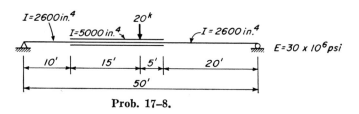

Prob. 17–8.

17–9. Compute the slopes and deflections at points A and B of the structure shown in the accompanying illustration.

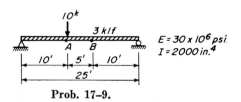

Prob. 17–9.

17–10. Determine the maximum deflection in the beam of Prob. 17–7. Use the conjugate-beam method for solving Probs. 17–11 to 17–19.

17–11. Solve Prob. 17–2 by using the conjugate-beam method instead of the moment-area method.

17–12. Solve Prob. 17–3 by using the conjugate-beam method instead of the moment-area method.

17–13. Draw a deflection curve for the overhanging beam shown in the accompanying illustration.

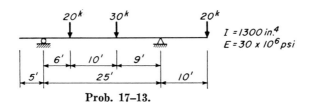

Prob. 17–13.

17–14. Determine the slope and deflection under each of the concentrated loads on the wooden beam shown in the accompanying illustration.

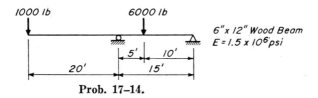

Prob. 17–14.

17–15. Determine the slope and deflections at points A and B for the beam shown in the accompanying illustration.

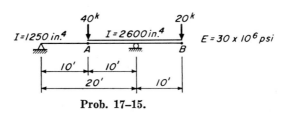

Prob. 17–15.

17–16. Determine deflections and slopes at points A and B on the frame shown in the accompanying illustration.

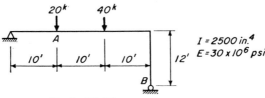

Prob. 17–16.

17–17. Determine the horizontal deflection at point A and the horizontal and vertical deflection of point B of the structure shown in the accompanying illustration.

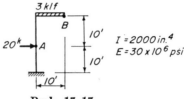

Prob. 17–17.

17–18. Determine slopes and deflections of points A and B of the structure shown in the accompanying illustration.

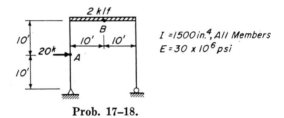

Prob. 17–18.

17–19. Determine slopes and deflections of points A and B on the rigid frame shown in the accompanying illustration.

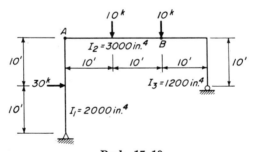

Prob. 17–19.

18 | DEFLECTIONS, CONTINUED

18-1. Virtual Work

The virtual-work method, often referred to as the method of work or dummy unit load method, has the widest range of application of any of the deflection methods. It applies equally well to trusses, frames, and beams, being particularly applicable to trusses.

Virtual work is based on the law of conservation of energy, according to which the work done by a set of external loads gradually applied to a structure equals the internal elastic energy stored in the structure. To make use of this law in the derivations to follow it is necessary that the following assumptions be made:

1) The external and internal forces are in equilibrium.
2) The elastic limit of the material is not exceeded.
3) There is no movement of the supports.

18-2. Truss Deflections by Virtual Work

The truss of Fig. 18-1 will be considered for this discussion. Loads P_1 to P_3 are applied to the truss, as shown, and cause stresses in the truss members. Each member of the truss shortens or lengthens depending on

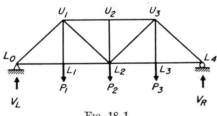

Fig. 18-1.

the character of its stress. These internal deformations cause external deflections, and each of the external loads moves through a short distance. The law of conservation of energy as it applies to the truss may now be stated in detail. The external work performed by the loads P_1 to P_3, as they move through their respective truss deflections, equals the internal work performed by the member stresses as they move through their respective changes in length.

To write an expression for the internal work performed by a truss member, it is necessary to develop an expression for the deformation of the member. For this purpose the bar of Fig. 18-2 is considered.

223

The force applied to the bar causes it to elongate by an amount Δl. The elongation may be computed from the properties of the bar. The unit elongation ϵ is equal to the total elongation divided by the length of the bar, and is also equal to the stress intensity divided by the modulus of elasticity. An expression for Δl may be developed as follows:

$$E = \frac{f}{\epsilon} = \frac{S/A}{\Delta l/l}$$

$$\Delta l = \frac{Sl}{AE}$$

In accordance with previous assumptions, the members of a truss have only axial stresses. These stresses are referred to as S stresses, and each member will change in length by an amount equal to Sl/AE.

It is desired that an expression for the deflection at a joint in the truss of Fig. 18–1 be developed. A convenient means of developing such an expression is to remove the external loads from the truss, place a unit load at the joint where deflection is desired, replace the external loads, and write an expression for the internal and external work performed by the unit load and its stresses when the external loads are replaced.

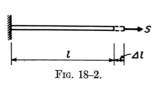

Fig. 18–2.

The stresses caused in the truss members by the unit load are called μ stresses. They cause small deformations of the members and small external deformations of the truss. When the external loads are returned to the truss, the stress in each of the members changes by the appropriate S stress, and the deformation of each member changes by its Sl/AE value. The truss deflects and the unit load is carried through a distance δ. The external work performed by the unit load when the external loads are returned to the structure may be expressed as follows:

$$W_e = 1 \times \delta$$

Internally the μ stress in each member is carried through a distance Sl/AE. The internal work performed by all of the μ stresses as they move through these distances is

$$W_i = \Sigma \frac{S\mu l}{AE}$$

By equating the internal and external work, the deflection at a joint in the truss may be expressed as follows:

$$\delta = \Sigma \frac{S\mu l}{AE}$$

18–3. Application of Virtual Work to Trusses

Examples 18–1 and 18–2 illustrate the application of virtual work to trusses. In each case the stresses due to the external loads are computed initially. Secondly, the external loads are removed, and a unit load is placed at the point and in the direction in which deflection is desired (not necessarily horizontal or vertical). The stresses due to the unit load are determined, and finally, the value of $S\mu l/AE$ for each of the members is found. To simplify the numerous multiplications, a table is used. The modulus of elasticity is carried through as a constant until the summation is made for all of the members, at which time its numerical value is used. Should there be members of different E's, it is necessary that their actual or their relative values be used for the individual multiplications. A positive value of $\Sigma(S\mu l/AE)$ indicates a deflection in the direction of the unit load.

EXAMPLE 18–1. Determine the horizontal and vertical components of deflection at joint L_4 in the truss shown in Fig. 18–3. Circled figures are areas, in square inches.

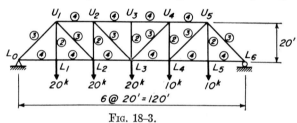

FIG. 18–3.

Solution: Stresses due to external loads:

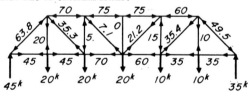

Stresses due to a vertical unit load at L_4:

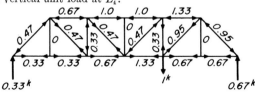

Stresses due to a horizontal unit load at L_4:

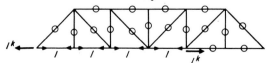

Member	l (in.)	A (sq in.)	$\dfrac{l}{A}$	S	μ_V	$\dfrac{S\mu_V l}{A}$	μ_H	$\dfrac{S\mu_H l}{A}$
L_0L_1	240	4	60	$+45$	$+0.33$	$+\ 900$	1.0	$+2700$
L_1L_2	240	4	60	$+45$	$+0.33$	$+\ 900$	1.0	$+2700$
L_2L_3	240	4	60	$+70$	$+0.67$	$+2800$	1.0	$+4200$
L_3L_4	240	4	60	$+60$	$+1.33$	$+4800$	1.0	$+3600$
L_4L_5	240	4	60	$+35$	$+0.67$	$+1400$	0	0
L_5L_6	240	4	60	$+35$	$+0.67$	$+1400$	0	0
L_0U_1	340	3	113.3	-63.8	-0.47	$+3400$	0	0
U_1U_2	240	4	60	-70	-0.67	$+2800$	0	0
U_2U_3	240	4	60	-75	-1.0	$+4500$	0	0
U_3U_4	240	4	60	-75	-1.0	$+4500$	0	0
U_4U_5	240	4	60	-60	-1.33	$+4800$	0	0
U_5L_6	340	3	113.3	-49.5	-0.95	$+5340$	0	0
U_1L_1	240	2	120	$+20$	0	0	0	0
U_1L_2	340	3	113.3	$+35.3$	$+0.47$	$+1880$	0	0
U_2L_2	240	2	120	$-\ 5$	-0.33	$+\ 200$	0	0
U_2L_3	340	3	113.3	$+\ 7.1$	$+0.47$	$+\ 378$	0	0
U_3L_3	240	2	120	0	0	0	0	0
L_3U_4	340	3	113.3	$+21.2$	-0.47	-1130	0	0
U_4L_4	240	2	120	-15	$+0.33$	$-\ 600$	0	0
L_4U_5	340	3	113.3	$+35.4$	$+0.95$	$+3810$	0	0
U_5L_5	240	2	120	$+10$	0	0	0	0
Σ	......	......	....	....	....	$+42,078$	....	$+13,200$

Vertical deflection:

$$E\delta_{L_2} = +42,078$$

$$\delta_{L_2} = \frac{42,078 \times 1000}{30,000,000} = +1.40 \text{ in. } \downarrow$$

Horizontal deflection:

$$E\delta_{L_2} = +13,200$$

$$\delta_{L_2} = \frac{13,200 \times 1000}{30,000,000} = +0.44 \text{ in.} \rightarrow$$

EXAMPLE 18–2. Determine the vertical component of deflection of joint L_4 in Fig. 18–4 by the virtual-work method. Circled figures are areas, in square inches.

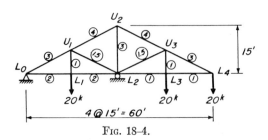

FIG. 18–4.

Solution: Stresses due to external loads:

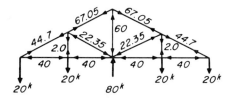

Stresses due to a vertical unit load at L_4:

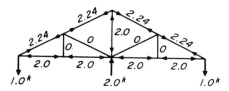

Member	l (in.)	A (sq in.)	$\dfrac{l}{A}$	S	μ	$\dfrac{S\mu l}{AE}$
L_0L_1	180	2	90	-40	-2.0	$+7200$
L_1L_2	180	2	90	-40	-2.0	$+7200$
L_2L_3	180	1	180	-40	-2.0	$+14,400$
L_3L_4	180	1	180	-40	-2.0	$+14,400$
L_0U_1	202	3	67.3	$+44.7$	$+2.24$	$+6730$
U_1U_2	202	4	50.5	$+67.05$	$+2.24$	$+7575$
U_2U_3	202	4	50.5	$+67.05$	$+2.24$	$+7575$
U_3L_4	202	3	67.3	$+44.7$	$+2.24$	$+6730$
U_1L_1	90	1	90	$+20$	0	0
U_1L_2	202	1.5	134.5	-22.35	0	0
U_2L_2	180	3	60	-60	-2.0	$+7200$
L_2U_3	202	1.5	134.5	-22.35	0	0
U_3L_3	90	1	90	$+20$	0	0
Σ	....	....	....	....	....	$\dfrac{79,010}{E}$

$$\text{Vertical deflection at } L_4 = \frac{(79,010)(1000)}{30 \times 10^6} = 2.63 \text{ in. } \downarrow$$

18–4. Deflections of Beams and Frames by Virtual Work

The law of conservation of energy may be used to develop an expression for the deflection at any point in a beam or frame. In the following derivation, each fiber of the structure is considered to be a "bar" or member such as the members of the trusses considered in the preceding sections. The summation of the internal work performed by the stress in each of the bars equals the external work performed by the loads.

For the following discussion the beam of Fig. 18–5 (a) is considered. Part (b) of the figure shows the beam cross section. It is desired to know the deflection δ at point A in the beam caused by the external loads P_1 to P_3. If the loads were removed from the beam and a unit load placed at A, small stresses and deformations would be developed in the bars, and a small deflection would occur at A. Replacing the external loads would cause increases in the bar stresses and deformations, and the unit load at A would deflect an additional amount δ. The internal work performed by the unit load stresses, as they are carried through the additional bar deformations, equals the external work performed by the unit load as it is carried through the additional deflection δ.

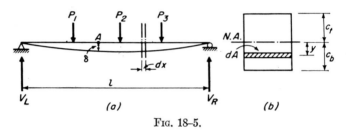

FIG. 18–5.

The following symbols are used in writing an expression for the internal work performed in a dx length of the beam: $M =$ the moment at any section in the beam due to the external loads and $m =$ the moment at any section due to the unit load. The stress in a differential area of the beam cross section due to the unit load can be found from the flexure formula as follows:

$$\text{Unit stress in } dA = \frac{my}{I}$$

$$\text{Total stress in } dA = \frac{my}{I} \, dA$$

The dA area has a thickness or length of dx which deforms by $\epsilon \, dx$ when the external loads are returned to the structure. The deformation is as follows:

$$\text{Unit stress due to external loads} = f = \frac{My}{I}$$

$$\text{Deformation of } dx \text{ length} = \epsilon \, dx = \frac{f}{E} \, dx = \frac{My}{EI} \, dx$$

The total stress in dA due to the unit load $\left(\frac{my}{I} \, dA\right)$ is carried through this deformation, and the work it performs is as follows:

$$\text{Work in } dA = \left(\frac{my}{I} \, dA\right)\left(\frac{My}{EI} \, dx\right) = \frac{Mmy^2}{EI^2} \, dA \, dx$$

The total work performed on the cross section equals the summation of the work in each dA area in the cross section.

$$\text{Work} = \int_{C_b}^{C_t} \frac{Mmy^2}{EI^2} \, dA \, dx = \frac{Mm}{EI^2} \int_{C_b}^{C_t} y^2 \, dA \, dx$$

The expression $\int y^2 \, dA$ is a familiar one, being the moment of inertia of the section, and the equation becomes

$$\text{Work} = \frac{Mm}{EI} \, dx$$

It is now possible to determine the internal work performed in the entire beam, because it equals the integral from 0 to l of this expression:

$$W_i = \int_0^l \frac{Mm}{EI} \, dx$$

The external work performed by the unit load as it is carried through the distance δ is $1 \times \delta$. By equating the external work and the internal work, an expression for the deflection at any point in the beam is obtained:

$$W_e = W_i$$

$$1 \times \delta = \int_0^l \frac{Mm}{EI} \, dx$$

$$\delta = \int_0^l \frac{Mm}{EI} \, dx$$

18–5. Application of Virtual Work to Beams and Frames

Examples 18–3 to 18–7 illustrate the application of virtual work to beams and frames. To apply the method, a unit load is placed at the point and in the direction in which deflection is desired. Expressions are written for M and m throughout the structure, and the results are integrated from 0 to l. It is rarely possible to write one expression for M or one expression for m which is correct in all parts of the structure. As an illustration, consider the beam of Fig. 18–6 and let the deflection under P_2

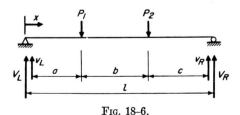

Fig. 18–6.

be desired. A unit load is placed at this point in the figure. The reactions V_L and V_R are due to loads P_1 and P_2, while v_L and v_R are due to the unit load.

The values of M and m are written with respect to the distance from the left support. From the left support to the unit load m may be represented by one expression, $v_L x$, but the expression for M is not constant for the full distance. Its value is $V_L x$ from the left support to P_1 and $V_L x - P_1$ $(x-a)$ from P_1 to P_2. The integration will be made from 0 to a for $V_L x$ and $v_L x$, and from a to b for $V_L x - P_1(x-a)$ and $v_L x$. Moment expressions for all parts of the beam are shown in the following table. The left support is used as the origin of x.

For $x=0$ to a: For $x=a$ to b:
$$M = V_L x \qquad\qquad M = V_L x - P_1(x-a)$$
$$m = v_L x \qquad\qquad m = v_L x$$

For $x=b$ to c:
$$M = V_L x - P_1(x-a) - P_2(x-a-b)$$
$$m = v_L x - 1(x-a-b)$$

$$\delta = \int_0^a \frac{Mm}{EI}\,dx + \int_a^{a+b} \frac{Mm}{EI}\,dx + \int_{a+b}^l \frac{Mm}{EI}\,dx$$

A positive sign is used for a moment which causes tension in the bottom fibers of a beam. If the result of integration is positive, the direction used for the unit load is the direction of the deflection.

EXAMPLE 18-3. Determine the deflection at point A, Fig. 18-7, by virtual work.

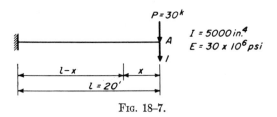

FIG. 18-7.

Solution: An expression is written for M (the moment due to the 30^k load) at any point a distance x from the free end. A unit load is placed at the free end, and an expression is written for the moment m it causes at any point. The origin of x may be selected at any point as long as the same point is used for writing M and m for that portion of the beam.

$$M = -Px$$
$$m = -1x$$

$$\delta_A = \int_0^l \frac{Mm}{EI}\,dx = \int_0^l \frac{(-Px)(-1x)}{EI}\,dx = \int_0^l \frac{Px^2}{EI}\,dx$$

$$\delta_A = \frac{P}{EI}\left[\frac{x^3}{3}\right]_0^l = \frac{Pl^3}{3EI}$$

$$\delta_A = \frac{(30{,}000)(20\times12)^3}{(3)(30\times10^6)(5000)} = 0.922 \text{ in.}$$

EXAMPLE 18–4. Determine the deflection at point A in Fig. 18–8.

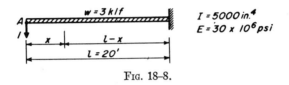

$I = 5000$ in.^{4}
$E = 30 \times 10^6$ psi

FIG. 18–8.

Solution:

$$M = -(w)(x)\left(\frac{x}{2}\right) = -\frac{wx^2}{2}$$

$$m = -1x$$

$$Mm = +\frac{wx^3}{2}$$

$$\delta_A = \int_0^l \frac{Mm}{EI}\,dx = \int_0^l \frac{wx^3}{2EI}\,dx$$

$$= \frac{w}{2EI}\left(\frac{x^4}{4}\right)_0^l = \frac{wl^4}{8EI}$$

$$= \frac{(3000/12)(20\times12)^4}{(8)(30\times10^6)(5000)} = 0.691 \text{ in.}$$

EXAMPLE 18–5. Determine the deflection at point B in the beam shown in Fig. 18–9.

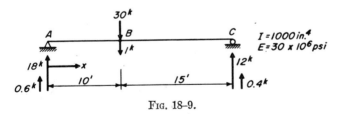

$I = 1000$ in.^{4}
$E = 30 \times 10^6$ psi

FIG. 18–9.

Solution: It is necessary to write one expression for M from A to B and another from B to C. The same is true for m. Frequently it is possible to simplify the mathematics by using different origins of x for different sections of the beam. The same results would have been obtained if for the M and m expressions from B to C the origin had been taken at C. The small reactions at A and C are those due to the unit load.

For $x=0$ to 10:

$M = 18\,x$

$m = 0.6\,x$

$Mm = 10.8x^2$

For $x=10$ to 25:

$M = 18x - (30)(x-10) = -12x + 300$

$m = 0.6x - 1(x-10) = -0.4x + 10$

$Mm = +4.8x^2 - 240x + 3000$

$$\delta_A = \int_0^{10} \frac{10.8x^2}{EI}\,dx + \int_{10}^{25} \frac{(4.8x^2 - 240x + 3000)}{EI}\,dx$$

$$= \frac{1}{EI}\left[3.6x^3 \right]_0^{10} + \frac{1}{EI}\left[1.6x^3 - 120x^2 + 3000x \right]_{10}^{25}$$

$$= \frac{3600}{EI} + \frac{25{,}000 - 19{,}600}{EI}$$

$$= \frac{9000 \text{ ft}^3\text{-k}}{EI} = \frac{(9000)(1728)(1000)}{(30 \times 10^6)(1000)} = 0.518 \text{ in.}$$

EXAMPLE 18–6. Determine the deflection at point B in the beam of Example 17–12 which is reproduced in Fig. 18–10.

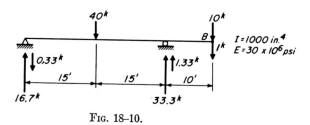

FIG. 18–10.

Solution: In writing the moment expressions from the left support to the right support, the left support is used for the origin of x. For the overhanging portion of the beam, the right end is used as the origin.

For $x=0$ to 15:

$M = 16.7x$

$m = -0.33x$

$Mm = -5.56x^2$

For $x=15$ to 30:

$M = 16.7x - (40)(x-15)$

$m = -23.3x + 600$

$m = -0.33x$

$Mm = +7.77x^2 - 200x$

For $x=0$ to 10:

$M = -10x$

$m = -x$

$Mm = +10x^2$

$$\delta_B = \frac{1}{EI}\int_0^{15} (-5.56x^2)\,dx + \frac{1}{EI}\int_{15}^{30} (7.77x^2 - 200x)\,dx + \frac{1}{EI}\int_0^{10} (10x^2)\,dx$$

$$= \frac{1}{EI}\left[-1.85x^3 \right]_0^{15} + \frac{1}{EI}\left[2.59x^3 - 100x^2 \right]_{15}^{30} + \frac{1}{EI}\left[3.33x^3 \right]_0^{10}$$

$$= \frac{-6250}{EI} + \frac{-20{,}000 + 13{,}750}{EI} + \frac{3330}{EI}$$

$$= -\frac{9170 \text{ ft}^3\text{-k}}{EI} = -0.528 \text{ in.} \uparrow$$

·EXAMPLE 18-7. Find the horizontal deflection at D in the frame shown in Fig. 18-11.

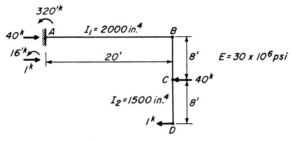

FIG. 18-11.

Solution: A unit load acting horizontally to the left is placed at D. With A as the origin for x, moment expressions are written for member AB. For the vertical member, the origin is taken at D, one pair of M and m expressions is written for the portion of the member from D to C, and another pair is written for the portion of the beam from C to B. The members do not have the same moments of inertia, and it is necessary to carry them separately as shown in the calculations.

For $x=0$ to 20:	For $x=0$ to 8:	For $x=8$ to 16:
$M=-320$	$M=0$	$M=-40(x-8)=-40x+320$
$m=-16$	$m=x$	$m=-x$
$Mm=+5120$	$Mm=0$	$Mm=40x^2-320x$

$$\delta_D = \int_0^{20}\left(\frac{5120}{EI_1}\right)dx + \int_8^{16}\left(\frac{40x^2-320x}{EI_2}\right)dx$$

$$= \frac{1}{EI_1}\left[5120x\right]_0^{20} + \frac{1}{EI_2}\left[\frac{40}{3}x^3-160x^2\right]_8^{16}$$

$$= \frac{102{,}400 \text{ ft}^3\text{-k}}{EI_1} + \frac{17{,}110 \text{ ft}^3\text{-k}}{EI_2} = +3.61 \text{ in.} \leftarrow$$

18-6. Rotations or Slopes by Virtual Work

Virtual work may be used to determine the slope at various points in a structure. To find the slope at point A in the beam of Fig. 18-12, a unit couple is applied at A, the external loads being removed from the structure. The value of moment at any point in the beam caused by the couple is m. Replacing the external loads will cause an additional moment, at any point, of M.

FIG. 18-12.

If the application of the loads causes the beam to rotate through an angle θ at A, the external work performed by the couple equals $1 \times \theta$. The internal work or the internal elastic energy stored is $\int \dfrac{Mm}{EI}\,dx$.

$$\theta = \int \frac{Mm}{EI}\,dx$$

If a clockwise couple is assumed at the position where slope is desired and the result of integration is positive, the rotation is clockwise. Examples 18–8 and 18–9 illustrate the determination of slopes by virtual work. The slopes obtained are in radians.

EXAMPLE 18–8. Find the slope at the free end A, Fig. 18–13.

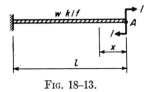

FIG. 18–13.

Solution:

$$M = \frac{wx^2}{2}$$

$$m = 1$$

$$Mm = \frac{wx^2}{2}$$

$$\theta_A = \int_0^l \frac{wx^2}{2EI}\,dx$$

$$\theta_A = \left[\frac{wx^3}{6EI}\right]_0^l = +\frac{wl^3}{6EI} \text{ clockwise}$$

EXAMPLE 18–9. Find the slope at the 30^k load, Fig. 18–14.

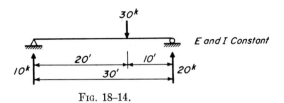

FIG. 18–14.

Solution: A separate diagram is drawn for the couple and the reactions it causes. For the beam to the left of the load, the left support is used for the origin of x and the right support is used for the origin for the portion of the beam to the right of the 30^k load.

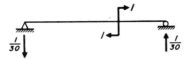

For $x = 0$ to 20:
$$M = 10x$$
$$m = -\tfrac{1}{30}x$$
$$Mm = -\tfrac{1}{3}x$$

For $x = 0$ to 10:
$$M = 20x$$
$$m = \tfrac{1}{30}x$$
$$Mm = \tfrac{2}{3}x^2$$

$$\theta = \int_0^{20} \left(-\frac{1x^2}{3EI}\right) dx + \int_0^{10} \left(\frac{2x^2}{3EI}\right) dx$$

$$= \left[-\frac{x^3}{9EI}\right]_0^{20} + \left[\frac{2x^3}{9EI}\right]_0^{10} = -\frac{888 \text{ ft}^2\text{-k}}{EI} + \frac{222 \text{ ft}^2\text{-k}}{EI}$$

$$= -\frac{666 \text{ ft}^2\text{-k}}{EI} \text{ counterclockwise}$$

18–7. Maxwell's Law of Reciprocal Deflections

The deflections of two points in a beam have a surprising relationship to each other. The student may have noticed this relationship, which was first published, by James Clerk Maxwell, in 1864. Maxwell's law may be stated as follows: *The deflection at one point A in a structure due to a load applied at another point B is exactly the same as the deflection at B if the same load is applied at A.* The rule is perfectly general and applies to any type of structure, whether it is truss, beam, or frame, which is made up of elastic materials following Hooke's law. The displacements may be caused by flexure, shear, or torsion. In preparing influence lines for continuous structures, in analyzing indeterminate structures, and in model-analysis problems this useful tool is frequently applied.

The law is not only applicable to the deflections in all of these types of structure but is also applicable to rotations. For instance, a unit couple at A will produce a rotation at B equal to the rotation caused at A if the same couple is applied at B.

Example 18–10 proves the law to be correct for a simple beam in which the deflections at two points are determined by the conjugate-beam method. Several applications of this law are made in Chapters 19 and 20.

EXAMPLE 18–10. Compute the deflections at points A and B for a load P applied first at B and then at A, Fig. 18–15.

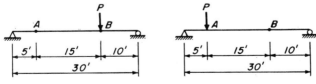

FIG. 18–15.

Solution:

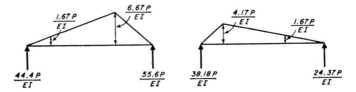

Deflection at A due to load at B: Deflection at B due to load at A:

$$\delta_A = \left(\frac{44.4P}{EI}\right)(5) - \left(\frac{1}{2}\right)\left(\frac{1.67P}{EI}\right)(5)(1.67) \qquad \delta_B = \left(\frac{24.37P}{EI}\right)(10) - \left(\frac{1}{2}\right)\left(\frac{1.67P}{EI}\right)(10)(3.33)$$

$$=\frac{222P}{EI} - \frac{7P}{EI} \qquad\qquad\qquad\qquad =\frac{243.7P}{EI} - \frac{28.7P}{EI}$$

$$=\frac{215P}{EI} \qquad\qquad\qquad\qquad\qquad =\frac{215P}{EI}$$

18–8. Truss Deflections Graphically

Truss deflections were determined by virtual work in Sec. 18–3. Virtual work is very satisfactory for calculating the deflections at one or two points in a truss, but should the deflection of all the joints in a large truss be desired, the process becomes so lengthy as to be impractical. For this reason graphical methods, by which the deflection of all points in a truss can be determined simultaneously, are frequently used. Another problem conveniently solved graphically is that of finding the exact fabrication dimensions necessary to camber trusses.

The members of a truss become longer or shorter depending on the character of the stresses to which they are subjected. Since they are assumed to be free from bending, they must remain straight. In view of this, it is seen that despite the changes in lengths of the members the triangles of a truss must remain perfect triangles. The change in length of a member due to a total axial stress S has previously been found to equal

$$\Delta l = \frac{Sl}{AE}$$

The resulting deformations are exceedingly small for common structural materials, an increase or decrease in length of $\frac{1}{1000}$ being an extreme value. Having calculated the deformations, it is theoretically possible to determine graphically the new position of each truss joint by plotting to scale the changed lengths of the members and drawing arcs with the new lengths as radii. The method, however, is completely impractical because it would require an enormous scale drawing for the deformations

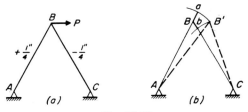

Fig. 18–16.

to be visible. Imagine a 30-ft member in a steel truss which elongates $\frac{3}{16}$ in. and the difficulty of showing the member and its deformation with the same scale on a normal-size drawing.

Nevertheless, this method is demonstrated in Figs. 18–16 to 18–18 as a background for the development of the Williot diagram. In Fig. 18–16 (a) a simple structure and the deformations of its members are shown. It is noted that points A and C may not deflect horizontally or vertically; however, the changes in length of AB and BC will cause some movement of joint B. In Fig. 18–16 (b) member AB is elongated by $\frac{1}{4}$ in. to point a and member BC is shortened $\frac{1}{4}$ in. to point b. The deformations are

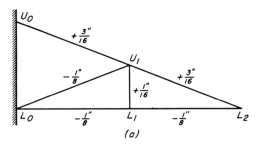

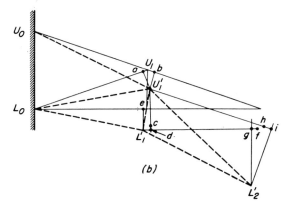

Fig. 18–17.

drawn to a tremendously exaggerated scale as compared to the one used for the member lengths. Since points a and b must coincide because the members do not pull apart at B, an arc of radius Aa is drawn with A as the center, and an arc of radius Cb is drawn with C as a center. The intersection of the two arcs must be the new location of joint B, B', and the dotted lines represent the new positions of the members.

The distorted position of the cantilever truss of Fig. 18–17 is determined in a similar manner. To develop the drawing, it is necessary that one point be assumed fixed in position and the direction of one line be assumed fixed. It is obvious that joints U_0 and L_0 cannot deflect and that the direction of a line through U_0 and L_0 remains vertical. In Fig. 18–17 (b) the deflection of the other joints is shown with respect to the non-deflecting references.

To develop the distorted shape of the structure, the first member considered is L_0U_1, which shortens by $\frac{1}{8}$ in. Because L_0 is fixed in position, $\frac{1}{8}$ in. is scaled off from U_1 toward L_0 to point a. Member U_0U_1 elongates by $\frac{3}{16}$ in., and this distance is measured to the right of U_1 to point b, because U_0 is unyielding. Points a and b must coincide at the new position of joint U_1; therefore, with U_0 as a center an arc of radius U_0b is drawn, and with L_0 as a center an arc of radius L_0a is drawn. The intersection of the arcs gives U'_1, the new position of U_1.

For locating the deflected positions of the joints in this truss and in subsequent trusses considered, perpendiculars are drawn to the radii, rather than using arcs. The distortions are so slight with respect to the radii that no appreciable error is caused by using perpendiculars, and results may be considered to be exact.

To locate the new position of joint L_1, member U_1L_1 is moved over so that U_1 coincides with U'_1, and the bottom end of the member is at c. The

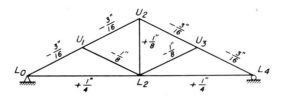

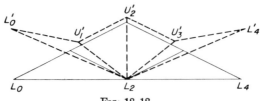

Fig. 18–18.

member U_1L_1 lengthens $\frac{1}{16}$ in. down to point d. Similarly, L_0L_1 shortens $\frac{1}{8}$ in. from L_1 to e. The new length of L_0L_1 is L_0e, and U'_1d is the new length of U_1L_1. The new position of L_1, L'_1, is found at the intersection of perpendiculars to the respective radii at e and d.

Finally, from L'_1 the original length of L_1L_2 is drawn to f. The member shortens $\frac{1}{8}$ in. to g. Member U_1L_2 is laid off parallel to its original position from U'_1 to h, and it lengthens $\frac{3}{16}$ in. to i. Perpendiculars are drawn at i and g, their intersection being L'_2. The new position of each of the truss members is shown by a dotted line.

The distorted shape of the truss of Fig. 18–8 was developed by the same process. The dimensions and member distortions were symmetrical about the center line, and it was therefore assumed that U_2L_2 was fixed in direction and that joint L_2 was fixed in position. It is noted that joint L_2 does deflect vertically and that, contrary to the deflection diagram, joints L_0 and L_4 do not. To obtain the correct deflection of the joints, the deflected truss should be moved downward until L'_0 and L'_4 fall on a line drawn through L_0 and L_4.

18–9. The Williot Diagram

The French engineer Williot discovered in 1877 that it is unnecessary to include member lengths in drawing truss-deflection diagrams. He found the same results are obtained for joint deflections if the original lengths of the members are assumed to be zero and if the changes in lengths of the members and perpendiculars to those changes are drawn exactly as before. His remarkable discovery enables the engineer to obtain excellent results, because he can draw large-scale diagrams with the actual distortions greatly exaggerated.

The distortion of the truss of Fig. 18–18 is developed by using the Williot diagram in Fig. 18–19. Joint L_2 is assumed fixed in position, and member U_2L_2 is assumed fixed in direction. The deflection of each of the joints is drawn with respect to L_2. If the distance from L_2 to a joint did not change in the distorted truss, that point would coincide with L_2 on the Williot diagram.

Starting with a point L_2 on the drawing, the position of U_2 is located. With respect to L_2, U_2 moves up $\frac{1}{8}$ in. vertically, and that point is marked on the paper. By having the position of U_2 and L_2, the computer can locate U_1. Member U_1U_2 shortens by $\frac{3}{16}$ in., meaning that U_1 moves $\frac{3}{16}$ in. towards U_2. A line is drawn from U_2 up and to the right parallel to the member. Member U_1L_2 shortens by $\frac{1}{8}$ in., causing U_1 to move $\frac{1}{8}$ in. down and to the right with respect to L_2. Perpendiculars are drawn at the end of each of the two distortions, their intersection being the deflected position of U_1.

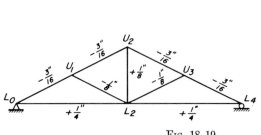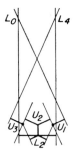

Fig. 18–19.

Joint L_0 moves $\frac{3}{16}$ in. to the right toward U_1 and parallel to L_0U_1, and with respect to L_2 it moves $\frac{1}{4}$ in. to the left, parallel to L_0L_2. Perpendiculars to the two distortions will intersect at L_0. The locations of joints U_3 and L_4 are found by a similar process, and they are opposite U_1 and L_0, respectively, because of the symmetry of the truss.

It is customary, as illustrated in these figures, to draw the distortions with dark heavy lines and the perpendiculars with light construction lines. Better accuracy can probably be obtained in locating points by extending the perpendiculars until they pass the intersection points, as shown in the sample Williot diagrams here.

Referring to the geometry of the truss, it is seen that a horizontal line from L_0 to L_4 must remain horizontal because the two supports do not deflect vertically. The vertical deflection of any joint in the truss may be found by measuring the vertical distance from a horizontal line through L_0 and L_4 in the Williot diagram. Similarly, it is seen that joint L_0 is a hinge and may not deflect horizontally. The horizontal deflection of any joint can be found by measuring to the joint in the Williot diagram from a vertical line through L_0.

In Fig. 18–20 the Williot diagram is drawn for the truss of Fig. 18–17. In this truss, joints U_0 and L_0 are fixed in position and U_0L_0 is fixed in

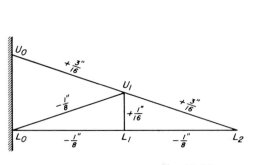

Fig. 18–20.

direction. With respect to U_0, U_1 moves down and to the right $\frac{3}{16}$ in., and with respect to L_0 it moves down and to the left $\frac{1}{8}$ in. Perpendiculars to these movements intersect at U_1. Joint L_1 moves to the left $\frac{1}{8}$ in. with respect to L_0 and vertically down $\frac{1}{16}$ in. with respect to U_1. Perpendiculars to these lines intersect at L_1. The deflected position of L_2 may be found in the same manner. The vertical deflection of a joint can be found by measuring the vertical distance on the diagram from a horizontal line through L_0, and the horizontal deflection is the horizontal distance from a vertical line through L_0. Examples 18–11 and 18–12 are two more illustrations of the application of the Williot diagram.

EXAMPLE 18–11. Determine the vertical and horizontal components of deflection for each of the joints of the truss shown in Fig. 18–21.

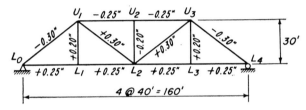

FIG. 18–21.

Solution: The Williot diagram is drawn with respect to joint L_2, which is assumed fixed in position, and with respect to member U_2L_2, which is assumed fixed in direction. The vertical components of deflection are measured from a horizontal line through L_0 and L_4, and the horizontal components of deflection are measured from a vertical line through L_0.

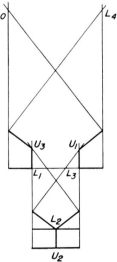

DEFLECTIONS (IN.)

Joint	Vertical	Horizontal
L_0	0	0
L_1	1.65 ↓	0.25 →
L_2	2.34 ↓	0.50 →
L_3	1.65 ↓	0.75 →
L_4	0	0.96 →
U_1	1.46 ↓	0.75 →
U_2	2.54 ↓	0.50 →
U_3	1.46 ↓	0.25 →

Example 18–12. Determine the increases in length of the top chord and end post members necessary to camber the truss of Fig. 18–22 by 4 in. at joint L_3.

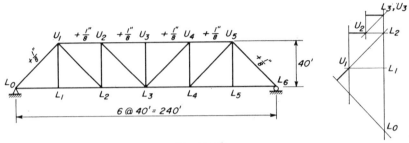

Fig. 18–22.

Solution: Each of the members in question is assumed to be increased in length by ⅛ in., and the resulting camber at L_3 is determined with the Williot diagram. A proportion may be written between the camber obtained and that desired as compared to the increases in length made and those necessary. In preparing the diagram, member U_3L_3 is assumed to remain vertical, and joint L_3 is assumed fixed in position.

L_3 deflects upward 0.81 in.; top members to be lengthened $\dfrac{4}{0.81} \times$ ⅛ = 0.617 in., say, ⅝ in. each.

Note: Trusses are often cambered for both dead and live loadings so that at no time will any of the lower-chord joints be below the horizontal. Another way to achieve camber is to change the length of each of the members from their normal length by an amount exactly equal and opposite to their shortenings or elongations under load. For the truss of Fig. 18–19, members U_1U_2 and U_2U_3 would each be made ³⁄₁₆ in. longer, members L_0L_2 and L_2L_4 ¼ in. shorter, etc. This method has the disadvantage in fabrication of having to make so many different length changes.

18–10.   The Williot-Mohr Diagram

Graphical solutions for deflections have been made for trusses which had at least one member whose direction was constant. The center verticals in the trusses of Figs. 18–19, 18–21, and 18–22 remain vertical because of the symmetry of the trusses and loadings about center lines. A line from U_0 to L_0 in the truss of Fig. 18–20 is fixed in direction and position. For cases such as these the Williot diagram will quickly and accurately give the joint deflections.

Should the diagram be drawn with respect to some other member which does rotate, the correct deflections may not be obtained directly. A correction must be made to take into account the rotation of that member. Trusses in which the directions of all the members change are often encountered, and the diagram must be drawn with respect to a rotating member.

The deflected shape of the truss of Fig. 18–19 is drawn in Fig. 18–23 (*b*) with the assumption that member L_0L_2 (which obviously rotates) remains

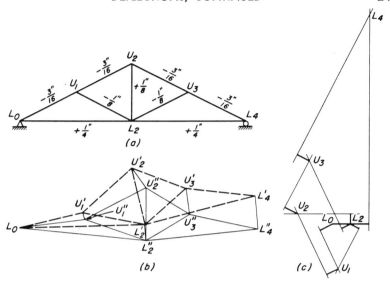

FIG. 18–23.

horizontal. A Williot diagram is drawn in Fig. 18–23 (c) on the basis of the same assumption. Both diagrams seem to indicate that the deflected position of joint L_4 is well above joint L_0. Obviously this situation is not possible, because a horizontal line through the supports L_0 and L_4 must remain horizontal. The deflection diagram needs to be rotated clockwise until L_4 lies on a horizontal line through L_0.

In 1887 Otto Mohr presented a simple method of correcting the Williot diagram when the reference member, which was assumed to be fixed in direction, actually rotated. Referring to the truss of Fig. 18–23 (a) and its deflected shape in part (b), it is obvious that the entire diagram needs to be rotated about L_0 until L'_4 is at L''_4, a distance $L'_4L''_4$. A perpendicular to the radius $L_0L'_4$ is used, because the difference between a perpendicular and an arc is negligible. The rotated positions of the other joints are indicated by L''_2, U''_3, etc.

The amount of rotation of any joint about L_0 is in proportion to the rotation $L'_4L''_4$ as the distance of the joint from L_0 is to $L_0L'_4$. For example, the rotation of L'_2 necessary to put it in its proper position is as follows:

$$\frac{L'_2L''_2}{L'_4L''_4} = \frac{L_0L'_2}{L_0L'_4}$$

$$L'_2L''_2 = L'_4L''_4 \times \frac{L_0L'_2}{L_0L'_4}$$

If the truss is rotated 90° to the position shown in Fig. 18–24, each of the members will be perpendicular to its original position. Although the truss may not be drawn to the same scale as before, a triangle such as $L_0U_1L_2$ in the first truss is similar to the corresponding triangle ADB in the second truss.

The trusses are proportional, and the following relations may be written:

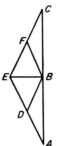

$$\frac{AE}{L_0U_2} = \frac{AC}{L_0L_4} \qquad AE = \frac{(L_0U_2)(AC)}{L_0L_4}$$

$$\frac{AD}{L_0U_1} = \frac{AC}{L_0L_4} \qquad AD = \frac{(L_0U_1)(AC)}{L_0L_4}$$

With reference to the distorted shape of the truss in Fig. 18–23 (b), the distance from L'_4 to L''_4 is the rotation of L'_4, and the rotation of U'_3 is $(L_0U'_3/L_0L'_4) \times L'_4L''_4$. Let the truss of Fig. 18–24 be drawn to such scale that AC equals the distance $L'_4L''_4$ in Fig. 18–23. Since AD is to L_0U_1 as AC is to L_0L_4 and since $U'_1U''_1$ is to $L'_4L''_4$ as $L_0U'_1$ is to $L_0L'_4$, AD equals the rotation correction that must be made to U'_1, AF equals the correction of joint U'_3, etc.

Fig. 18–24.

Professor Mohr's ingenious idea was to draw a truss proportional to the real truss above the point in the Williot diagram corresponding to the assumed fixed support of the truss. A horizontal line is then drawn through the point on the diagram corresponding to the expansion support of the truss. The fictitious truss is at 90° with the actual truss, and its length between supports equals the distance from the fixed support to a horizontal line through the expansion support in the Williot diagram. The Williot diagram of Fig. 18–23 is repeated in Fig. 18–25, and the Mohr correction is made. The correct deflection of any point in the truss is the distance from the joint number in the correction truss to the corresponding joint number in the regular Williot diagram.

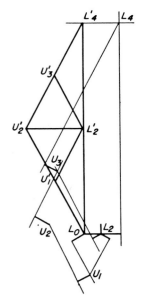

Fig. 18–25.

The deflection of joint U_2, in magnitude and direction, in the actual truss is the distance from U'_2 to U_2 in the figure. In Examples 18–13 to 18–16, joint deflections for four more trusses are determined with the Williot-Mohr diagram. An effort should be made to select a member whose direction rotates as little as possible to use as a reference in drawing the Williot diagram. The smaller the rotation, the smaller the Mohr correction diagram will be and the greater the accuracy of the deflection obtained will be, because the Williot diagram may be drawn to a larger scale on the same size paper.

There is one particular point that should be noted in Example 18–15. The roller joint L_3 falls below the pinned joint L_0 on the Williot diagram. A horizontal line is drawn through L_3, and the correction diagram is rotated clockwise so that L'_3 falls on the horizontal line, which means that L'_4 extends below as shown. The deflections are measured as usual from the joints on the correction diagram to the joints on the Williot diagram.

The supports of the truss of Example 18–16 are not on the same level, and the supporting surface beneath the roller is inclined. During the distortion of the truss under load the roller will move along a plane parallel to the supporting surface; therefore, a line is drawn parallel to the supporting surface, through the position of the roller joint (L_3) on the standard Williot diagram. The Mohr correction diagram is drawn by rotating the truss 90° about the hinge joint (L_0) and fitting it to the proper size so that L'_3 will fall on the line through the roller joint.

EXAMPLE 18–13. Draw the Williot-Mohr diagram for the truss of Fig. 18–26; assume L_0 fixed in position and L_0L_1 fixed in direction.

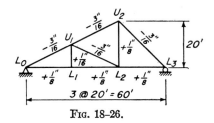

FIG. 18–26.

Solution:

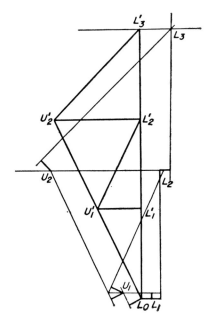

EXAMPLE 18–14. By using the Williot-Mohr diagram, determine the vertical and horizontal components of deflection of joints U_2 and L_3, Fig. 18–27. Assume joint L_0 is fixed in position and member L_0L_1 is fixed in direction.

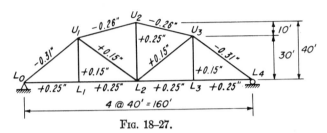

FIG. 18–27.

Solution:

Deflections:
  U_2 Vertical $=1.70''$ ↓
  U_2 Horizontal $=0.48''$ →
  L_3 Vertical $=1.60''$ ↓
  L_3 Horizontal $=0.77''$ →

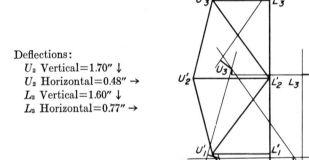

EXAMPLE 18–15. Draw the Williot-Mohr diagram for the truss of Fig. 18–28. Assume L_0 fixed in position and L_0U_1 fixed in direction.

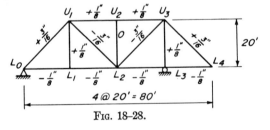

FIG. 18–28.

Solution:

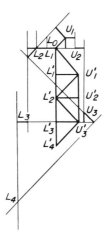

EXAMPLE 18–16.   Draw the Williot-Mohr diagram for the truss shown in Fig. 18–29; assume L_0 fixed in position and L_0U_1 fixed in direction.

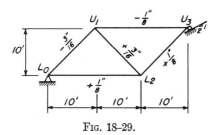

FIG. 18–29.

Solution:

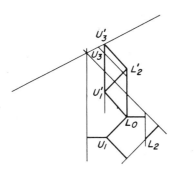

Problems

Use the virtual-work method for solving Probs. 18–1 to 18–7.

18–1.   Determine the slope and deflection at points A and B of the structure shown in the accompanying illustration.

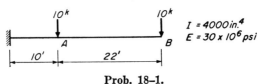

Prob. 18-1.

18-2. Determine slope and deflection at points 6 and 12 ft from the left support of the structure shown in the accompanying illustration.

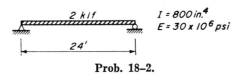

Prob. 18-2.

18-3. Determine the deflection underneath each of the concentrated loads shown in the accompanying illustration.

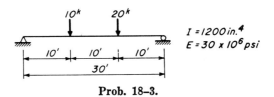

Prob. 18-3.

18-4. Determine the slope and deflection at the 40^k load on the structure shown in the accompanying illustration.

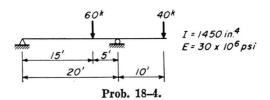

Prob. 18-4.

18-5. Determine the center-line deflection of the structure shown in the accompanying illustration.

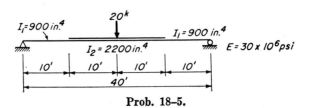

Prob. 18-5.

18-6. Determine the deflections at each of the points lettered on the frames shown in the accompanying illustration.

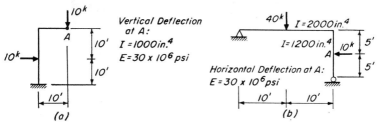

Prob. 18-6.

18-7. Determine the deflection of each of the joints marked on the trusses shown in the accompanying illustration. The circled figures are areas. ($E=30\times10^6$ psi, all trusses.)

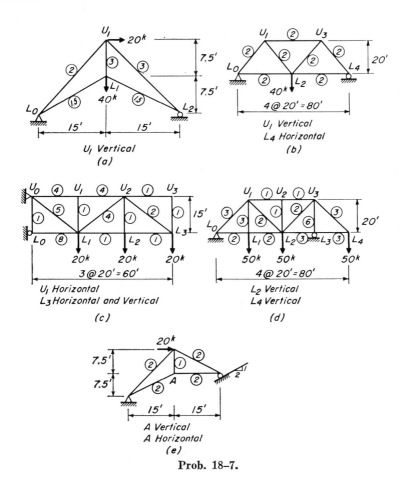

Prob. 18-7.

18–8. Draw a Williot-Mohr diagram for the truss of Prob. 18–7 (a). Assume L_0 fixed in position and L_0L_1 fixed in direction.

18–9. Draw a Williot-Mohr diagram for the truss of Prob. 18–7 (b). Assume U_1 fixed in position and U_1L_2 fixed in direction.

18–10. Draw a Williot-Mohr diagram for the truss of Prob. 18–7 (c). Assume U_1 fixed in position and U_1L_1 fixed in direction.

18–11. Draw a Williot-Mohr diagram for the truss of Prob. 18–7 (d). Assume L_0 fixed in position and L_0U_1 fixed in direction.

19 | DEFLECTION METHODS OF ANA-LYZING INDETERMINATE BEAMS

19–1. Introduction

James Clerk Maxwell published in 1864 the first consistent method of analyzing indeterminate structures. His method was based upon a consideration of deflections, but the presentation (which included the reciprocal deflection theorem) was rather brief and attracted little attention. Ten years later Otto Mohr independently extended the theory to almost its present stage of development. Analysis of redundant structures with the use of deflection computations is often referred to as the Maxwell-Mohr method or the method of consistent distortions.[1,2]

The computation of deflections is probably not as common for its own sake as it is as a part of the analysis of indeterminate structures. Analysis of continuous beams will be discussed in this chapter, and redundant trusses will be considered in Chapter 20. The process of analyzing a continuous beam consists in 1) the removal of enough supports to make the beam determinate, 2) the calculation of the deflections at the points where supports are removed, and 3) the determination of the forces necessary to push the support points back to their original nondeflected positions. These forces are equal to the redundant reactions.

19–2. Beams with One Redundant

The two-span beam of Fig. 19–1 (a) is assumed to consist of a material following Hooke's law. This statically indeterminate structure supports the loads P_1 and P_2 and is in turn supported by reaction components at points A, B, and C. Removal of support B would leave a statically determinate beam, proving the structure to be statically indeterminate to the first degree. It is a simple matter to find the deflection at B, δ_B in Fig. 19–1 (b), caused by the external loads.

If the external loads are removed from the beam and a unit load is placed at B, a deflection at B equal to δ_{bb} will be developed, as indicated in Fig. 19–1 (c). Deflections due to external loads are denoted with capital letters herein. The deflection at point C on a beam due to external

---

[1] Parcel and Moorman, *Analysis of Statically Indeterminate Structures* (New York: John Wiley & Sons, Inc., 1955), p. 48.

[2] Kinney, *Indeterminate Structural Analysis* (Reading, Mass.: Addison-Wesley Publishing Company, 1957), pp. 12–13.

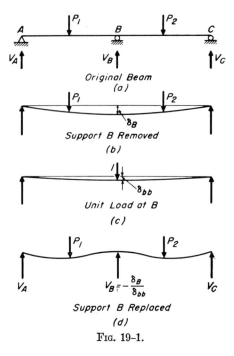

Fig. 19-1.

loads would be δ_C. Deflections due to the imaginary unit load are denoted with two small letters. The first letter indicates the location of the deflection, and the second letter indicates the location of the unit load. The deflection at E caused by a unit load at B would be δ_{eb}.

Support B is unyielding, and its removal is merely a convenient assumption. An upward force is present at B and is sufficient to prevent any deflection, or, continuing with the fictitious line of reasoning, there is a force at B which is large enough to push point B back to its original non-deflected position. The distance the support must be pushed is δ_B.

A unit load at B causes a deflection at B equal to δ_{bb}, and a 10^k load at B will cause a deflection of $10\delta_{bb}$. Similarly, an upward reaction at B of V_B will push B up an amount $V_B\delta_{bb}$. The total deflection at B due to the external loads and the reaction V_B is zero and may be expressed as follows:

$$\delta_B + V_B\delta_{bb} = 0$$

$$V_B = -\frac{\delta_B}{\delta_{bb}}$$

The minus sign in this expression indicates V_B is in the opposite direction from the downward unit load. If the solution of the expression yields a positive value, the reaction is in the same direction as the unit load. Examples 19–1 to 19–4 illustrate the deflection method of computing the reactions for indeterminate beams having one redundant reaction component. Example 19–5 shows that the method may be extended to include indeterminate frames as well. The necessary deflections for all of the examples are determined with the conjugate-beam procedure. After the value of the redundant reaction in each problem is found, the other reactions are determined by statics, and shear and moment diagrams are drawn.

EXAMPLE 19–1. Determine the reactions and draw shear and moment diagrams for the two-span beam of Fig. 19–2; assume V_B to be the redundant. E and I are constant.

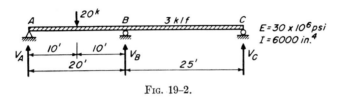

FIG. 19–2.

Solution:

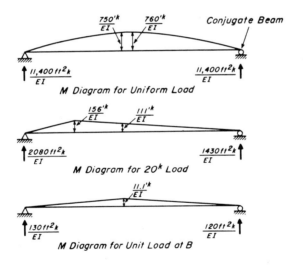

$$EI\delta_B = (20)(11{,}400) - (\tfrac{1}{2})(20)(750)(6.67) - \frac{(3)(20)^3}{12}(10)$$
$$+ (1430)(25) - (\tfrac{1}{2})(25)(111)(8.33)$$

$$EI\delta_B = 182{,}100 \text{ ft}^3\text{-k}$$

$$EI\delta_{bb} = (20)(130) - (\tfrac{1}{2})(20)(11.1)(6.67)$$

$$EI\delta_{bb} = 1860 \text{ ft}^3\text{-k}$$

$$V_B = -\frac{\delta_B}{\delta_{bb}} = -\frac{182{,}100}{1860} = -98^k \uparrow$$

By computing reactions at A and C by statics,

$$\Sigma M_A = 0$$
$$(20)(10) + (45)(3)(22.5) - (20)(98) - 45V_C = 0$$
$$V_C = 28.5^k \uparrow$$

$$\Sigma V = 0$$
$$20 + (3)(45) - 98 - 28.5 - V_A = 0$$
$$V_A = 28.5^k \uparrow$$

Shear and Moment Diagrams

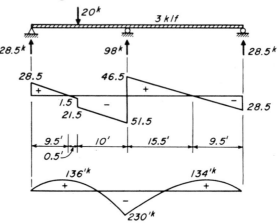

EXAMPLE 19–2. Determine the reactions and draw shear and moment diagrams for the propped beam shown in Fig. 19–3. Consider V_B to be the redundant; E and I are constant.

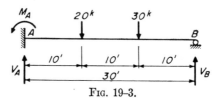

FIG. 19–3.

Solution:

$EI\delta_B = (\frac{1}{2})(200)(10)(26.67) + (\frac{1}{2})(600)(20)(23.33) = 166,670$ ft²-k

$EI\delta_{bb} = (\frac{1}{2})(30)(30)(20) = 9000$ ft²-k

$$V_B = -\frac{166,670}{9000} = -18.5^k \uparrow$$

By statics

$$V_A = 31.5^k \uparrow \quad \text{and} \quad M_A = 245'^k \, \backslash$$

Shear and Moment Diagrams

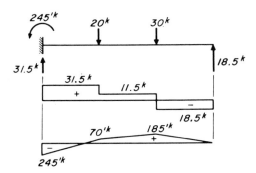

EXAMPLE 19–3. Rework Example 19–2 by using the resisting moment at the fixed end as the redundant.

Solution: Any one of the reactions may be considered to be the redundant and taken out, provided a stable structure remains. If the resisting moment at A is removed, a simple support remains, and the beam loads cause the tangent to the elastic curve to rotate an amount θ_A. A brief discussion of this condition will reveal a method of determining the moment.

The value of θ_A equals the shear at A in the conjugate beam. If a unit moment is applied at A, the tangent to the elastic curve will rotate an amout θ_{aa}, which can be found from the conjugate beam. The tangent to the elastic curve at A actually does not rotate; therefore, when M_A is replaced, it must be of sufficient magnitude to rotate the tangent back to its original horizontal position. The following expression equating θ_A to zero may be written and solved for the redundant M_A.

$$\theta_A + M_A \theta_{aa} = 0 \qquad M_A = -\frac{\theta_A}{\theta_{aa}}$$

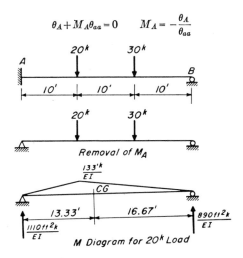

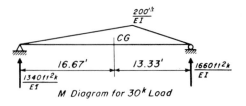

M Diagram for 30^k Load

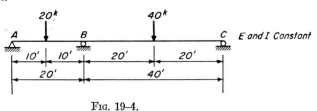

M Diagram for a
Clockwise Unit Moment at A

$$\theta_A = \frac{1110 + 1340}{EI} = \frac{2450 \text{ ft}^2\text{-k}}{EI}$$

$$\theta_{aa} = \frac{10 \text{ ft}^2\text{-k}}{EI}$$

$$M_A = -\frac{\theta_A}{\theta_{aa}} = -\frac{2450}{10} = -245'^k \text{ counterclockwise}$$

EXAMPLE 19–4. Find the reactions and draw the shear and moment diagrams for the two-span beam shown in Fig. 19–4. Assume the moment at the interior support to be the redundant.

FIG. 19–4.

Solution: Removal of moment from the interior support changes the support into a hinge, and the beam is free to slope independently on each side, as indicated by the angles θ_{b_1} and θ_{b_2} in the deflection curve shown. The numerical values of the angles can be found by placing the M/EI diagram on the conjugate structures and computing the shear on each side of the support. In the actual beam, there is no change of slope of the tangent to the elastic curve from a small distance to the left of B to a small distance to the right of B.

The angle represented in the diagram by θ_B is the angle between the tangents to the elastic curve on each side of the support (i.e., $\theta_{b_1} + \theta_{b_2}$). The actual moment M_B, when replaced, must be of sufficient magnitude to bring the tangents back together or reduce θ_B to zero. A unit moment applied on each side of the hinge produces a change of slope of θ_{bb}; therefore, the following expression is applicable:

$$M_B = -\frac{\theta_B}{\theta_{bb}}$$

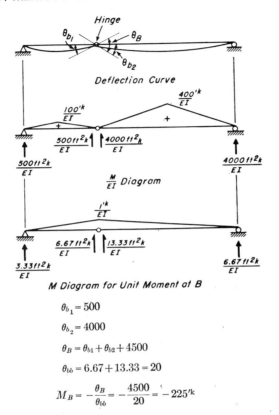

$$\theta_{b_1} = 500$$

$$\theta_{b_2} = 4000$$

$$\theta_B = \theta_{b1} + \theta_{b2} + 4500$$

$$\theta_{bb} = 6.67 + 13.33 = 20$$

$$M_B = -\frac{\theta_B}{\theta_{bb}} = -\frac{4500}{20} = -225'^k$$

By statics the following reactions are found:

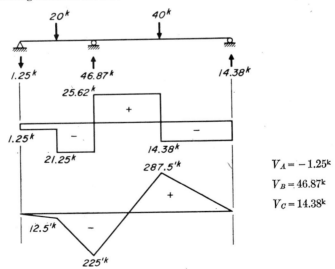

$$V_A = -1.25^k$$

$$V_B = 46.87^k$$

$$V_C = 14.38^k$$

EXAMPLE 19–5. Compute the reactions and draw the moment diagram for the structure shown in Fig. 19–5.

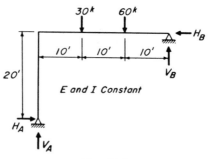

FIG. 19–5.

Solution: Remove H_A as the redundant (which changes A to a roller type of support), load the conjugate structure with the M/EI diagram, and compute the reactions.

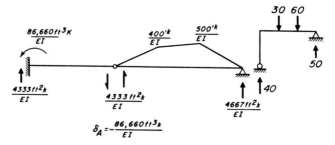

Apply a unit load at A and place the resulting M/EI diagram on the conjugate structure.

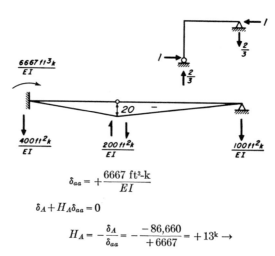

$$\delta_{aa} = +\frac{6667 \text{ ft}^3\text{-k}}{EI}$$

$$\delta_A + H_A \delta_{aa} = 0$$

$$H_A = -\frac{\delta_A}{\delta_{aa}} = -\frac{-86{,}660}{+6667} = +13^k \rightarrow$$

Compute the remaining reactions by statics:

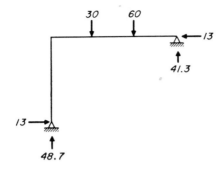

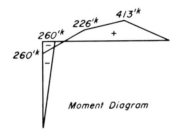

Moment Diagram

19–3. Beams with Two or More Redundants

The deflection method of analyzing beams with one redundant may be extended to beams having two or more redundants. The continuous beam of Fig. 19–6, which has two redundant reactions, is considered here.

To make the beam statically determinate, it is necessary to remove two supports. Supports B and C are assumed to be removed, and their deflections δ_B and δ_C due to the external loads are computed. The external loads

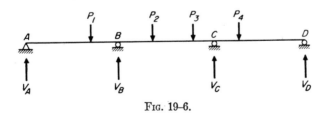

FIG. 19–6.

are theoretically removed from the beam; a unit load is placed at B; and the deflections at B and C, δ_{bb} and δ_{cb}, are found. The unit load is moved to C, and the deflections at the two points, δ_{bc} and δ_{cc}, are again determined.

The reactions at supports B and C push these points up until they are in their original positions of zero deflection. The reaction V_B will raise B an amount $V_B \delta_{bb}$ and C an amount $V_B \delta_{cb}$. The reaction V_C raises C by $V_C \delta_{cc}$ and B by $V_C \delta_{bc}$.

An equation may be written for the deflection at each of the supports. Both equations contain the two unknowns, V_B and V_C, and their values may be obtained by solving the equations simultaneously.

$$\delta_B + V_B \delta_{bb} + V_C \delta_{bc} = 0$$
$$\delta_C + V_B \delta_{cb} + V_C \delta_{cc} = 0$$

The deflection method of computing redundant reactions may be extended indefinitely for beams with any number of redundants. The calculations become quite lengthy, however, if there are more than two or

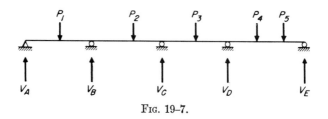

FIG. 19-7.

three redundants. (Chapters 21 to 23 present more satisfactory methods for handling multiredundant structures.) Considering the beam of Fig. 19-7, the following expressions may be written:

$$\delta_B + V_B \delta_{bb} + V_C \delta_{bc} + V_D \delta_{bd} = 0$$
$$\delta_C + V_B \delta_{cb} + V_C \delta_{cc} + V_D \delta_{cd} = 0$$
$$\delta_D + V_B \delta_{db} + V_C \delta_{dc} + V_D \delta_{dd} = 0$$

Example 19-6 illustrates the analysis of a continuous beam with two redundants. The deflections necessary for the solution of the problem are determined with the conjugate-beam procedure. Since E and I are constant, they do not appear in the calculations.

EXAMPLE 19-6. Find the reactions and draw shear and moment diagrams for the continuous beam shown in Fig. 19-8.

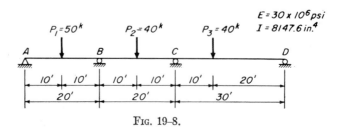

FIG. 19-8.

Solution:

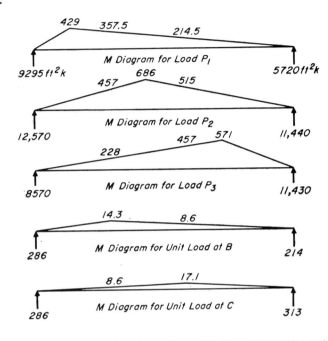

$\delta_B = (5720)(50) - (\tfrac{1}{2})(50)(357.5)(1667) + (12,570 + 8570)(20) - (\tfrac{1}{2})(20)(457 + 228)(6.67)$

$\delta_B = 514,350$

$\delta_C = (5720 + 11,440)(30) - (\tfrac{1}{2})(30)(214.5 + 515)(10) + (8570)(40) - (\tfrac{1}{2})(40)(457)(13.33)$

$\delta_C = 625,300$

$\delta_{bb} = (20)(286) - (\tfrac{1}{2})(20)(14.3)(6.67) = 4765$

$\delta_{cc} = (30)(313) - (\tfrac{1}{2})(30)(17.1)(10) = 6820$

$\delta_{bc} = \delta_{cb} = (20)(286) - (\tfrac{1}{2})(20)(8.6)(6.67) = 5140$

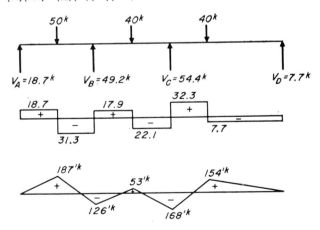

By writing the deflection equations:

$$\delta_B + V_B \delta_{bb} + V_C \delta_{bc} = 0$$

$$514{,}350 + 4765 V_B + 5140 V_C = 0 \tag{1}$$

$$\delta_C + V_B \delta_{cb} + V_C \delta_{cc} = 0$$

$$625{,}300 + 5140 V_B + 6820 V_C = 0 \tag{2}$$

Simultaneous solution of Eqs. 1 and 2 gives V_B and V_C; values of V_A and V_D are found by statics.

19–4. Support Settlement

Continuous beams with unyielding supports have been considered in the preceding sections. Should the supports settle or deflect from their theoretical positions, major changes may occur in the reactions, shears, moments, and stresses. Whatever the factors causing displacement (weak foundations, temperature changes, poor erection or fabrication, etc.), analysis may be made with the deflection expressions previously developed for continuous beams.

An expression for deflection at point B in the two-span beam of Fig. 19–1 was written in Sec. 19–2. The expression was developed on the assumption that support B was temporarily removed from the structure, allowing point B to deflect, after which the support was replaced. The reaction at B, V_B, was assumed to be of sufficient magnitude to push B up to its original position of zero deflection. Should B actually settle 1.0 in., V_B will be smaller because it will only have to push B up an amount $\delta_B - 1.0$ in., and the deflection expression may be written as follows:

$$\delta_B - 1.0 + V_B \delta_{bb} = 0$$

If three men are walking along with a log on their shoulders and one of them lowers his shoulder slightly, he will not have to support as much of the total weight as before. He has, in effect, backed out from under the log and thrown more of its weight to the other men. The settlement of a support in a continuous beam has the same effect.

The values of δ_B and δ_{bb} must be calculated in inches if the support movement is given in inches; they are calculated in feet if the support movement is given in feet; etc. Example 19–7 illustrates the analysis of the two-span beam of Example 19–1 with the assumption of a $\frac{3}{4}$ in. settlement of the interior support. The moment diagram is drawn after settlement occurs and is compared with the diagram before settlement. The seemingly small displacement has completely changed the moment picture.

When several or all of the supports are displaced, the analysis may be conducted on the basis of relative settlement values. For example, if all of the supports of the beam of Fig. 19–9 (a) were to settle 1.5 in., the

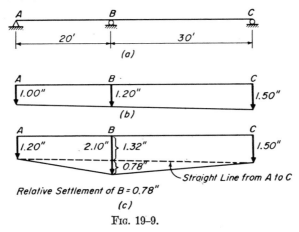

Fig. 19-9.

stress conditions would be unchanged. If the supports settle different amounts but remain in a straight line, as illustrated in Fig. 19–9 (b), the situation theoretically is the same as before settlement.

Where inconsistent settlements occur and the supports no longer lie in a straight line, the stress conditions change because the beam is twisted. The situation may be handled by drawing a line through the displaced positions of two of the supports, usually the end ones. The distances of the other supports from this line are determined and used in the calculations, as illustrated in Fig. 19–9 (c) and Example 19–8.

EXAMPLE 19–7. Determine the reactions and draw shear and moment diagrams for the beam of Example 19–1, which is reproduced in Fig. 19–10, if support B settles ¾ in.

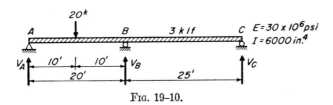

Fig. 19-10.

·Solution: The values of δ_B and δ_{bb} previously found are computed in inches, and the effect of the support settlement on V_B is determined. By statics the new values of V_A and V_B are found and the shear and moment diagrams are drawn. The moment diagram before settlement is repeated to illustrate the striking changes.

$$V_B = \frac{182{,}100 \text{ ft}^3\text{-k}}{EI} = 1.748 \text{ in.}$$

$$\delta_{bb} = \frac{1860 \text{ ft}^3\text{-k}}{EI} = 0.0179 \text{ in.}$$

$$\delta_B + V_B \delta_{bb} = 0.750$$

$$V_B = -\frac{1.748 - 0.750}{0.0179} = -55.7^k \uparrow$$

$$V_A = 52.1^k \uparrow$$

$$V_C = 47.2^k \uparrow$$

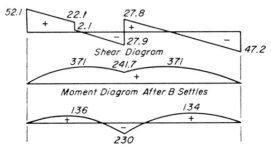

Moment Diagram Before Settlement

EXAMPLE 19-8. Determine the reactions and draw shear and moment diagrams for the beam of Example 19-6, which is reproduced in Fig. 19-11, if the supports settle as follows: $A = 1.25$ in., $B = 2.40$ in., $C = 2.75$ in., and $D = 1.10$ in.

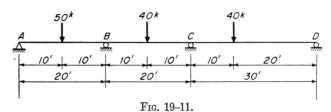

FIG. 19-11.

Solution: The reactions at supports B and C are considered to be the redundants; therefore, a diagram of the settlements is plotted to determine the relative settlements of B and C.

Settlement Diagram

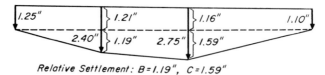

Relative Settlement: $B = 1.19''$, $C = 1.59''$

From Example 19-6:

$$\delta_B = \frac{514{,}350 \text{ ft}^3\text{-k}}{EI} = 3.63 \text{ in.}$$

$$\delta_C = \frac{625{,}300 \text{ ft}^3\text{-k}}{EI} = 4.42 \text{ in.}$$

$$\delta_{bb} = \frac{4765 \text{ ft}^3\text{-k}}{EI} = 0.0337 \text{ in.}$$

$$\delta_{cc} = \frac{6820 \text{ ft}^3\text{-k}}{EI} = 0.0482 \text{ in.}$$

$$\delta_{bc} = \delta_{cb} = \frac{5140 \text{ ft}^3\text{-k}}{EI} = 0.0362 \text{ in.}$$

$$\delta_B + V_B\delta_{bb} + V_c\delta_{bc} = 0$$

$$3.63 + 0.0337V_B + 0.0362V_c = 1.19 \tag{1}$$

$$\delta_c + V_B\delta_{cb} + V_c\delta_{cc} = 0$$

$$4.42 + 0.0362V_B + 0.0482V_c = 1.59 \tag{2}$$

Solving Eqs. 1 and 2 simultaneously gives values of V_B and V_C, and by statics V_A and V_D are determined.

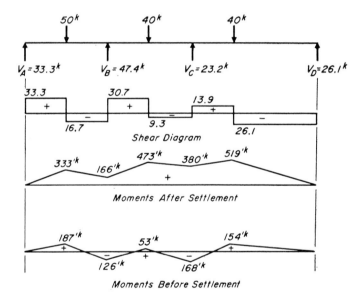

19–5.   Influence Lines for Indeterminate Beams

The uses of influence lines for indeterminate structures are the same as those for determinate structures. They enable the designer to locate the critical positions for live loads and to compute stresses for various positions of the loads. Influence lines for indeterminate structures are not as simple to draw as they are for determinate structures. For the latter case it is possible to compute the ordinates for a few controlling points and connect those values with a set of straight lines. Unfortunately, influence lines for continuous structures require the computation of ordinates at a large number of points because the diagrams are either curved or made up of a series of chords. The chord-shaped diagram occurs where loads can only be transferred to the structure at intervals, as at the panel points of a truss or at joists framing into a girder.

The problem of preparing the diagrams is not as difficult as the preceding paragraph seems to indicate, because a large percentage of the work may be eliminated by applying Maxwell's law of reciprocal deflections. The preparation of an influence line for the interior reaction of the two-span beam of Fig. 19–12 is considered in the following paragraphs.

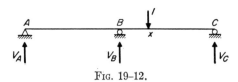

FIG. 19–12.

The procedure for calculating V_B has been to remove it from the beam and then compute δ_B and δ_{bb} and substitute their values in the usual formula. The same procedure may be used in drawing an influence line for V_B. A unit load is placed at some point x causing δ_B to equal δ_{bx}, from which the following expression is written.

$$V_B = -\frac{\delta_B}{\delta_{bb}} = -\frac{\delta_{bx}}{\delta_{bb}}$$

At first glance it appears that the unit load will have to be placed at numerous points on the beam and the value of δ_{bx} laboriously computed for each. A study of the deflections caused by a unit load at point x, however, proves these computations to be unnecessary. By Maxwell's law the deflection at B due to a unit load at x (δ_{bx}) is identical with the deflection at x due to a unit load at B (δ_{xb}). The expression for V_B becomes:

$$V_B = -\frac{\delta_{xb}}{\delta_{bb}}$$

It is now evident that the unit load need only be placed at B, and the deflections at various points across the beam are then computed. Dividing each of these values by δ_{bb} gives the ordinates for the influence line. If a deflection curve is plotted for the beam for a unit load at B (support B being removed), an influence line for V_B may be obtained by dividing each of the deflection ordinates by δ_{bb}. Another way of expressing this principle is as follows: If a unit deflection is caused at a support for which the influence line is desired, the beam will draw its own influence line, because the deflection at any point in the beam is the ordinate of the influence line at that point for the reaction in question.

Maxwell's presentation of his theorem in 1864 was so brief that its value was not fully appreciated until 1886 when Prof. Heinrich Müller-Breslau clearly showed its true worth as described in the preceding paragraph.[3] Müller-Breslau's principle may be stated in detail as follows: *The deflected shape of a structure represents the influence line for a function such as stress, shear, moment, or reaction component if the function is allowed to act through a unit distance.* The principle is applicable to statically determinate and indeterminate beams, frames, and trusses.

The influence line for the reaction at the interior support of a two-span beam is presented in Example 19-9. Influence lines are also shown for the end reactions, the values for ordinates having been obtained by statics from those computed for the interior reaction. The conjugate-beam procedure is an excellent method of determining the beam deflections necessary for preparing the diagrams.

EXAMPLE 19-9. Draw influence lines for reactions at each support of the structure shown in Fig. 19-13.

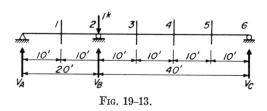

FIG. 19-13.

Solution: Remove V_B, place a unit load at B, and compute the deflections caused at 10-ft intervals by the conjugate-beam method:

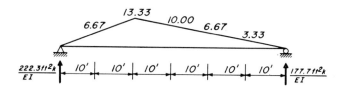

$$\delta_1 = (222.3)(10) - (\tfrac{1}{2})(10)(6.67)(3.33) = 2112$$
$$\delta_2 = (222.3)(20) - (\tfrac{1}{2})(20)(13.33)(6.67) = 3550$$
$$\delta_3 = (177.7)(30) - (\tfrac{1}{2})(30)(10.00)(10.00) = 3831$$
$$\delta_4 = (177.7)(20) - (\tfrac{1}{2})(20)(6.67)(6.67) = 3109$$
$$\delta_5 = (177.7)(10) - (\tfrac{1}{2})(10)(3.33)(3.33) = 1722$$

Noting $\delta_{bb} = \delta_2$, the values of the influence-line ordinates for V_B are found by dividing each deflection by δ_2.

[3] Kinney, *op. cit., Indeterminate Structural Analysis*, p. 14.

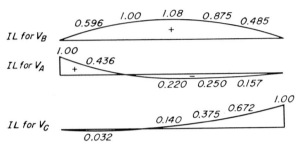

Check results by removing support C, place a unit load there, and compute deflections at 10-ft intervals.

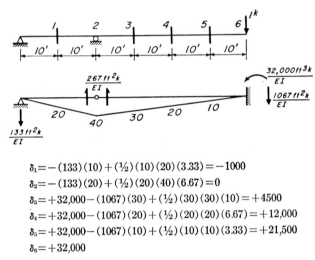

$$\delta_1 = -(133)(10) + (\tfrac{1}{2})(10)(20)(3.33) = -1000$$
$$\delta_2 = -(133)(20) + (\tfrac{1}{2})(20)(40)(6.67) = 0$$
$$\delta_3 = +32,000 - (1067)(30) + (\tfrac{1}{2})(30)(30)(10) = +4500$$
$$\delta_4 = +32,000 - (1067)(20) + (\tfrac{1}{2})(20)(20)(6.67) = +12,000$$
$$\delta_5 = +32,000 - (1067)(10) + (\tfrac{1}{2})(10)(10)(3.33) = +21,500$$
$$\delta_6 = +32,000$$

Noting that $\delta_{cc} = \delta_6$, find the ordinates of the influence line for V_c by dividing each deflection by δ_6.

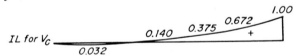

The next problem is to draw the influence lines for beams continuous over three spans, which have two redundants. For this discussion the beam of Fig. 19–14 is considered, and the reactions V_B and V_C are assumed to be the redundants.

It will be necessary to remove the redundants and compute the deflections at various sections in the beam for a unit load at B and also for a unit load at C. By Maxwell's law a unit load at any point x causes a deflection at B (δ_{bx}) equal to the deflection at x due to a unit load at B (δ_{xb}). Similarly, $\delta_{cx} = \delta_{xc}$. After computing δ_{xb} and δ_{xc} at the several sections,

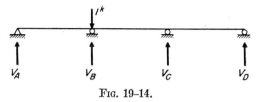

FIG. 19–14.

their values at each section may be substituted into the following simultaneous equations, whose solution will yield the values of V_B and V_C.

$$\delta_{xb} + V_B\delta_{bb} + V_C\delta_{bc} = 0$$
$$\delta_{xc} + V_B\delta_{cb} + V_C\delta_{cc} = 0$$

The simultaneous equations are solved quickly, even though a large number of ordinates are being computed, because the only variables in the equations are δ_{xb} and δ_{xc}. After the influence lines are prepared for the redundant reactions of a beam, the ordinates for any other function (moment, shear, etc.) can be determined by statics. Example 19–10 illustrates the calculations necessary for preparing influence lines for several functions of a three-span continuous beam.

EXAMPLE 19–10. Draw influence lines for V_B, V_C, V_D, M_7, and shear at section 6, Fig. 19–15.

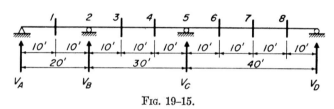

FIG. 19–15.

Solution: Remove V_B and V_C, place a unit load at B, and load the conjugate beam with the M/EI diagram.

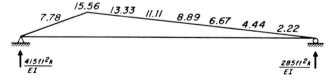

Place a unit load at C and load the conjugate beam with the M/EI diagram.

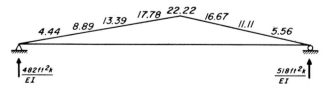

Compute the values of δ_{xb} and δ_{xc}, from which V_B and V_C are obtained by solving the simultaneous equations. Ordinates for M_7, V_b, and shear at section 6 are obtained by statics.

Section	δ_{xb}	δ_{xc}	V_B	V_C	V_D	M_7	V_6
1	4020	4746	+0.646	−0.0735	+0.008	+0.160	−0.008
2	7255 = δ_{bb}	9040 = δ_{bc}	+1.00	0	0	0	0
3	9100	12,460	+0.855	+0.320	−0.0344	−0.688	+0.0344
4	9630	14,540	+0.432	+0.720	−0.0513	−1.026	+0.0513
5	9040 = δ_{cb}	14,825 = δ_{cc}	0	+1.00	0	0	0
6	7550	13,040	−0.227	+1.02	+0.1504	+3.008	−0.1504
							+0.8496
7	5404	9618	−0.257	+0.805	+0.388	+7.76	+0.612
8	2813	5088	−0.159	+0.440	+0.688	+3.68	+0.316

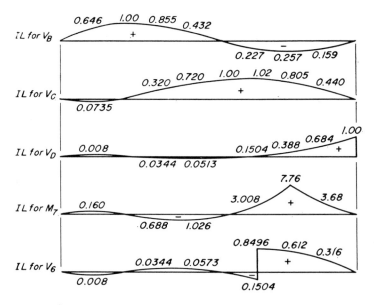

19–6. Qualitative Influence Lines

Müller-Breslau's principle is of such importance that space is taken to emphasize its value. The shape of the usual influence line needed for continuous structures is so simple to obtain from his principle that in many situations it is unnecessary to perform the labor needed to compute the numerical values of the ordinates. It is possible to roughly sketch the diagram with sufficient accuracy to locate the critical positions for live load for various functions of the structure. This possibility is of particular importance for building frames, as will be illustrated in subsequent paragraphs.

If the influence line is desired for the left reaction of the continuous beam of Fig. 19–16 (a), its general shape can be determined by letting the reaction act upward through a unit distance as shown in Fig. 19–16 (b) of the figure. If the left end of the beam were pushed up, the beam would take the shape shown. This distorted shape can be easily sketched, remembering the other supports are unyielding. Influence lines obtained by sketching are said to be *qualitative influence* lines, while the exact ones are said to be *quantitative influence lines*. The influence line for V_C in Fig. 19–16 (c) is another example of qualitative sketching for reaction components.

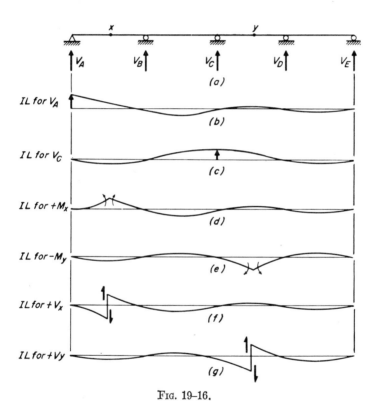

Fig. 19–16.

Figure 19–16 (d) shows the influence line for positive moment at point x near the center of the left-hand span. The beam is assumed to have a pin or hinge inserted at x and a couple applied adjacent to each side of the pin which will cause compression on the top fibers (+ moment). Twisting the beam on each side of the pin causes the left span to take the shape indicated, and the deflected shape of the remainder of the beam may be roughly sketched. A similar procedure is used to draw the influence line for negative moment at point y in the third span, except that a moment couple is applied at the assumed pin which will tend to cause compression on the bottom beam fibers, corresponding with negative moment.

Finally, qualitative influence lines are drawn for positive shear at points x and y. At point x the beam is assumed to be cut, and two vertical forces of the nature required to give positive shear are applied to the beam on the sides of the cut section. The beam will take the shape shown in Fig. 19–16 (f). The same procedure is used to draw the diagram for positive shear at point y.

From these diagrams considerable information is available concerning critical live-loading conditions. If a maximum positive value of V_A were desired for a uniform live load, the load would be placed in spans *1* and *3*, where the diagram has positive ordinates; if maximum negative moment were required at point x, spans *2* and *4* would be loaded; etc.

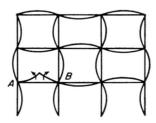

FIG. 19–17.

Qualitative influence lines are particularly valuable for determining critical load positions for buildings, as shown by the moment influence line for the building frame of Fig. 19–17. In drawing the diagrams for an entire frame, the joints are assumed to be free to rotate, but the members at each joint are assumed rigidly connected to each other so that the angles between them do not change during rotation. The diagram of this figure is sketched for positive moment at the center of beam AB.

The spans which should be loaded to cause maximum positive moment are obvious from the diagram. It should be noted that loads on a beam more than approximately three spans away have little effect on the function under consideration. This fact can be seen in the influence lines of Example 19–10, where the ordinates even two spans aways are quite small.

A warning should be given regarding qualitative influence lines. They should be drawn for functions near the center of spans or at the supports, but for sections near one-fourth points they should not be sketched without out a good deal of study. Near the one-fourth point of a span is a point called the *fixed point* at which the influence line changes in type. The subject of fixed points is discussed at some length in the text *Continuous Frames of Reinforced Concrete* by Cross and Morgan.

Problems

19-1 to 19-8. Compute the reactions and draw shear and moment diagrams for the continuous beams. E and I are constant unless noted otherwise.

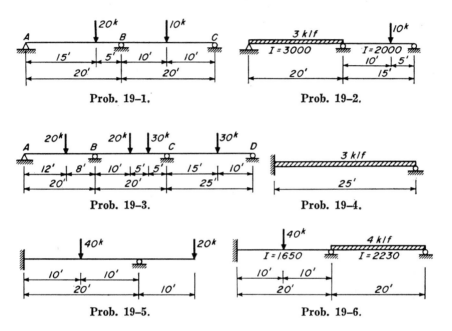

Prob. 19-1. **Prob. 19-2.**

Prob. 19-3. **Prob. 19-4.**

Prob. 19-5. **Prob. 19-6.**

19-7. The beam of Prob. 19-1 assuming the supports settle as follows: $A=0.85$ in., $B=1.35$ in., and $C=0.64$ in.

19-8. The beam of Prob. 19-3 assuming the following support settlements: $A=0.40$ in., $B=0.75$ in., $C=1.25$ in., and $D=0.55$ in.

Draw quantitative influence lines for the situations listed in Probs. 19-9 to 19-12.

19-9. Reactions at all supports for the beam of Prob. 19-1.

19-10. Shear and moment at the fixed-end support of the beam of Prob. 19-4.

19-11. Shear and moment at the expansion support of the beam of Prob. 19-5.

19-12. Shear and moment at a point 10 ft from the left support of Prob. 19-6.

By using Müller-Breslau's principle, sketch influence lines qualitatively for the functions indicated in the structures of Probs. 19-13 to 19-15.

19-13. With reference to the accompanying illustration: (a) reactions at B and E, (b) positive moment at x and y, and (c) positive shear at x.

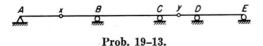

Prob. 19-13.

19–14. With reference to the beam of Prob. 19–3: (a) negative moments at B and C, (b) positive moment at C.

19–15. With reference to the accompanying illustration: (a) positive moment at A, (b) positive shear at A, and (c) negative moment at B.

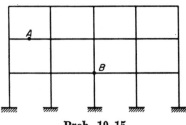

Prob. 19–15.

20 | DEFLECTION METHODS OF ANA-
LYZING INDETERMINATE TRUSSES

20–1. Analysis of Externally Redundant Trusses

Trusses may be statically indeterminate because of redundant reactions, redundant members, or a combination of redundant reactions and members. Externally redundant trusses will be considered initially, and they will be analyzed on the basis of deflection computations in a manner closely related to the procedure used for indeterminate beams.

The two-span continuous truss of Example 20–1 is considered for the following discussion. One reaction component, for example, V_B, is removed, and the deflection at that point caused by the external loads is determined. Next the external loads are removed from the truss, and the deflection at the support point due to a unit load at that point is determined. The reaction is replaced, and it supplies the force necessary to push the support back to its original position. The familiar deflection expression is written as follows:

$$\delta_B + V_B \delta_{bb} = 0$$
$$V_B = -\frac{\delta_B}{\delta_{bb}}$$

The stresses in the truss members due to the external loads, when the redundant is removed, are not the correct final stresses and are referred to as S' stresses. The deflection at the removed support due to the external loads can be computed by $\Sigma(S'\mu l/AE)$. The deflection caused at the support by placing a unit load there can be found by applying the same virtual work expression, except the unit load is now the external load and the stresses caused are the same as the μ stresses. The deflection at the support due to the unit load is $\Sigma(\mu_B^2 l/AE)$, and the redundant reaction may be expressed as follows:

$$V_B = -\frac{\Sigma(S'\mu_B l/AE)}{\Sigma(\mu_B^2 l/AE)}$$

Example 20–1 illustrates the complete analysis of a two-span truss by the method just described. After the redundant reaction is found, the other reactions and the final member stresses may be determined by statics. Another method, however, is available for finding the final stresses and should be used as a mathematics check. When the redundant reaction V_B is returned to the truss, it causes the stress in each member to change by V_B times its μ stress value. The final stress in a member becomes:

$$S = S' + V_B \mu$$

It should be evident that the deflection procedure may be used to analyze trusses which have two or more redundant reactions. The truss of Example 20–2 is continuous over three spans, and the reactions at the interior supports, V_B and V_C, are considered to be the redundants. The following expressions, previously written for a three-span continuous beam, are applicable to the truss:

$$\delta_B + V_B \delta_{bb} + V_C \delta_{bc} = 0$$

$$\delta_C + V_B \delta_{cb} + V_C \delta_{cc} = 0$$

The stresses due to a unit load at B are called the μ_B stresses; the ones due to a unit load at C are called the μ_C stresses. A unit load at B will cause a deflection at C equal to $\Sigma(\mu_B \mu_C l / AE)$, while a unit load at C causes the same deflection at B, $\Sigma(\mu_C \mu_B l / AE)$, which is thus another illustration of Maxwell's law. The deflection expressions become:

$$\Sigma \frac{S' \mu_B l}{AE} + V_B \Sigma \frac{\mu_B^2 l}{AE} + V_C \Sigma \frac{\mu_B \mu_C l}{AE} = 0$$

$$\Sigma \frac{S' \mu_C l}{AE} + V_B \Sigma \frac{\mu_C \mu_B l}{AE} + V_C \Sigma \frac{\mu_C^2 l}{AE} = 0$$

A simultaneous solution of these equations will yield the values of the redundants. Should support settlement occur, the deflections would have to be worked out numerically in the same units given for the settlements.

EXAMPLE 20–1. Compute the reactions and stresses for the two-span continuous truss shown in Fig. 20–1. Circled figures are member areas, in square inches.

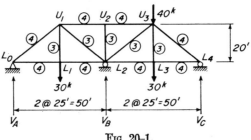

FIG. 20–1.

Solution: Remove center support as the redundant and compute S' stresses.

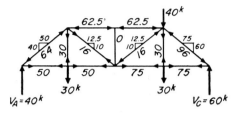

Remove the external loads and place a unit load at the center support; then compute the μ stresses.

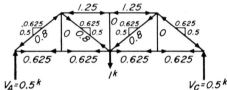

Member	l (in.)	A (sq in.)	$\dfrac{l}{A}$	S'	μ	$\dfrac{S'\mu l}{AE}$	$\dfrac{\mu^2 l}{AE}$	$S = S' + X\mu$
L_0L_1	300	4	75	$+50$	$+0.625$	$+2340$	$+29.2$	$+15.0$
L_1L_2	300	4	75	$+50$	$+0.625$	$+2340$	$+29.2$	$+15.0$
L_2L_3	300	4	75	$+75$	$+0.625$	$+3510$	$+29.2$	$+40.0$
L_3L_4	300	4	75	$+75$	$+0.625$	$+3510$	$+29.2$	$+40.0$
L_0U_1	384	4	96	-64	-0.800	$+4920$	$+61.4$	-19.2
U_1U_2	300	4	75	-62.5	-1.25	$+5850$	$+117.0$	$+7.5$
U_2U_3	300	4	75	-62.5	-1.25	$+5850$	$+117.0$	$+7.5$
U_3L_4	384	4	96	-96	-0.800	$+7370$	$+61.4$	-51.2
U_1L_1	240	3	80	$+30$	0	0	0	$+30.0$
U_1L_2	384	3	128	$+16$	$+0.800$	$+1640$	$+82.0$	-28.8
U_2L_2	240	3	80	0	0	0	0	0
U_2U_3	384	3	128	-16	$+0.800$	-1640	$+82.0$	-60.8
U_3L_3	240	3	80	$+30$	0	0	0	$+30.0$
Σ	......	......	......	......	......	$35,690$	637.6	......

$$V_B = -\frac{35,690}{637.6} = -56.0^k \uparrow$$

The reactions and stresses are found by statics in order to check the final values in the table.

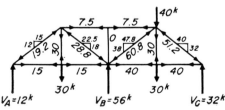

EXAMPLE 20–2. Analyze the ·three-span truss shown in Fig. 20–2. Assume the· reactions at the interior supports to be the redundants. Circled figures are member areas, in square inches.

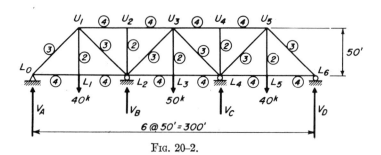

FIG. 20–2.

Solution: Remove the redundants and compute the S' stresses, the μ_B stresses, and the μ_C stresses.

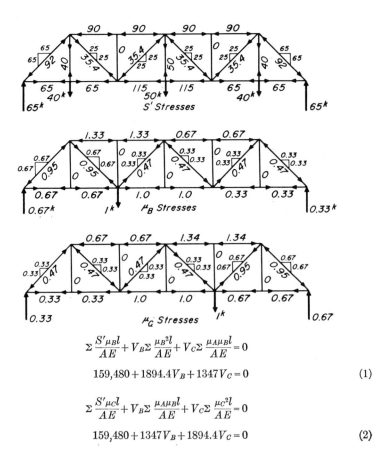

$$\Sigma \frac{S'\mu_B l}{AE} + V_B \Sigma \frac{\mu_B{}^2 l}{AE} + V_C \Sigma \frac{\mu_A \mu_B l}{AE} = 0$$

$$159{,}480 + 1894.4 V_B + 1347 V_C = 0 \tag{1}$$

$$\Sigma \frac{S'\mu_C l}{AE} + V_B \Sigma \frac{\mu_A \mu_B l}{AE} + V_C \Sigma \frac{\mu_C{}^2 l}{AE} = 0$$

$$159{,}480 + 1347 V_B + 1894.4 V_C = 0 \tag{2}$$

Member	l (in.)	$\dfrac{A}{\text{(sq in.)}}$	$\dfrac{l}{A}$	S'	μ_B	μ_C	$\dfrac{S'\mu_B l}{AE}$	$\dfrac{S'\mu_C l}{AE}$	$\dfrac{\mu_B{}^2 l}{AE}$	$\dfrac{\mu_C{}^2 l}{AE}$	$\dfrac{\mu_C\mu_B l}{AE}$	$S = V\mu_B + V\mu_C + S'$
L_0L_1	600	4	150	+ 65	+0.67	+0.33	+ 6500	+ 3250	+ 67.4	+ 16.4	+ 33.0	+ 15.6
L_1L_2	600	4	150	+ 65	+0.67	+0.33	+ 6500	+ 3250	+ 67.4	+ 16.4	+ 33.0	+ 15.6
L_2L_3	600	4	150	+ 115	+1.00	+1.00	+17,250	+17,250	+150.0	+150.0	+150.0	+ 16.4
L_3L_4	600	4	150	+ 115	+1.00	+1.00	+17,250	+17,250	+150.0	+150.0	+150.0	+ 16.4
L_4L_5	600	4	150	+ 65	+0.33	+0.67	+ 3250	+ 6500	+ 16.4	+ 67.4	+ 33.0	+ 15.6
L_5L_6	600	4	150	+ 65	+0.33	+0.67	+ 3250	+ 6500	+ 16.4	+ 67.4	+ 33.0	+ 15.6
L_0U_1	848	3	283	− 92	−0.95	−0.47	+24,800	+12,400	+256.0	+ 62.5	+126.5	− 22.0
U_1U_2	600	4	150	− 90	−1.33	−0.67	+18,000	+ 9000	+265.0	+ 67.4	+133.5	+ 8.7
U_2U_3	600	4	150	− 90	−1.33	−0.67	+18,000	+ 9000	+265.0	+ 67.4	+133.5	+ 8.7
U_3U_4	600	4	150	− 90	−0.67	−1.33	+ 9000	+18,000	+ 67.4	+265.0	+133.5	+ 8.7
U_4U_5	600	4	150	− 90	−0.67	−1.33	+ 9000	+18,000	+ 67.4	+265.0	+133.5	+ 8.7
U_5L_6	848	3	283	− 92	−0.47	−0.95	+12,400	+24,800	+ 62.5	+255.0	+126.5	− 22.0
U_1L_1	600	2	300	+ 40	0	0	0	0	0	0	0	+40.0
U_1L_2	848	3	283	+ 35.4	+0.95	+0.47	+ 9520	+ 4760	+256.0	+ 62.5	+126.5	−34.6
U_2L_2	600	2	300	0	0	0	0	0	0	0	0	0
L_2U_3	848	3	283	− 35.4	+0.47	−0.47	− 4760	+ 4760	+ 62.5	+ 62.5	− 62.5	−35.4
U_3L_3	600	2	300	+ 50	0	0	0	0	0	0	0	+50.0
U_3L_4	848	3	283	− 35.4	−0.47	+0.47	+ 4760	− 4760	+ 62.5	+ 62.5	− 62.5	−35.4
U_4L_4	600	2	300	0	0	0	0	0	0	0	0	0
L_4U_5	848	3	283	+ 35.4	+0.47	+0.95	+ 4760	+ 9520	+ 62.5	+255.0	+126.5	−34.6
U_5L_5	600	2	300	+ 40	0	0	0	0	0	0	0	+40.0
Σ							+159,480	+159,480	+1894.4	+1894.4	+1347	

By solving Eqs. 1 and 2 simultaneously for V_B and V_C and finding V_A and V_D by statics,

$$V_A = -15.7^k \uparrow$$
$$V_B = -49.4^k \uparrow$$
$$V_C = -49.4^k \uparrow$$
$$V_D = -15.7^k \uparrow$$

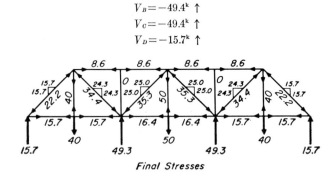

Final Stresses

20–2. Analysis of Internally Redundant Trusses

The truss of Example 20–3 has one more member than necessary for stability and is, therefore, statically indeterminate to the first degree, as can be proved by applying the equation $m = 2j - 3$.

Internally redundant trusses may be analyzed in a manner closely related to the one used for externally redundant trusses. One member is assumed to be the redundant and is theoretically cut or removed from the structure. The remaining members must form a statically determinate and stable truss. The S' stresses in these members are assumed to be of a nature causing the joints at the ends of the removed member to pull apart, the distance being $\Sigma(S'\mu l/AE)$.

The redundant member is replaced in the truss and is assumed to have a unit tensile stress. The μ stresses in each of the members are computed owing to the redundant's stress of $+1$, and they will cause the joints to be pulled together an amount equal to $\Sigma(\mu^2 l/AE)$. If the redundant has an actual stress of X, the joints will be pulled together an amount equal to $X \Sigma(\mu^2 l/AE)$.

If the member had been sawed in half, the S' stresses would have opened a gap of $\Sigma(S'\mu l/AE)$; therefore, X must be sufficient to close the gap, and the following expressions may be written:

$$X \Sigma \frac{\mu^2 l}{AE} + \Sigma \frac{S'\mu l}{AE} = 0$$

$$X = -\frac{\Sigma(S'\mu l/AE)}{\Sigma(\mu^2 l/AE)}$$

The application of this very common method of analyzing internally redundant trusses is illustrated by Example 20–3. After the true stress in the redundant member is found, the stress in any other member equals

Delaware River Turnpike Bridge. (American Bridge)

its S' stress plus X times its μ stress. Final stresses may also be calculated by statics as a check on the mathematics.

For trusses which have more than one redundant internally, simultaneous equations are necessary in the solution. Example 20–4 illustrates the analysis of a truss which is statically indeterminate internally to the second degree. Two members, with stresses of X_A and X_B, assumed to be the redundants are theoretically cut. The S' stresses in the remaining truss members pull the cut places apart by $\Sigma(S'\mu_A l/AE)$ and $\Sigma(S'\mu_B l/AE)$, respectively. Replacing the first redundant member with a stress of $+1$ causes μ_A stresses in the truss members and causes the gaps to close by $\Sigma(\mu_A{}^2 l/AE)$ and $\Sigma\mu_A\mu_B l/AE$. Repeating the process with the other redundant causes μ_B stresses and additional gap closings of $\Sigma(\mu_B\mu_A l/AE)$ and $\Sigma(\mu_B{}^2 l/AE)$. The redundant stresses must be sufficient to close the gaps, permitting the writing of the following equations:

$$\Sigma\frac{S'\mu_A l}{AE}+X_A\Sigma\frac{\mu_A{}^2 l}{AE}+X_B\Sigma\frac{\mu_A\mu_B l}{AE}=0$$

$$\Sigma\frac{S'\mu_B l}{AE}+X_A\Sigma\frac{\mu_B\mu_A l}{AE}+X_B\Sigma\frac{\mu_B{}^2 l}{AE}=0$$

EXAMPLE 20–3. Determine the stresses in the members of the internally redundant truss shown in Fig. 20–3. Circled figures are member areas, in square inches.

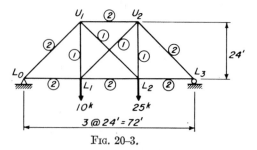

Fig. 20–3.

Solution: Assume L_1U_2 to be the redundant, remove it, and compute the S' stresses.

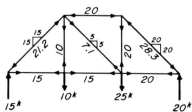

Replace L_1U_2 with a stress of $+1$ and compute the μ stresses.

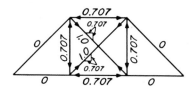

Member	l	A	$\dfrac{l}{A}$	S'	μ	$\dfrac{S'\mu l}{AE}$	$\dfrac{\mu^2 l}{AE}$	$S = S' + X\mu$
L_0L_1	288	2	144	$+15$	0	0	0	$+15.00$
L_1L_2	288	2	144	$+15$	-0.707	-1530	$+72$	$+13.47$
L_2L_3	288	2	144	$+20$	0	0	0	$+20.00$
L_0U_1	408	2	204	-21.2	0	0	0	-21.20
U_1U_2	288	2	144	-20	-0.707	$+2040$	$+72$	-21.53
U_2L_3	408	2	204	-28.3	0	0	0	-28.30
U_1L_1	288	1	288	$+10$	-0.707	-2040	$+144$	$+8.47$
U_1L_2	408	1	408	$+7.1$	$+1.0$	$+2900$	$+408$	$+9.26$
L_1U_2	408	1	408	0	$+1.0$	0	$+408$	$+2.16$
U_2L_2	288	1	288	$+20$	-0.707	-4070	$+144$	$+18.47$
Σ	......	....	....	....	....	-2700	$+1248$	....

$$X = -\frac{\Sigma(S'\mu l/AE)}{\Sigma(\mu^2 l/AE)} = -\frac{-2700}{+1248} = +2.16^k$$

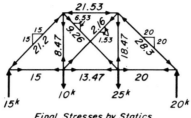

Final Stresses by Statics

EXAMPLE 20-4. Analyze the truss shown in Fig. 20-4; assume L_1U_2 and U_2L_3 to be the redundants. Circled figures are member areas, in square inches.

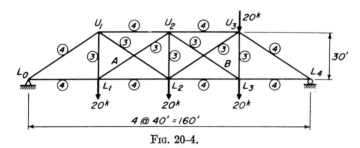

FIG. 20-4.

Solution: Remove the redundants and compute the S' stresses.

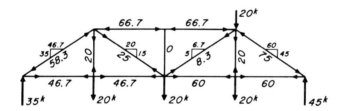

Replace L_1U_2 with a stress of $+1$ and compute the μ_A stresses.

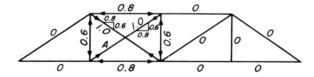

Replace U_2L_3 with a stress of $+1$ and compute the μ_B stresses.

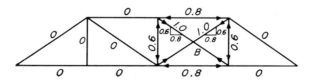

Member	l	A	$\dfrac{l}{A}$	S'	μ_A	μ_B	$\dfrac{S'\mu_A l}{AE}$	$\dfrac{S'\mu_B l}{AE}$	$\dfrac{\mu_A^2 l}{AE}$	$\dfrac{\mu_B^2 l}{AE}$	$\dfrac{\mu_A\mu_B l}{AE}$	$S = S' + X_A\mu_A + X_B\mu_B$
L_0L_1	480	4	120	+46.7	0	0	0	0	0	0	0	+46.7
L_1L_2	480	4	120	+46.7	−0.8	0	−4490	0	+76.8	0	0	+53.5
L_2L_3	480	4	120	+60.0	0	−0.8	0	−5760	0	+43.2	0	+60.63
L_3L_4	480	4	120	+60.0	0	0	0	0	0	0	0	+60.0
L_0U_1	600	4	150	−58.3	0	0	0	0	0	0	0	−58.3
U_1U_2	480	4	120	−66.7	−0.8	0	+6410	0	+76.8	0	0	−59.9
U_2U_3	480	4	120	−66.7	0	−0.8	0	+6410	0	+76.8	0	−66.06
U_3L_4	600	4	150	−75.0	0	0	0	0	0	0	0	−75.0
U_1L_1	360	3	120	+20.0	−0.6	0	−1440	0	+43.2	0	0	+25.1
U_1L_2	600	3	200	+25.0	+1.0	0	+5000	0	+200.0	0	0	+16.5
L_1U_2	600	3	200	0	+1.0	0	0	0	+200.0	0	0	− 8.5
U_2L_2	360	3	120	0	−0.6	−0.6	0	0	+43.2	+43.2	+43.2	+ 5.57
U_2L_3	600	3	200	0	0	+1.0	0	0	0	+200.0	0	− 0.79
L_2U_3	600	3	200	+ 8.3	0	+1.0	0	+1660	0	+200.0	0	+ 7.51
U_3L_3	360	3	120	+20.0	0	−0.6	0	−1440	0	+43.2	0	+20.47
Σ							+5480	+ 870	+640	+640	+43.2	

$$\Sigma \frac{S'\mu_A l}{AE} + X_A \Sigma \frac{\mu_A{}^2 l}{AE} + X_B \Sigma \frac{\mu_A \mu_B l}{AE} = 0$$

$$+5480 + 640 X_A + 43.2 X_B = 0 \tag{1}$$

$$\Sigma \frac{S'\mu_B l}{AE} + X_A \Sigma \frac{\mu_A \mu_B l}{AE} + X_B \Sigma \frac{\mu_B{}^2 l}{AE} = 0$$

$$+870 + 43.2 X_A + 640 X_B = 0 \tag{2}$$

Simultaneous solutions of Eqs. 1 and 2 gives values of X_A and X_B of -8.5^k and -0.79^k, respectively. These values are used in computing final stresses by statics as a check on figures obtained in the last column of the table.

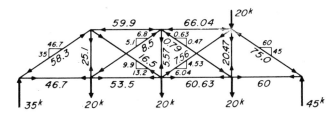

20–3. Analysis of Trusses Redundant Internally and Externally

Deflection equations have been written so frequently in the past few sections that the student is probably able to set up his own equations for types of indeterminate beams and trusses not previously encountered. Nevertheless, one more group of equations is developed here, these being the ones necessary for the analysis of a truss which is statically indeterminate internally and externally. For the following discussion, the truss of Fig. 20–5, which has two redundant members and one redundant reaction component, will be considered.

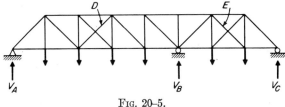

Fig. 20–5.

The diagonals lettered D and E and the interior reaction V_B are removed from the truss, which leaves a statically determinate structure. The openings of the gaps in the cut members and the deflections at the interior support may be computed from the following:

$$\delta_B = \Sigma \frac{S'\mu_B l}{AE} \qquad \delta_D = \Sigma \frac{S'\mu_D l}{AE} \qquad \delta_E = \Sigma \frac{S'\mu_E l}{AE}$$

Placing a unit load at the interior support will cause deflections at the gaps in the cut members as well as at the point of application.

$$\delta_{bb} = \Sigma \frac{\mu_B^2 l}{AE} \qquad \delta_{db} = \Sigma \frac{\mu_B \mu_D l}{AE} \qquad \delta_{eb} = \Sigma \frac{\mu_B \mu_E l}{AE}$$

Replacing member D and assuming it to have a positive unit tensile stress will cause the following deflections:

$$\delta_{bd} = \Sigma \frac{\mu_B \mu_D l}{AE} \qquad \delta_{dd} = \Sigma \frac{\mu_D^2 l}{AE} \qquad \delta_{ed} = \Sigma \frac{\mu_E \mu_D l}{AE}$$

Similarly, replacement of member E with a stress of $+1$ will cause these deflections:

$$\delta_{be} = \Sigma \frac{\mu_B \mu_E l}{AE} \qquad \delta_{de} = \Sigma \frac{\mu_D \mu_E l}{AE} \qquad \delta_{ee} = \Sigma \frac{\mu_E^2 l}{AE}$$

Computation of these sets of deflections permits the calculation of the numerical values of the redundants, because the total deflection at each may be equated to zero.

$$\delta_B + V_B \delta_{bb} + X_D \delta_{bd} + X_E \delta_{be} = 0$$
$$\delta_D + V_B \delta_{db} + X_D \delta_{dd} + X_E \delta_{de} = 0$$
$$\delta_E + V_B \delta_{eb} + X_D \delta_{ed} + X_E \delta_{ee} = 0$$

Nothing new is involved in the solution of this type of problem, and space is not taken for the lengthy calculations necessary for an illustrative example.

20–4. Influence Lines for Statically Indeterminate Trusses

For analyzing indeterminate trusses, influence lines are necessary to determine the critical positions for live loads as they were for statically determinate trusses.

The discussion of the details of construction of these diagrams for indeterminate trusses is quite similar to the one presented for indeterminate beams in the preceding chapter. To prepare the influence line for a reaction of a continuous truss, the support is removed and a unit load is placed at the support point. For this position of the unit load, the deflection at each of the truss joints is determined. For example, the preparation of an influence line for the interior reaction of the truss of Fig. 20–6 is considered. The value of the reaction when the unit load is at joint x may be expressed as follows:

$$V_B = -\frac{\delta_{xb}}{\delta_{bb}} = -\frac{\Sigma(\mu_x\mu_B l/AE)}{\Sigma(\mu_B^2 l/AE)}$$

After the influence line for V_B has been plotted, the influence line for another reaction may be prepared by repeating the process of removing it as the redundant, introducing a unit load there, and computing the necessary deflections. A simpler procedure is to compute the other reactions, or any other functions for which influence lines are desired, by statics after the diagram for V_B is prepared. This method is employed in Example 20–5 for a two-span truss for which influence lines are desired for the reactions and several member stresses.

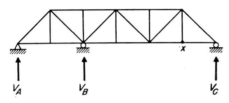

FIG. 20–6.

Example 20–6 shows that influence lines for members of an internally redundant truss may be prepared by an almost identical procedure. The member assumed to be the redundant is given a unit stress, and deflections caused thereby at each of the joints are calculated. The ordinates of the diagram for the member are obtained by dividing each of these deflections by the deflection at the member. All other influence lines are prepared by statics.

EXAMPLE 20–5. Draw influence lines for the three vertical reactions and for stresses in members U_1U_2, L_0U_1, and L_2U_3, Fig. 20–7. Circled figures are member areas, in square inches.

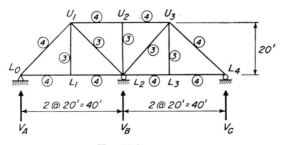

FIG. 20–7.

Solution: Remove the interior support and compute the stresses for a unit load at L_1 and at L_2. (Note that the deflection at L_1 caused by a unit load at L_2 is the same as the deflection caused at L_3 due to symmetry).

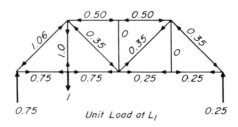

Unit Load at L_1

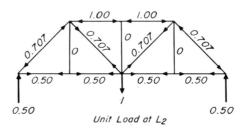

Unit Load at L_2

Member	l	A	$\dfrac{l}{A}$	μ_B	μ_A	$\dfrac{\mu_B{}^2 l}{AE}$	$\dfrac{\mu_B \mu_A l}{AE}$
L_0L_1	240	4	60	+0.50	+0.75	+15	+22.5
L_1L_2	240	4	60	+0.50	+0.75	+15	+22.5
L_2L_3	240	4	60	+0.50	+0.25	+15	+ 7.5
L_3L_4	240	4	60	+0.50	+0.25	+15	+ 7.5
L_0U_1	340	4	85	−0.707	−1.06	+42.5	+63.6
U_1U_2	240	4	60	−1.00	−0.50	+60	+30.0
U_2U_3	240	4	60	−1.00	−0.50	+60	+30.0
U_3L_4	340	4	85	−0.707	−0.35	+42.5	+21.0
U_1L_1	240	3	80	0	+1.00	0	0
U_1L_2	340	3	113	+0.707	−0.35	+56.5	−28.0
U_2L_2	240	3	80	0	0	0	0
L_2U_3	340	3	113	+0.707	+0.35	+56.5	+28.0
U_3L_3	240	3	80	0	0	0	0
Σ	....	....	....	....	....	$\dfrac{378}{E}$	$\dfrac{204.6}{E}$

Divide each of the values by δ_{bb} to obtain the influence-line ordinates for V_B and compute the ordinates for the other influence diagrams by statics.

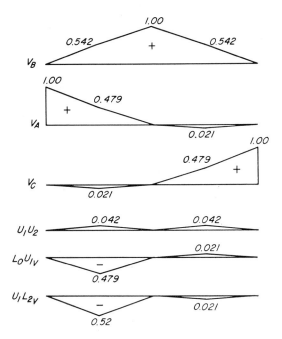

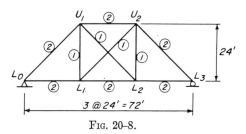

EXAMPLE 20–6. Prepare influence lines for stress in members L_1U_2, U_1U_2, and U_2L_2 of the truss of Example 20–3, which is reproduced in Fig. 20–8. Circled members are member areas, in square inches.

FIG. 20–8.

Solution: Remove L_1U_2 as the redundant and compute the stresses caused by unit loads at L_1 and L_2; replace L_1U_2 with a stress of $+1$ and compute the stresses in the remaining truss members.

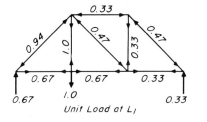

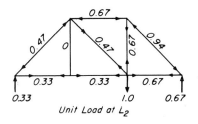

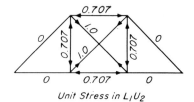

Unit Stress in L_1U_2

Member	l	A	$\dfrac{l}{A}$	μ_{L_1}	μ_{L_2}	μ_A	$\delta_{AL_1}=\dfrac{\mu_{L_1}\mu_Al}{AE}$	$\delta_{AL_1}=\dfrac{\mu_{L_2}\mu_Al}{AE}$	$\delta_{aa}=\dfrac{\mu_A{}^2l}{AE}$
L_0L_1	288	2	144	$+0.67$	$+0.33$	0	0	0	0
L_1L_2	288	2	144	$+0.67$	$+0.33$	-0.707	-68	-34	$+72$
L_2L_3	288	2	144	$+0.33$	$+0.67$	0	0	0	0
L_0U_1	408	2	204	-0.94	-0.47	0	0	0	0
U_1U_2	288	2	144	-0.33	-0.67	-0.707	$+34$	$+68$	$+72$
U_2L_3	408	2	204	-0.47	-0.94	0	0	0	0
U_1L_1	288	1	288	$+1.00$	0	-0.707	-204	0	$+144$
U_1L_2	408	1	408	-0.47	$+0.47$	$+1.00$	-192	$+192$	$+408$
L_1U_2	408	1	408	0	0	$+1.00$	0	0	$+408$
U_2L_2	288	1	288	$+0.33$	$+0.67$	-0.707	-34	-136	$+144$
Σ	.....	....	.....	......	......	......	$\dfrac{-498}{E}$	$\dfrac{+90}{E}$	$\dfrac{+1248}{E}$

Draw the influence line for the redundant, L_1U_2, and note that the stress in any other member equals $S' + X\mu$.

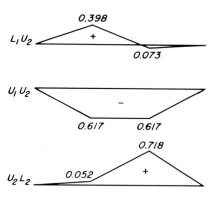

Problems

20–1 to 20–7. Determine the reactions and member stresses for the trusses. Circled figures are member areas, in square inches; E is constant.

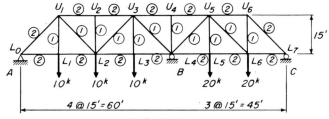

Prob. 20-1.

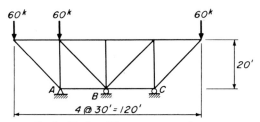

Prob. 20-2. All areas are equal.

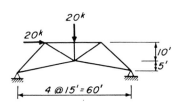

Prob. 20-3. All areas are equal.

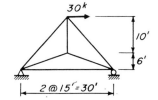

Prob. 20-4. All areas are equal.

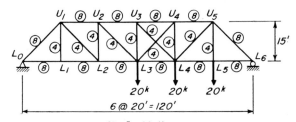

Prob. 20-5.

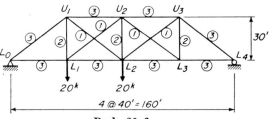

Prob. 20-6.

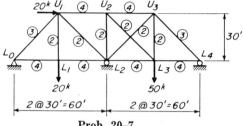

Prob. 20–7.

20–8. For Prob. 20–1 draw influence lines for each of the reactions.

20–9. Draw influence lines for stress in members U_1L_2, U_3U_4, and L_4L_5 of the truss of Prob. 20–1.

20–10. Draw influence lines for the reactions of Prob. 20–2. Assume the loads are moving across the top of the structure.

20–11. Draw influence lines for stress in members L_3L_4, U_1U_2, and U_2L_2 of the truss of Prob. 20–5.

20–12. Draw influence lines for stress in members L_1U_2 and U_2L_3 of the truss of Prob. 20–6.

20–13. Draw influence lines for stress in member L_2U_3 and for the center reaction of the truss of Prob. 20–7.

20–14. Rework Prob. 20–1 for support settlement as follows: $A=1.25$ in., $B=2.25$ in., and $C=0.75$ in.

20–15. Rework Prob. 20–2 for support settlement as follows: $A=1.75$ in., $B=1.25$ in., and $C=1.50$ in.

21

LEAST WORK AND THE THREE-MOMENT THEOREM

21-1. Method of Least Work

An Italian railway engineer, Alberto Castigliano, published an original and elaborate book in 1879 on the study of indeterminate structures. His book contained the two theorems known as Castigliano's first and second theorems. The first theorem presents a method of computing deflections which is not included in this text. The method is applicable to structures which are subject to gradually applied loads and consists in equating the deflection to the first partial derivative of the total internal work of the structure.

Castigliano's second theorem, commonly known as the method of least work, has played an important role in the development of structural analysis through the years and is often used today. It is closely related to the method of consistent distortions discussed in the two preceding chapters and is very effective in the analysis of indeterminate structures, particularly trusses and composite structures. (Composite structures have some members with axial stress only and others with axial stress and bending.) Although applicable to beams and frames, the moment-distribution method is more satisfactory. The method of least work has the disadvantage that it is not applicable in its usual form to stresses caused by displacements due to temperature changes, support settlements, and fabrication errors.

The discussion of virtual work showed that, when a structure is caused to deflect, internal work is performed or internal elastic energy is stored by the various parts of the structure. Assuming the elastic limit of the material is not exceeded, the members of the structure will change in length the absolute minimum necessary consistent with equilibrium.

The columns and girders meeting at a joint in a building will all deflect the same amount: the smallest possible value. Neglecting the effect of the other ends of these members, it can be seen that each member does no more work than necessary, and the total work performed by all of the members at the joint is the least possible.

From the foregoing discussion the theorem of least work may be stated: *The internal work accomplished by each member or each portion of an indeterminate structure subjected to a set of external loads is the least possible necessary to maintain equilibrium in supporting the loads.*

21-2. Application of Least Work

To analyze an indeterminate structure with Castigliano's theorem, certain members are assumed to be the redundants and are considered removed from the structure. The removal of the members must be sufficient to leave a statically determinate and stable base structure. The S' stresses in the structure are determined by means of the external loads; the redundants are replaced as loads X_1, X_2, etc.; and the stresses the loads cause are determined.

The total internal work of deformation may be set up in terms of the S' stresses and the stresses caused by the redundant loads. The result is differentiated successively with respect to the redundants. The derivatives are made equal to zero in order to determine the values of the redundants.

Examples 21-1 to 21-3 illustrate the analysis of indeterminate structures by least work. Although the least-work and consistent-distortion methods are the most general methods for analyzing various types of indeterminate structures, they will not be used in every case, because other methods are more satisfactory for special types.

EXAMPLE 21-1. Analyze the truss of Example 20-1, reproduced in Fig. 21-1, by the least-work method. Circled numbers are member areas, in square inches.

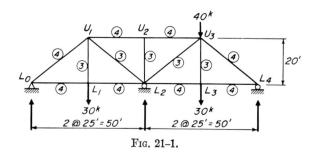

FIG. 21-1.

Solution: Remove the center support and compute the S' stresses.

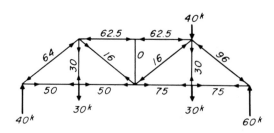

Replace the center support and determine its effect on member stresses in terms of V_B.

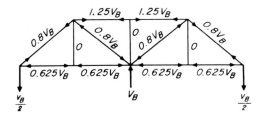

Member	l	A	$\dfrac{l}{A}$	S	$\dfrac{Sl}{A}$	$\dfrac{\partial S}{\partial V_B}$	$\dfrac{Sl}{A}\dfrac{\partial S}{\partial V_B}$
L_0L_1	300	4	75	$+50\ -0.625V_B$	$+3750-\ 46.9V_B$	-0.625	$-2345+\ 29.3V_B$
L_1L_2	300	4	75	$+50\ -0.625V_B$	$+3750-\ 46.9V_B$	-0.625	$-2345+\ 29.3V_B$
L_2L_3	300	4	75	$+75\ -0.625V_B$	$+5625-\ 46.9V_B$	-0.625	$-3520+\ 29.3V_B$
L_3L_4	300	4	75	$+75\ -0.625V_B$	$+5625-\ 46.9V_B$	-0.625	$-3520+\ 29.3V_B$
L_0U_1	384	4	96	$-64\ +0.8V_B$	$-6144+\ 76.8V_B$	$+0.8$	$-4915+\ 61.4V_B$
U_1U_2	300	4	75	$-62\ 5+1.25V_B$	$-4687+\ 93.8V_B$	$+1.25$	$-5860+117.2V_B$
U_2U_3	300	4	75	$-62.5+1.25V_B$	$-4687+\ 93.8V_B$	$+1.25$	$-5860+117.2V_B$
U_3U_4	384	4	96	$-96\ +0.8V_B$	$-9216+\ 76.8V_B$	$+0.8$	$-7373+\ 61.4V_B$
U_1L_1	240	3	80	$+30\ +0$	$+2400+\ 0$	0	$0+\ 0$
U_1L_2	384	3	128	$+16\ -0.8V_B$	$+2048-102.4V_B$	-0.8	$-1638+\ 81.9V_B$
U_2L_2	240	3	80	$0\ +0$	$0+\ 0$	0	$0+\ 0$
L_2U_3	384	3	128	$-16\ -0.8V_B$	$-2048-102.4V_B$	-0.8	$+1638+\ 81.9V_B$
U_3L_3	240	3	80	$+30\ +0$	$+2400+\ 0$	0	$0+\ 0$
Σ	.....	...	.....	....	....	0	$-35,738$ $+638.2V_B$

$$E\,\frac{\partial S}{\partial V_B}=\frac{Sl}{A}\,\frac{\partial S}{\partial V_B}$$

$$-35{,}738+638.2V_B=0$$

$$V_B=+56^{k}\uparrow$$

EXAMPLE 21–2. Determine the value of the reaction at support C, Fig. 21–2, by the method of least work.

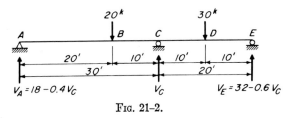

FIG. 21–2.

Solution:

Section	M	$\dfrac{\partial M}{\partial V_C}$	$\int M \dfrac{\partial M}{\partial V_B}\dfrac{dx}{EI}=0$
A to B	$18x-0.4V_Cx$	$-0.4x$	$\int_0^{20}(-7.2x^2+0.16V_Cx^2)\,dx$
B to C	$-2x-0.4V_Cx-8V_C+360$	$-0.4x-8$	$\int_0^{10}(+0.8x^2+0.16V_Cx^2+6.4V_Cx$ $-128x\times64V_C-2880)\,dx$
E to D	$32x-0.6V_Cx$	$-0.6x$	$\int_0^{10}(-19.2x^2+0.36V_Cx^2)\,dx$
D to C	$2x-0.6V_Cx-6V_C+320$	$-0.6x-6$	$\int_0^{10}(-1.2x^2+0.36V_Cx^2+7.2V_Cx$ $-204x+36V_C-1920)\,dx$

By integrating the $\int M \dfrac{\partial M}{\partial V_B}\dfrac{dx}{EI}$ expressions and substituting the values of the proper limits, the result for the entire beam is:

$$-89{,}533+2400.3V_C=0$$
$$V_C=+37.4^{\text{k}}\ \uparrow$$

EXAMPLE 21–3. Find the stresses in all members of the king post truss shown in Fig. 21–3.

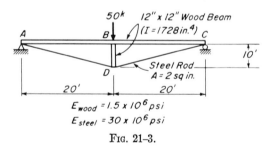

$E_{wood}=1.5\times10^6\,psi$
$E_{steel}=30\times10^6\,psi$

Fig. 21–3.

Solution: By letting BD be the redundant with a stress of S, the deflection of the beam at B is found in terms of S.

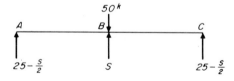

From A to B and from C to B:

$$M=25x-\frac{S}{2}x \qquad \frac{\partial M}{\partial S}=-\frac{x}{2}$$

$$\int M \frac{\partial M}{\partial S} \frac{dx}{EI} = 2 \int_0^{20} \frac{(-12.5x^2 + 0.25Sx^2)\, dx}{EI}$$

$$\frac{2\left[-12.5x^3/3 + 0.25Sx^3/3 \right]_0^{20}}{EI} = \frac{-66,600 + 1333S}{EI}$$

$$\frac{-66,600 + 1333S}{1.5} = -44,400 + 886S$$

Determine the stresses in the various members in terms of the unknown stress S.

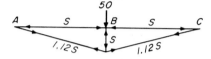

Member	l	A	E	$\dfrac{l}{AE}$	S'	$\dfrac{S'l}{AE}$	$\dfrac{\partial W}{\partial S}$	$\dfrac{\partial W}{\partial S} \times \dfrac{S'l}{AE}$
AC	960	144	1.5×10^6	4.44	$-S$	$-4.44S$	-1	$+4.44S$
BD	120	144	1.5×10^6	0.555	$-S$	$-0.555S$	-1	$+0.555S$
AD	268	2	30×10^6	4.47	$+1.12S$	$+5.02S$	$+1.12$	$+5.62S$
DC	268	2	30×10^6	4.47	$+1.12S$	$+5.02S$	$+1.12$	$+5.62S$
Σ	......	......	....	......	....	....	....	$16.235S$

$$-44,400 + 886S + 16.235S = 0$$
$$S = 49.3^k$$

Final stresses:

$$AC = -(1)(49.3) = -49.3^k \qquad AD = +(1.12)(49.3) = +55.3^k$$
$$BD = -(1)(49.3) = -49.3^k \qquad DC = +(1.12)(49.3) = +55.3^k$$

21–3. The Three-Moment Theorem

An essential subject in the study of the "classical" methods of analyzing indeterminate structures is the three-moment theorem, initiated in 1855 by the Frenchman, Bertot. Extensions of his original theorem were presented in 1857 by Clapeyron and in 1862 by Bresse, both Frenchmen.[1]

The theorem, which presents a relationship between the moments at the supports in a continuous beam, is usually developed for beams of constant cross section between each pair of supports. Theoretically, beams of varying sections may be considered, but the results are so complicated as to be of little practical value. The conjugate-beam method is convenient for developing the relationship between support moments. The resulting equation applies to the moments at any three consecutive sup-

[1] Sutherland and Bowman, *Structural Theory* (New York: John Wiley & Sons, Inc., 1954), Chap. 8.

ports, as long as the beam is continuous between those supports (i.e., no internal hinges or other breaks in the continuity of the beam).

Considering the continuous beam of Fig. 21–4, the three-moment theorem can be written as follows: for the moments at supports A, B, and C; for the moments at supports B, C, and D; and finally, for the moments at supports C, D, and E. Supports A and E are simple ends and must have zero moments. Three unknown moments (M_B, M_C, and M_D) remain, but three simultaneous equations are available from which their values may be determined. The theorem applies equally well to beams with fixed ends, as will be seen in the following sections.

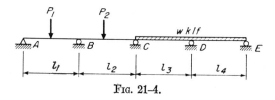

Fɪɢ. 21–4.

21–4. Development of the Theorem

The elastic curve of a continuous beam has the same numerical value of slope (in radians), an infinitesimal distance on each side of an interior support, although the signs of slope are different. Considering three consecutive interior supports of a continuous beam and loading the beam with the M/EI diagrams, expressions may easily be written for the slope on each side of the center support. The two expressions which are numer-

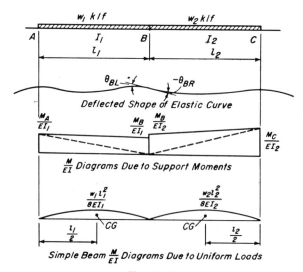

Fɪɢ. 21–5.

ically equal are equated to each other, the result being a statement of a relationship between the moments at the three supports.

Figure 21–5 shows a section of a uniformly loaded beam, the deflected shape of the elastic curve of the beam, and the M/EI diagrams for the section. The first M/EI diagram is for the negative support moments, and the second M/EI diagram is for the positive simple beam moments caused by the uniform loads.

Span 1. The slope θ_{BL} is equal to the shear or the upward force at the center support. By elastic weights the slope can be expressed as follows:

$$\theta_{BL}$$
$$=\frac{(\tfrac{1}{2})(M_A/EI_1)(l_1)(\tfrac{1}{3}l_1)+(\tfrac{1}{2})(M_B/EI_1)(l_1)(\tfrac{2}{3}l_1)+(\tfrac{2}{3})(w_1l_1^2/8EI_1)(l_1)(l_1/2)}{l_1}$$

$$=\frac{M_Al_1}{6EI_1}+\frac{M_Bl_1}{3EI_1}+\frac{w_1l_1^3}{24EI_1}$$

Span 2. A similar expression is written for the slope θ_{BR} to the right of support B.

$$\theta_{BR}$$
$$=\frac{(\tfrac{1}{2})(M_C/EI_2)(l_2)(\tfrac{1}{3}l_2)+(\tfrac{1}{2})(M_B/EI_2)(l_2)(\tfrac{2}{3}l_2)+(\tfrac{2}{3})(w_2l_2^2/8EI_2)(l_2)(l_2/2)}{l_2}$$

$$=\frac{M_Cl_2}{6EI_2}+\frac{M_Bl_2}{3EI_2}+\frac{w_2l_2^3}{24EI_2}$$

The slope on the left of the center support is equal to minus the slope on the right, or $\theta_{BL}=-\theta_{BR}$. Equating the two expressions results in an equation for the three support moments.

$$\frac{M_Al_1}{6EI_1}+\frac{M_Bl_1}{3EI_1}+\frac{w_1l_1^3}{24EI_1}=-\frac{M_Cl_2}{6EI_2}-\frac{M_Bl_2}{3EI_2}-\frac{w_2l_2^2}{24EI_2}$$

$$\frac{M_Al_1}{6EI_1}+\frac{M_B}{3E}\left(\frac{l_1}{I_1}+\frac{l_2}{I_2}\right)+\frac{M_Cl_2}{6EI_2}=-\frac{w_1l_1^3}{24EI_1}-\frac{w_2l_2^3}{24EI_2}$$

Assuming the beam to consist of the same material throughout results in the elimination of E. Multiplying through by 6 changes the expression into a more convenient form.

$$\frac{M_Al_1}{I_1}+2M_B\left(\frac{l_1}{I_1}+\frac{l_2}{I_2}\right)+\frac{M_Cl_2}{I_2}=-\frac{w_1l_1^3}{4I_2}-\frac{w_2l_2^3}{4I_2}$$

The derivation has considered the spans to be loaded with uniform loads only, but concentrated loads may be easily included by taking into account their triangular-shaped simple beam M/EI diagrams. The general equation for both concentrated and uniform loads (dimensions and symbols from Fig. 21–6) is as follows:

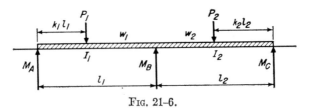

FIG. 21-6.

General Equation

$$\frac{M_A l_1}{I_1} + 2M_B\left(\frac{l_1}{I_1} + \frac{l_2}{I_2}\right) + \frac{M_C l_2}{I_2} = -\Sigma\frac{P_1 l_1^3}{I_1}(k_1 - k_1^3) - \Sigma\frac{P_2 l_2^3}{I_2}(k_2 - k_2^3) - \frac{w_1 l_1^3}{4 I_1} - \frac{w_2 l_2^3}{4 I_2}$$

If the moments of inertia are the same for both spans, the expression becomes:

Constant I

$$M_A l_1 + 2M_B(l_1 + l_2) + M_C l_2 = -\Sigma P_1 l_1^2(k_1 - k_1^3) - \Sigma P_2 l_2^2(k_2 - k_2^3) - \frac{w_1 l_1^3}{4} - \frac{w_2 l_2^3}{4}$$

If both span lengths and moments of inertia should be equal, the equation becomes:

Constant I and Equal Spans

$$M_A + 4M_B + M_C = -\Sigma P_1 l(k_1 - k_1^3) - \Sigma P_2 l(k_2 - k_2^3) - \frac{w_1 l^2}{4} - \frac{w_2 l^2}{4}$$

21-5. Application of the Three-Moment Theorem

The determination of support moments by the three-moment theorem is illustrated by Examples 21-4 to 21-8. Little explanation is necessary for the analysis of the beams in the first three examples. These beams are simply supported on each end, indicating zero moments. It will be seen that application of the theorem to a simply end-supported continuous beam presents two less equations than supports, but the end-support moments are zero, and the equations may be solved simultaneously for the unknowns.

A slightly different approach is needed for the solution of Examples 21-7 and 21-8. The beam of Example 21-7 is fixed on the left end, while the beam of Example 21-8 is fixed on both ends. It would appear that there are not going to be enough equations for the unknowns, because the fixed-end supports have moments. The problem is solved, however, by assuming a fixed end to create another span beyond it having a length of zero. The three-moment theorem is written for the assumed span and the adjoining span, as shown in these two examples, giving the required number of equations.

Shear and moment diagrams are drawn for several of the examples to present a complete picture of the stress conditions throughout the beam.

When the solution of an equation yields a negative support moment, it indicates the beam is bending over the support, which causes tension in the top fibers ($\underset{\uparrow}{\overline{-m}}$).

EXAMPLE 21-4. Determine the support moments of the structure in Fig. 21-7 by the three-moment theorem and draw shear and moment diagrams.

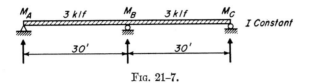

FIG. 21-7.

Solution: For equal spans and constant I:

$$M_A + 4M_B + M_C = -\Sigma P_1 l(k_1 - k_1{}^3) - \Sigma P_2 l(k_2 - k_2{}^3) - \frac{w_1 l^2}{4} - \frac{w_2 l^2}{4}$$

$$M_A = M_C = 0$$

$$4M_B = -\frac{(3)(30)^2}{4} - \frac{(3)(30)^2}{4} = -675 - 675 = -1350$$

$$M_B = -337.5'^k$$

ΣM_B to left $= -337.5$

$$-337.5 = (V_A)(30) - (3 \times 30)(15)$$

$$-337.5 = 30V_A - 1350$$

$$V_A = \frac{1012.5}{30} = +33.75^k$$

ΣM_B to right $= +337.5$

$$+337.5 = -(V_C)(30) + (3)(30)(15)$$

$$+337.5 = -30V_C + 1350$$

$$V_C = \frac{1012.5}{30} = +33.75^k$$

$\Sigma V = 0$

$$33.75 + V_B + 33.75 = (3)(60) = 180$$

$$V_B = 112.5^k$$

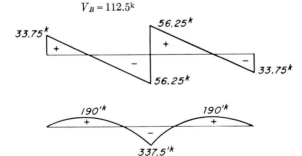

EXAMPLE 21–5. By using the three-moment theorem, determine all support moments of the structure in Fig. 21–8.

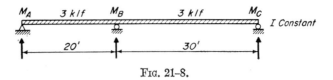

FIG. 21–8.

Solution: For constant I:

$$M_A l_1 + 2M_B(l_1 + l_2) + M_C l_2 = -\Sigma P_1 l_1^2(k_1 - k_1^3) - \Sigma P_2 l_2^2(k_2 - k_2^3) - \frac{w_1 l_1^3}{4} - \frac{w_2 l_2^3}{4}$$

$$M_A = M_C = 0$$

$$2M_B(20 + 30) = -\frac{(3)(20)^3}{4} - \frac{(3)(30)^3}{4} = -6000 - 20{,}250$$

$$100M_B = -26{,}250$$

$$M_B = -262.5'^k$$

ΣM_B to left $= -262.5$

$$-262.5 = 20V_A - (3)(20)(10)$$

$$-262.5 = 20V_A - 600$$

$$V_A = \frac{337.5}{20} = 16.9^k$$

ΣM_B to right $= +262.5$

$$+262.5 = -(30)(V_C) + (3 \times 30)(15)$$

$$+262.5 = -30V_C + 1350$$

$$V_C = \frac{1087.5}{30} = 36.2$$

$\Sigma V = 0$

$$16.9 + V_B + 36.2 - 150 = 0$$

$$V_B = 96.9^k$$

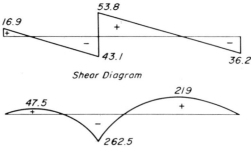

Shear Diagram

Moment Diagram

EXAMPLE 21–6. Draw shear and moment diagrams for the structure of Fig. 21–9.

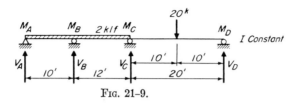

FIG. 21–9.

Solution: For constant I:

$$M_A l_1 + 2M_B(l_1 + l_2) + M_C l_2 = -\Sigma P_1 l_1^2(k_1 - k_1^3) - \Sigma P_2 l_2^2(k_2 - k_2^3) - \frac{w_1 l_1^3}{4} - \frac{w_2 l_2^3}{4}$$

$$M_A = M_D = 0$$

$$2M_B(10 + 12) + M_C(12) = -\frac{(2)(10)^3}{4} - \frac{(2)(12)^3}{4} = -500 - 864 = -1364$$

$$44M_B + 12M_C = -1364 \tag{1}$$

$$M_B l_2 + 2M_C(l_2 + l_3) + M_D l_3 = -\Sigma P_2 l_2^2(k_2 - k_2^3) - \Sigma P_3 l_3^2(k_3 - k_3^3) - \frac{w_2 l_2^3}{4} - \frac{w_3 l_3^3}{4}$$

$$M_B(12) + 2M_C(12 + 20) = -(20)(20)^2(\tfrac{1}{2} - \tfrac{1}{2}^3) - \frac{(2)(12)^3}{4}$$

$$12M_B + 64M_C = -3864 \tag{2}$$

By solving Eqs. 1 and 2 simultaneously for M_B and M_C,

$$M_B = -15.3'^k \qquad M_C = -57.5'^k$$

By determining reactions by statics,

$$V_A = \ 8.5^k \qquad V_C = 28.4^k$$
$$V_B = 20.0^k \qquad V_D = \ 7.1^k$$

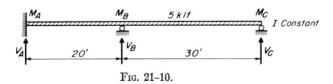

Shear Diagram

Moment Diagram

EXAMPLE 21–7. Draw shear and moment diagrams for the structure shown in Fig. 21–10.

FIG. 21–10.

Solution: For constant I:

$$M_A l_1 + 2M_B(l_1 + l_2) + M_C l_2 = -\Sigma P_1 l_1^2(k_1 - k_1^3) - \Sigma P_2 l_2^2(k_2 - k_2^3) - \frac{w_1 l_1^3}{4} - \frac{w_2 l_2^3}{4}$$

By assuming a span of zero length to left of fixed end,

$$M_0 l_0 + 2M_A(l_0 + l_1) + M_B l_1 = -\frac{w_0 l_0^3}{4} - \frac{w_1 l_1^3}{4}$$

$$M_0 = 0$$

$$2M_A(0 + 20) + M_B(20) = -\frac{(5)(20)^3}{4}$$

$$40M_A + 20M_B = -10,000 \tag{1}$$

$$M_A(20) + 2M_B(20 + 30) = -\frac{(5)(20)^3}{4} - \frac{(5)(30)^3}{4}$$

$$20M_A + 100M_B = -43,750 \tag{2}$$

By solving Eqs. 1 and 2 simultaneously,

$$M_A = -34.75'^k$$

$$M_B = -430.5'^k$$

By computing reactions by statics,

$$V_A = +\ 30.3^k$$

$$V_B = +159.0^k$$

$$V_C = +\ 60.7^k$$

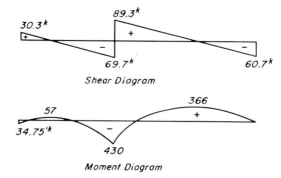

Shear Diagram

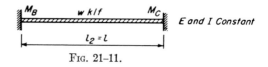

Moment Diagram

EXAMPLE 21–8. Determine the moments at the ends of the uniformly loaded fixed-ended beam shown in Fig. 21–11.

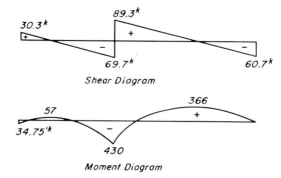

FIG. 21–11.

Solution: By assuming spans of zero length (l_1 and l_3) outside each end with zero moments (M_A and M_D),

$$M_A l_1 + 2M_B(l_1+l_2) + M_C l_2 = -\frac{w_1 l_1^3}{4} - \frac{w_2 l_2^3}{4}$$

$$M_A = 0 = M_D$$

$$2M_B(l) + M_C(l) = -\frac{wl^3}{4} \tag{1}$$

$$2M_B l + M_C l = -\frac{wl^3}{4}$$

$$M_B l_2 + 2M_C(l_2+l_3) + M_D l_3 = -\frac{wl^3}{4}$$

$$M_B l + 2M_C l = -\frac{wl^3}{4} \tag{2}$$

By solving Eqs. 1 and 2 simultaneously

$$M_B = -\frac{wl^3}{12}$$

$$M_C = -\frac{wl^3}{12}$$

The moments at the ends of a fixed-ended beam loaded with a concentrated load can be determined in a similar manner, with the following results:

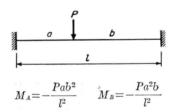

$$M_A = -\frac{Pab^2}{l^2} \qquad M_B = -\frac{Pa^2b}{l^2}$$

These expressions will be needed for solution of later problems.

21-6.   Effect of Support Settlements by the Three-Moment Theorem

The three-moment theorem as presented in Sec. 21–4 was developed on the basis of unyielding supports. Should the supports be displaced from their theoretical positions because of settlement, fabrication errors, etc., the equation will have to be adjusted accordingly. The values of θ_{BL} and θ_{BR} were the slopes of the elastic curve of a beam on each side of the center support of any three consecutive supports being considered. Settlement of any of the three supports, provided they settle unequally and do not remain in a straight line, will change the values of the slopes.

Supports A, B, and C of the beam of Fig. 21–12 are assumed to settle δ_A, δ_B, and δ_C, respectively. If a horizontal line were drawn through the newly deflected position of support B, the angle θ_{BL} would be changed by $(\delta_A - \delta_B)/l_1$, and θ_{BR} would be changed by $(\delta_C - \delta_B)/l_2$. (It is to be remembered that the angle is small and the tangent of the angle change in question is the same as the angle in radians.)

By letting a downward value of the support settlements be positive, the

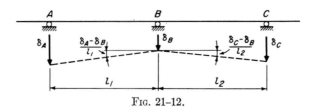

FIG. 21-12.

values of θ_{BL} and θ_{BR} for a beam loaded with concentrated and uniform loads become

$$\theta_{BL} = \frac{M_A l_1}{6EI_1} + \frac{M_B l_1}{3EI_1} + \frac{w_1 l_1^3}{24EI_1} + \Sigma \frac{P_1 l_1^2}{I_1}(k_1 - k_1^3) + \frac{\delta_A - \delta_B}{l_1}$$

$$\theta_{BR} = \frac{M_C l_2}{6EI_2} + \frac{M_B l_2}{3EI_2} + \frac{w_2 l_2^3}{24EI_2} + \Sigma \frac{P_2 l_2^2}{I_2}(k_2 - k_2^3) + \frac{\delta_C - \delta_B}{l_2}$$

Equating these two expressions, because $\theta_{BL} = -\theta_{BR}$, gives the general equation when support displacement occurs.

$$\frac{M_A l_1}{I_1} + 2M_B\left(\frac{l_1}{I_1} + \frac{l_2}{I_2}\right) + \frac{M_C l_2}{I_2} = -\Sigma\frac{P_1 l_1^2}{I_1}(k_1 - k_1^3) - \Sigma\frac{P_2 l_2^3}{I_2}(k_2 - k_2^3)$$
$$- \frac{w_1 l_1^3}{4EI_1} - \frac{w_2 l_2^3}{4EI_2} - 6E\left(\frac{\delta_A - \delta_B}{l_1} + \frac{\delta_C - \delta_B}{l_2}\right)$$

Examples 21-9 and 21-10 illustrate the application of the three-moment theorem to continuous beams having some support displacement. Keeping the units in terms of feet and kilopounds, as illustrated in these examples, makes the mathematics quite simple.

EXAMPLE 21-9. Draw the shear and moment diagrams for the two-span beam shown in Fig. 21-13 if the interior support settles 0.25 in., or 0.0208 ft.

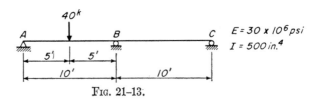

FIG. 21-13.

Solution:

$$2M_B\left(\frac{10}{I} + \frac{10}{I}\right) = -\frac{(40)(10)^2}{I}(\tfrac{1}{2} - \tfrac{1}{2}^3) - 6E\left(\frac{0 - 0.0208}{10} + \frac{0 - 0.0208}{10}\right)$$

$$\frac{40M_B}{I} = -\frac{1500}{I} + 0.02496E$$

$$40M_B = -1500 + 0.02496EI$$

$$M_B = -37.5 + 0.00624EI$$

$$M_B = -37.5 + \frac{(0.00624)(30 \times 10^6)(500)}{(144)(1000)}$$

$$M_B = +27.5'^k$$

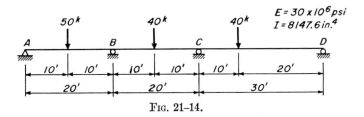

Shear Diagram

Moment Diagram

EXAMPLE 21-10. Determine the moments at the interior supports of the beam of Example 19-8, reproduced in Fig. 21-14, for which the following support settlements are assumed to occur:

$$A = 1.25 \text{ in.} = 0.104 \text{ ft} \qquad C = 2.75 \text{ in.} = 0.229 \text{ ft}$$
$$B = 2.40 \text{ in.} = 0.200 \text{ ft} \qquad D = 1.10 \text{ in.} = 0.0917 \text{ ft}$$

FIG. 21-14.

Solution:

$$2M_B\left(\frac{20}{I} + \frac{20}{I}\right) + \frac{20M_C}{I} = -\frac{(50)(20)^2}{I}(\tfrac{1}{2} - \tfrac{1}{2}^3) - \frac{(40)(20)^2}{I}(\tfrac{1}{2} - \tfrac{1}{2}^3) -$$
$$6E\left(\frac{0.104 - 0.200}{20} + \frac{0.229 - 0.200}{20}\right)$$

$$4M_B + M_C = -375 - 300 + 0.001005EI \qquad (1)$$

$$4M_B + M_C = +1020$$

$$\frac{20M_B}{I} + 2M_C\left(\frac{20}{I} + \frac{30}{I}\right) = -\frac{(40)(20)^2}{I}(\tfrac{1}{2} - \tfrac{1}{2}^3) - \frac{(40)(30)^2}{I}(\tfrac{2}{3} - \tfrac{2}{3}^3) -$$
$$6E\left(\frac{0.200 - 0.229}{20} + \frac{0.0917 - 0.229}{30}\right)$$

$M_B + 5M_C = -997 + 0.001809EI$

$M_B + 5M_C = +2063$ (2)

By solving Eqs. 1 and 2 simultaneously,

$M_B = +164'^k$

$M_C = +380'^k$

Problems

21–1 to 21–9.   Analyze the structures by the method of least work.

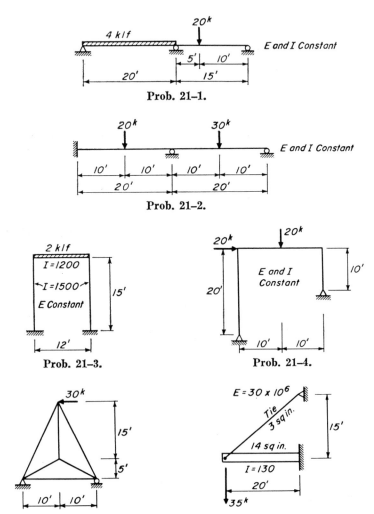

Prob. 21–1.

Prob. 21–2.

Prob. 21–3.

Prob. 21–4.

Prob. 21–5.   All areas equal 2 sq in.

Prob. 21–6.   Find stress in tie.

21–7. Problem 20–2.

21–8. Problem 20–6.

21–9. Problem 20–7.

21–10 to **21–16.** Compute all moments for the continuous beams by using the three-moment theorem. Draw shear and moment diagrams.

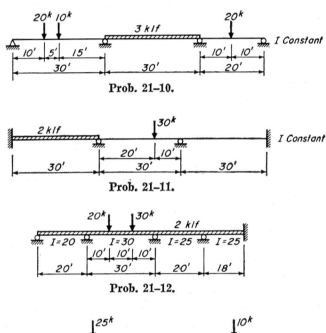

Prob. 21–10.

Prob. 21–11.

Prob. 21–12.

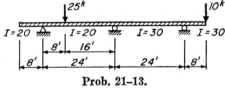

Prob. 21–13.

21–14. Problem 19–3.

21–15. Problem 19–4.

21–16. Problem 19–5.

22 |

SLOPE DEFLECTION

22–1. Introduction

Professor George A. Maney introduced slope deflection in a 1915 University of Minnesota engineering publication. His work was an extension of earlier studies of secondary stresses by Manderla and Mohr. For nearly fifteen years, until the introduction of moment distribution, slope deflection was the popular "exact" method used for the analysis of continuous frames in the United States. Even today, a few engineers are more satisfied with results obtained by slope deflection than with those obtained by moment distribution; therefore, its use has not entirely ended.

Although slope deflection for many types of beams and frames has been made "obsolete" by moment distribution, its study is of advantage for several reasons. They are:

1) For a few structures slope deflection may present the quickest possible solution.

2) A study of slope deflection serves as an excellent background for understanding moment distribution.

3) Slope deflection is a good method for checking results obtained by moment distribution.

4) The slopes and deflections which are determined draw a picture of the deformed shape of the structure.

5) Slope deflection has the widest range of application of any of the methods of analyzing indeterminate structures considered to this point.

22–2. Derivation of Slope-Deflection Equations

The name "slope deflection" comes from the fact that the moments at the ends of the members in indeterminate structures are expressed in terms of the rotations (or slopes) and deflections of the joints. For developing the equations, members are assumed to be of constant section between each pair of supports. Although it is possible to derive expressions for members of varying section, the results are so complex as to be of little practical value. It is further assumed that the joints in a structure may rotate or deflect, but the angles between the members meeting at a joint remain unchanged.

Span AB of the continuous beam of Fig. 22–1 (a) is considered for the following discussion. If the span were completely fixed at each end, the slope of the elastic curve of the beam at the ends would be zero. External loads produce fixed-end moments, and these moments cause the

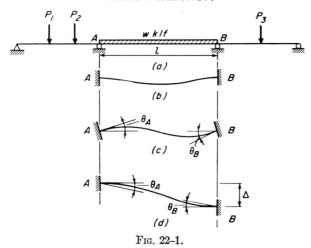

Fig. 22–1.

span to take the shape shown in Fig. 22–1 (b). Joints A and B are actually not fixed and will rotate slightly under load to some position such as the one shown in Fig. 22–1 (c). In addition to the rotation of the joints, there may possibly be some settlement of one or both of the supports which will cause a chord rotation of the member as shown in part (d), where support B is assumed to have settled an amount Δ.

From the study of Fig. 22–1 the values of the end moments at A and B (M_{AB} and M_{BA}) are seen to be equal to the sum of the moment caused by the following:

1) The fixed-end moments (FEM_{AB} and FEM_{BA}), which can be determined by the expressions developed in Example 21–8.

2) The moments caused by the rotations of joints A and B (θ_A and θ_B).

3) The moments caused by chord rotation (ψ) if one or both of the joints settles or deflects.

Rotations of the joints in a structure causes changes in the slopes of the tangents to the elastic curves at those points. For a particular beam, the

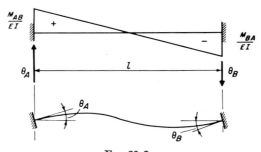

Fig. 22–2.

change in slope equals the end shear of the beam when it is loaded with the M/EI diagram. The beam is assumed to have the fixed-end moments, M_{AB} and M_{BA}, shown in Fig. 22–2. A moment is considered positive when the joints rotate in a counterclockwise direction. The fixed-end moments of beam AB of Fig. 22–1 are seen to be $+$ on the left end and $-$ on the right end. These are the signs used for M_{AB} and M_{BA} in Fig. 22–2.

The end reactions or end slopes are as follows:

$$\theta_A = \frac{(\frac{1}{2})(M_{AB}/EI)(l)(\frac{2}{3}l) - (\frac{1}{2})(M_{BA}/EI)(l)(\frac{1}{3}l)}{l}$$

$$= \frac{l}{6EI}(2M_{AB} - M_{BA})$$

$$\theta_B = \frac{(\frac{1}{2})(M_{BA}/EI)(l)(\frac{2}{3}l) - (\frac{1}{2})(M_{AB}/EI)(l)(\frac{1}{3}l)}{l}$$

$$= \frac{l}{6EI}(2M_{BA} - M_{AB})$$

If one of the supports of the beam settled or deflected an amount Δ, the angles θ_A and θ_B caused by joint rotation would be changed by Δ/l (or ψ), as illustrated in Fig. 22–1 (d). Adding chord rotation to the expressions results in the following total values for the slopes of the tangents to the elastic curves at the ends of the beams.

$$\theta_A = \frac{l}{6EI}(2M_{AB} - M_{BA}) + \psi$$

$$\theta_B = \frac{l}{6EI}(2M_{BA} - M_{AB}) + \psi$$

Solving the equations simultaneously for M_{AB} and M_{BA} gives the values of the end moments due to slopes and deflections. In these expressions I/l has been replaced with K, the so-called stiffness factor (see Chapter 23).

$$M_{AB} = 2EK(2\theta_A + \theta_B - 3\psi)$$

$$M_{BA} = 2EK(\theta_A + 2\theta_B - 3\psi)$$

The final end moments are equal to the moments due to slopes and deflections plus the fixed-end moments. The slope-deflection equations are as follows:

$$M_{AB} = 2EK(2\theta_A + \theta_B - 3\psi) + FEM_{AB}$$

$$M_{BA} = 2EK(\theta_A + 2\theta_B - 3\psi) + FEM_{BA}$$

With these equations it is possible to express the end moments in a structure in terms of joint rotations and settlements. By previous methods it has been necessary to write one equation for each redundant in the structure. The number of unknowns in each equation totaled the number of redundants. The work of solving those equations was considerable for highly redundant structures. Slope deflection appreciably reduces the amount of work involved in analyzing multiredundant structures because the unknown moments are expressed in terms of only a few unknown joint rotations and settlements. Even for multistory frames, the number of unknown θ and ψ values appearing in any one equation is rarely more than five or six, while the degree of indeterminancy of the structure is several times that figure.

22–3. Application of Slope-Deflection Equations to Continuous Beams

Examples 22–1 to 22–4 illustrate the analysis of indeterminate beams with the slope-deflection equations. Each member in the beams is considered individually; its fixed-end moments are computed; and one equation is written for the moment at each end of the member. For span AB of Example 22–1, equations for M_{AB} and M_{BA} are written; for span BC equations for M_{BC} and M_{CB} are written; etc.

The moment equations are written in terms of the unknown values of θ at the supports. The two moments at an interior support must total zero, as $M_{BA} + M_{BC} = 0$ at support B in Example 22–1. Expressions are, therefore, written for the total moment at each support, which gives a set of simultaneous equations from which the unknown θ values may be obtained. Two conditions which will simplify the solution of the equations may exist. These are fixed ends for which the θ values must be zero and simple ends for which the moment is zero. A special expression is derived at the end of Example 22–2 for end spans which are simply supported.

The beams of Examples 22–1 and 22–2 have unyielding supports, and ψ is zero for all of the equations. Some support settlement occurs for the beams of Examples 22–3 and 22–4, and ψ is included in the equations. Chord rotation is considered positive when the chord of a beam is rotated clockwise by the settlements, meaning that the sign is the same no matter which end is being considered as the entire beam rotates in that direction.

When span lengths, moduli of elasticity, and moments of inertia are constant for the spans of a continuous beam, the $2EK$ values are constant and may be canceled from the equations. Should the values of K vary from span to span, as they often do, it is convenient to express them in terms of relative values, as is done in Example 22–4.

To fully understand the deformations that take place in a structure and the sign convention for positive and negative moments, Fig. 22–3 is

presented. Several beams are shown bending as they would under certain
conditions of positive or negative moments.

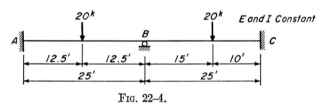

$M_{AB} = +$ $M_{BA} = -$
(a)

$M_{AB} = -$ $M_{BA} = +$
(b)

$M_{AB} = +$ $M_{BA} = +$
(c)

$M_{AB} = -$ $M_{BA} = -$
(d)

Fig. 22–3.

EXAMPLE 22–1. Determine all support moments of the structure in Fig. 22–4 by
the method of slope deflection.

Fig. 22–4.

Solution: By computing fixed-end moments,

$$FEM_{AB} = -\frac{(20)(12.5)(12.5)^2}{(25)^2} = -62.5'^k$$

$$FEM_{BA} = +\frac{(20)(12.5)(12.5)^2}{(25)^2} = +62.5'^k$$

$$FEM_{BC} = -\frac{(20)(15)(10)^2}{(25)^2} = -48'^k$$

$$FEM_{CB} = +\frac{(20)(10)(15)^2}{(25)^2} = +72'^k$$

By writing the equations, and noting $\theta_A = \theta_C = \psi = 0$,

$$M_{AB} = 2EK\theta_B - 62.5$$
$$M_{BA} = 4EK\theta_B + 62.5$$
$$M_{BC} = 4EK\theta_B - 48$$
$$M_{CB} = 2EK\theta_B + 72$$

$$\Sigma M_B = 0 = M_{BA} + M_{BC}$$
$$4EK\theta_B + 62.4 + 4EK\theta_B - 48$$
$$EK\theta_B = -1.8125$$

Final moments:

$$M_{AB} = (2)(-1.8125) - 62.5 = -66.125'^k$$
$$M_{BA} = (4)(-1.8125) + 62.5 = +55.25'^k$$
$$M_{BC} = (4)(-1.8125) - 48 = -55.25'^k$$
$$M_{CB} = (2)(-1.8125) + 72 = +68.375'^k$$

EXAMPLE 22-2. Find all moments in the structure of Fig. 22-5 by slope deflection. Use the modified equation for simple ends developed in the discussion at the end of the problem.

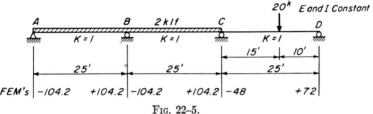

FIG. 22-5.

Solution: $M_{BA} = 3EK(\theta_B - \psi) + FEM_{BA} - \frac{1}{2}FEM_{AB}$
$M_{AB} = 2EK(2\theta_A + \theta_B - 3\psi) + FEM_{AB}$

By writing the equations, and canceling EK because it is constant for all spans,

$$M_{AB} = M_{DC} = 0$$
$$M_{BA} = (3)(\theta_B) + 104.2 - (\frac{1}{2})(-104.2) = 3\theta_B + 156.3$$
$$M_{BC} = (2)(2\theta_B + \theta_C) - 104.2 = 4\theta_B + 2\theta_C - 104.2$$
$$M_{CB} = (2)(\theta_B + 2\theta_C) + 104.2 = 2\theta_B + 4\theta_C + 104.2$$
$$M_{CD} = (3)(\theta_C) - 48 - (\frac{1}{2})(+72) = 3\theta_C - 84$$
$$\Sigma M_B = 0 = M_{BA} + M_{BC}$$
$$3\theta_B + 156.3 + 4\theta_B + 2\theta_C - 104.2 = 0$$
$$7\theta_B + 2\theta_C = -52.1 \tag{1}$$
$$\Sigma M_C = 0 = M_{CB} + M_{CD}$$
$$2\theta_B + 4\theta_C + 104.2 + 3\theta_C - 84 = 0$$
$$2\theta_B + 7\theta_C = -20.2 \tag{2}$$

By solving Eqs. 1 and 2 simultaneously,

$$\theta_B = -7.2$$
$$\theta_C = -0.83$$

Final end moments:

$$M_{BA} = (3)(-7.2) + 156.3 = +134.7$$
$$M_{BC} = (4)(-7.2) + (2)(-0.83) - 104.2 = -134.7$$
$$M_{CB} = (2)(-7.2) + (4)(-0.83) + 104.2 = +86.5$$
$$M_{CD} = (3)(-0.83) - 84 = -86.5$$

Discussion. For a beam with simply supported ends, it is obvious that the moments at those ends must be zero for equilibrium ($M_{AB} = M_{DC} = 0$). Application of the usual slope-deflection equations will yield zero moments, but it seems a waste of time to go through a process to determine the value of all of the moments in the beam when two of them by inspection are obviously zero. The usual slope-deflection equations are as follows:

$$M_{AB} = 2EK(2\theta_A + \theta_B - 3\psi) + FEM_{AB} \tag{1}$$
$$M_{BA} = 2EK(\theta_A + 2\theta_B - 3\psi) + FEM_{BA} \tag{2}$$

Assuming end A to be simply end-supported, the value of M_{AB} is zero. Solving the two equations simultaneously by eliminating θ_A gives a simplified expression for M_{BA} which has only one unknown, θ_B. The resulting simplified equation will expedite considerably the solution of continuous beams with simple ends.

Twice Eq. 2 $2M_{BA} = 2EK(2\theta_A + 4\theta_B - 6\psi) + 2FEM_{BA}$
Minus Eq. 1 $\phantom{2M_{BA}} 0 = 2EK(2\theta_A + \theta_B - 3\psi) + FEM_{AB}$

$$2M_{BA} = 2EK(3\theta_B - 3\psi) + 2FEM_{BA} - FEM_{AB}$$
$$M_{BA} = 3EK(\theta_B - \psi) + FEM_{BA} - \tfrac{1}{2}FEM_{AB}$$

EXAMPLE 22–3. Find the moment at support B in the beam of Example 21–9, reproduced in Fig. 22–6, assuming B settles 0.25 in., or 0.0208 ft.

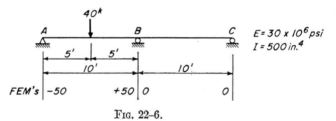

FIG. 22–6.

Solution: By writing the equations, and noting that $M_{AB} = M_{CB} = 0$,

$$M_{BA} = 3EK\left(\theta_B - \frac{+0.0208}{10}\right) + 50 - (\tfrac{1}{2})(-50)$$

$$M_{BA} = 3EK\theta_B - 0.00624EK + 75$$

$$M_{BC} = 3EK\left(\theta_B - \frac{-0.0208}{10}\right)$$

$$M_{BC} = 3EK\theta_B + 0.00624EK$$

$\Sigma M_B = 0 = M_{BA} + M_{BC}$

$$3EK\theta_B - 0.0624EK + 75 + 3EK\theta_B + 0.0624EK = 0$$

$$6EK\theta_B + 75 = 0$$

$$EK\theta_B = -12.5$$

$$M_{BA} = (3)(-12.5) - 0.00624EK + 75$$

Solution: By computing fixed-end moments,

$$FEM_{BC} = -\frac{(2)(20)^2}{12} = -66.7'^k$$

$$FEM_{CB} = +\frac{(2)(20)^2}{12} = +66.7'^k$$

By writing the equations, and noting $\theta_A = \theta_D = \psi = 0$ and $2EK$ is constant for all members, which permits it to be neglected,

$$M_{AB} = \theta_B$$
$$M_{BA} = 2\theta_B$$
$$M_{BC} = 2\theta_B + \theta_C - 66.7$$
$$M_{CB} = \theta_B + 2\theta_C + 66.7$$
$$M_{CD} = 2\theta_C$$
$$M_{DC} = \theta_C$$
$$\Sigma M_B = 0 = M_{BA} + M_{BC}$$
$$2\theta_B + 2\theta_B + \theta_C - 66.7 = 0$$
$$4\theta_B + \theta_C = 66.7 \qquad (1)$$
$$\Sigma M_C = 0 = M_{CB} + M_{CD}$$
$$\theta_B + 2\theta_C + 66.7 + 2\theta_C = 0$$
$$\theta_B + 4\theta_C = -66.7 \qquad (2)$$

By solving Eqs. 1 and 2 simultaneously,

$$\theta_B = +22.2$$
$$\theta_C = -22.2$$

Final end moments

$M_{AB} = +22.2'^k$	$M_{CB} = +44.4'^k$
$M_{BA} = +44.4'^k$	$M_{CD} = -44.4'^k$
$M_{BC} = -44.4'^k$	$M_{DC} = -22.2'^k$

22–5. Analysis of Frames with Sidesway

The loads, moments of inertia, and dimensions of the frame of Fig. 22–10 are not symmetrical about the center line, and the frame will obviously sway to one side. Joints B and C deflect to the right, which causes chord rotations in members AB and CD, there being theoretically

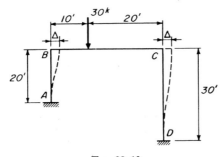

FIG. 22–10.

no rotation of BC. Neglecting axial deformation of BC, each of the joints deflects the same distance Δ.

The chord rotations of members AB and CD, due to sidesway, can be seen to equal Δ/l_{AB} and Δ/l_{CD}, respectively. (Notice that the shorter a member for the same Δ, the larger its chord rotation and thus the larger the effect on its moment). For this frame ψ_{AB} is $\frac{3}{2}$ as large as ψ_{CD} because l_{AB} is only two-thirds of l_{CD}. It is convenient to work with only one unknown chord rotation, and in setting up the slope-deflection equations, relative values are used. The value ψ is used for the two equations for member AB, while $\frac{2}{3}\psi$ is used for the equation for member CD.

Example 22–6 presents the analysis of the frame of Fig. 22–10. By noticing $\theta_A = \theta_D = 0$, it will be seen that the six end-moment equations for the entire structure contain a total of three unknowns: θ_B, θ_C, and ψ. There are present, however, three conditions which permit their determination. They are:

1) The sum of the moments at B is zero $(\Sigma M_B = 0 = M_{BA} + M_{BC})$.

2) The sum of the moments at C is zero $(\Sigma M_C = 0 = M_{CB} + M_{CD})$.

3) The sum of the horizontal forces on the entire structure must be zero. The only horizontal forces are the horizontal reactions at A and D, and they will be equal in magnitude and opposite in direction. Horizontal reactions may be computed for each of the columns by dividing the column moments by the column heights. The sum of the two must be zero.

$$H_A = \frac{M_{AB} + M_{BA}}{l_{AB}} \qquad H_D = \frac{M_{CD} + M_{DC}}{l_{DC}}$$

$$\Sigma H = 0 = \frac{M_{AB} + M_{BA}}{l_{AB}} + \frac{M_{CD} + M_{DC}}{l_{CD}}$$

EXAMPLE 22–6. Determine all of the moments for the frame shown in Fig. 22–11, for which E and I are constant.

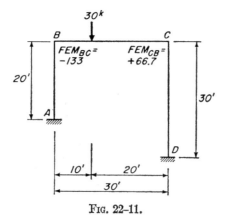

Fig. 22–11.

Solution: By using relative ψ values,

$$\psi_{AB} = \frac{\Delta}{20} \qquad \psi_{CD} = \frac{\Delta}{30} \qquad \frac{\psi_{AB}}{\psi_{CD}} = \frac{3}{2}$$

By using relative $2EK$ values,

$$\text{For } AB \qquad 2EK = \frac{2E}{20} : 3$$

$$\text{For } BC \qquad 2EK = \frac{2E}{30} : 2$$

$$\text{For } CD \qquad 2EK = \frac{2E}{30} : 2$$

By writing the equations, and noting $\theta_A = \theta_D = \psi_{BC} = 0$,

$$M_{AB} = 3(\theta_B - 3\psi) = 3\theta_B - 9\psi$$
$$M_{BA} = 3(2\theta_B - 3\psi) = 6\theta_B - 9\psi$$
$$M_{BC} = 2(2\theta_B + \theta_C) - 133 = 4\theta_B + 2\theta_C - 133$$
$$M_{CB} = 2(\theta_B + 2\theta_C) + 66.7 = 2\theta_B + 4\theta_C + 66.7$$
$$M_{CD} = 2[2\theta_C - (3)(\tfrac{2}{3}\psi)] = 4\theta_C - 4\psi$$
$$M_{DC} = 2[\theta_C - (3)(\tfrac{2}{3}\psi)] = 2\theta_C - 4\psi$$

$\Sigma M_B = 0 = M_{BA} + M_{BC}$

$$6\theta_B - 9\psi + 4\theta_B + 2\theta_C - 133 = 0$$
$$10\theta_B + 2\theta_C - 9\psi = 133 \tag{1}$$

$\Sigma M_C = 0 = M_{CB} + M_{CD}$

$$2\theta_B + 4\theta_C + 66.7 + 4\theta_C - 4\psi = 0$$
$$2\theta_B + 8\theta_C - 4\psi = -66.7 \tag{2}$$

$\Sigma H = 0 = \dfrac{H_A}{l_{AB}} + \dfrac{H_D}{l_{CD}}$

$$\frac{M_{AB} + M_{BA}}{l_{AB}} + \frac{M_{CD} + M_{DC}}{l_{CD}} = 0$$

$$\frac{3\theta_B - 9\psi + 6\theta_B - 9\psi}{20} + \frac{4\theta_C - 4\psi + 2\theta_C - 4\psi}{30} = 0$$

$$27\theta_B + 12\theta_C - 70\psi = 0 \tag{3}$$

By solving Eqs. 1, 2, and 3 simultaneously

$$\theta_B = +21.2$$
$$\theta_C = -10.5$$
$$\psi = +6.4$$

Final moments:

$$M_{AB} = +\ 6.0'^{k} \qquad\qquad M_{CB} = +67.4'^{k}$$
$$M_{BA} = +69.4'^{k} \qquad\qquad M_{CD} = -67.4'^{k}$$
$$M_{BC} = -69.4'^{k} \qquad\qquad M_{DC} = -46.6'^{k}$$

Slope deflection can be applied to frames with more than one condition of sidesway, such as the two-story frame of Fig. 22–12. Analysis of frames of this type is usually handled more conveniently by the moment-distribution method, but a knowledge of the slope-deflection solution is valuable in understanding the moment-distribution solution.

The horizontal loads cause the structure to lean to the right; the joints B and E deflect horizontally a distance Δ_1; and joints C and D deflect horizontally $\Delta_1 + \Delta_2$, as shown in Fig. 22–12. The chord rotations for the columns, ψ_1, and ψ_2 will therefore equal Δ_1/l_{AB} for the lower level and Δ_2/l_{BC} for the upper level.

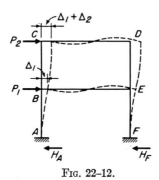

FIG. 22–12.

The slope-deflection equations may be written for the moment at each end of the six members, and the usual joint-condition equations are available as follows:

$$\Sigma M_B = 0 = M_{BC} + M_{BE} \tag{1}$$

$$\Sigma M_C = 0 = M_{BC} + M_{CD} \tag{2}$$

$$\Sigma M_D = 0 = M_{DC} + M_{DE} \tag{3}$$

$$\Sigma M_E = 0 = M_{ED} + M_{EB} + M_{EF} \tag{4}$$

These equations involve six unknowns (θ_B, θ_C, θ_D, θ_E, ψ_1, and ψ_2), noting that θ_A and θ_F are equal to zero. Two more equations are necessary for determining the unknowns, and they are found by considering the horizontal forces or shears on the frame. It is obvious that the sum of the horizontal resisting forces on any level must be equal and opposite to the external horizontal shear on the level. For the bottom level the horizontal shear equals $P_1 + P_2$, and the reactions at the base of each column equal the end moments divided by the column heights. Therefore:

$$H_A + H_F = P_1 + P_2$$

$$H_A = \frac{M_{AB} + M_{BA}}{l_{AB}}$$

$$H_F = \frac{M_{EF} + M_{FE}}{l_{BA}}$$

$$\frac{M_{AB} + M_{BA}}{l_{AB}} + \frac{M_{EF} + M_{FE}}{l_{EF}} = P_1 + P_2 \qquad (5)$$

A similar condition equation may be written for the top level, which has an external shear of P_2. The moments in the columns produce shears equal and opposite to P_2, which permits the writing of the following equation for the level:

$$\frac{M_{BC} + M_{CB}}{l_{BC}} + \frac{M_{DE} + M_{ED}}{l_{DE}} = P_2 \qquad (6)$$

Six condition equations are available for determining the six unknowns in the end-moment equations, and the problem may be solved as illustrated in Example 22–7. It is desirable to assume all θ and ψ values to be positive in setting up the equations. In this way the signs of the answers will take care of themselves.

No matter how many floors the building has, one shear-condition equation is available for each floor. The slope-deflection procedure is not very practical for multistory buildings. For a six-story building four bays wide there will be 6 unknown ψ values and 30 unknown θ values, or a total of 36 simultaneous equations to solve.

EXAMPLE 22–7. Find the moments for the frame of Fig. 22–13 by the method of slope deflection.

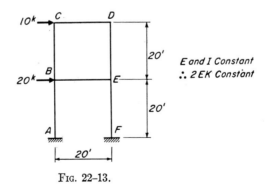

FIG. 22–13.

Solution: By noting that chords BE and CD do not rotate,

$$\psi_{AB} = \psi_{EF} = \psi_1 \qquad \psi_{BC} = \psi_{DE} = \psi_2$$

By writing the equations, and noting that $\theta_A = \theta_F = 0$,

$$M_{AB} = \theta_B - 3\psi_1 \qquad\qquad M_{DC} = \theta_C + 2\theta_D$$

$$M_{BA} = 2\theta_B - 3\psi_1 \qquad\qquad M_{DE} = 2\theta_D + \theta_E - 3\psi_2$$

$$M_{BC} = 2\theta_B + \theta_C - 3\psi_2 \qquad\qquad M_{ED} = \theta_D + 2\theta_E - 3\psi_2$$

$$M_{BE} = 2\theta_B + \theta_E \qquad\qquad M_{EB} = \theta_B + 2\theta_E$$

$$M_{CB} = \theta_B + 2\theta_C - 3\psi_2 \qquad\qquad M_{EF} = 2\theta_E - 3\psi_1$$

$$M_{CD} = 2\theta_C + \theta_D \qquad\qquad M_{FE} = \theta_E - 3\psi_1$$

$$\Sigma M_B = 0 = M_{BA} + M_{BC} + M_{BE}$$
$$2\theta_B - 3\psi_1 + 2\theta_B + \theta_C - 3\psi_2 + 2\theta_B + \theta_E = 0$$
$$6\theta_B + \theta_C + \theta_E - 3\psi_1 - 3\psi_2 = 0 \qquad\qquad (1)$$

$$\Sigma M_C = 0 = M_{CB} + M_{CD}$$
$$\theta_B + 2\theta_C - 3\psi_2 + 2\theta_2 + \theta_D = 0$$
$$\theta_B + 4\theta_C + \theta_D - 3\psi_2 = 0 \qquad\qquad (2)$$

$$\Sigma M_D = 0 = M_{DC} + M_{DE}$$
$$\theta_C + 2\theta_D + 2\theta_D + \theta_E - 3\psi_2 = 0$$
$$\theta_C + 4\theta_D + \theta_E - 3\psi_2 = 0 \qquad\qquad (3)$$

$$\Sigma M_E = 0 = M_{ED} + M_{EB} + M_{EF}$$
$$\theta_D + 2\theta_E - 3\psi_2 + \theta_B + 2\theta_E + 2\theta_E - 3\psi_1 = 0$$
$$\theta_B + \theta_D + 6\theta_E - 3\psi_1 - 3\psi_2 = 0 \qquad\qquad (4)$$

$\Sigma H = 10$; top level

$$\frac{M_{BC} + M_{CB}}{20} + \frac{M_{DE} + M_{ED}}{20} = 10$$

$$\frac{2\theta_B + \theta_C - 3\psi_2 + \theta_B + 2\theta_C - 3\psi_2}{20} + \frac{2\theta_D + \theta_E - 3\psi_2 + \theta_D + 2\theta_E - 3\psi_2}{20} = 10$$

$$3\theta_B + 3\theta_C + 3\theta_D + 3\theta_E - 12\psi_2 = 200 \qquad\qquad (5)$$

$\Sigma H = 30$; bottom level

$$\frac{M_{AB} + M_{BA}}{20} + \frac{M_{EF} + M_{FE}}{20} = 30$$

$$\frac{\theta_B - 3\psi_1 + 2\theta_B - 3\psi_1}{20} + \frac{2\theta_E - 3\psi_1 + \theta_E - 3\psi_1}{20} = 30$$

$$3\theta_B + 3\theta_E - 12\psi_1 = 600 \qquad\qquad (6)$$

By solving equations simultaneously,

$$\theta_B = \theta_E = -52.75 \qquad\qquad \psi_1 = -76.37$$
$$\theta_C = \theta_D = -21.82 \qquad\qquad \psi_2 = -53.95$$

Final moments

$$M_{AB} = M_{FE} = +176.4'^k \qquad\qquad M_{BE} = M_{EB} = -158.2'^k$$
$$M_{BA} = M_{EF} = +123.6'^k \qquad\qquad M_{CB} = M_{DE} = +65.5'^k$$
$$M_{BC} = M_{ED} = +34.6'^k \qquad\qquad M_{CD} = M_{DC} = -65.5'^k$$

Transit Shed, Port of Long Beach, California. (Courtesy of American Institute of Steel Construction, Inc.)

22-6. Analysis of Frames with Sloping Members

The frames with possible sidesway discussed in Sec. 22-5 were assumed to have horizontal members which had no chord rotations even though the columns had them. When a frame with sloping legs is encountered, such as the trapezoidal frame of Fig. 22-14 (a), the chord of each horizontal member does rotate. Similarly, the chords of all of the members of the gabled structure of Fig. 22-14 (b) may rotate.

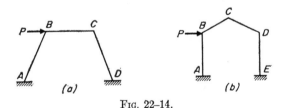

(a)

(b)

Fig. 22-14.

Another item of importance is the fact that the vertical reactions need to be considered in writing the expressions for shear for sloping members. The deflected shape of a trapezoidal shaped structure, acted upon by a horizontal load, is shown in Fig. 22-15.

Neglecting axial deformation, joints B and C move through the same distance z. To be absolutely correct, the deflected distances of the joints should be shown as arcs, but the distances are small, and perpendiculars are perfectly satisfactory. Each of the members has a chord rotation

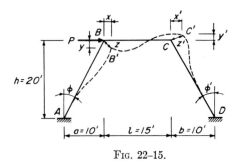

F<small>IG</small>. 22–15.

which needs to be included in applying the slope-deflection equations. A study of the trigonometry involved shows that the chord rotations may be expressed quite simply in relation to each other.

Suppose joint B moves a distance horizontally x and a vertical distance y and let the angle between member AB and the vertical be ϕ. The values of z and y will then be

$$z = \frac{x}{\cos \phi} \qquad y = x \tan \phi$$

Therefore, the chord rotation of AB is as follows, noting $l_{AB} = h/\cos \phi$:

$$\psi_{AB} = \frac{z}{l_{AB}} = \frac{x/\cos \phi}{h/\cos \phi} = \frac{x}{h}$$

Similarly, the rotation of CD is x'/h. The value of y' is $x' \tan \phi'$ and the chord rotation of BC is developed as follows:

$$\psi_{BC} = \frac{y + y'}{l_{BC}} = \frac{x(\tan \phi + \tan \phi')}{l_{BC}}$$

But $\tan \phi = a/h$ and $\tan \phi' = b/h$, and ψ_{BC} becomes:

$$\psi_{BC} = \frac{x(a/h + b/h)}{l_{BC}}$$

$$= \frac{x(a+b)}{h l_{BC}}$$

For the dimensions shown on the frame, the values of the three chord rotations may all be expressed in terms of one unknown, x. Similar relations may be derived trigonometrically for chord rotation for more complicated structures, but space is not taken to include them.

$$\psi_{AB} = \frac{x}{h} = \frac{x}{20}$$

$$\psi_{BC} = \frac{x(a+b)}{hl_{BC}} = \frac{x}{15}$$

$$\psi_{CD} = \frac{x'}{h} = \frac{x}{20}$$

Problems

22–1 to 22–4. Compute the end moments for the beams of Probs. 21–10 to 21–13 with the slope-deflection equations. Sketch the deformed shape of each beam.

22–5 to 22–12. Determine the end moments for the members of all of the structures by using the slope deflection equations. Sketch the deformed shape of each structure.

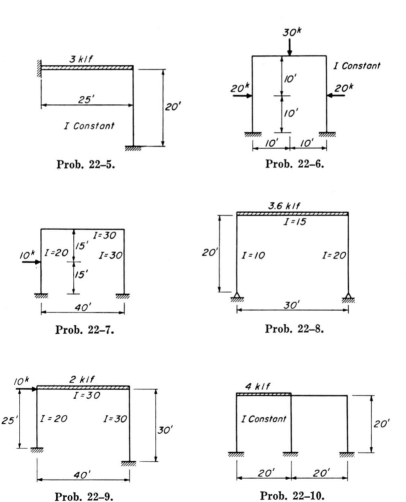

Prob. 22–5.

Prob. 22–6.

Prob. 22–7.

Prob. 22–8.

Prob. 22–9.

Prob. 22–10.

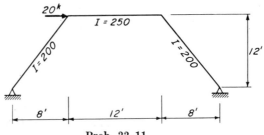

Prob. 22–11.

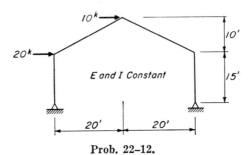

Prob. 22–12.

23 | MOMENT DISTRIBUTION

23–1. General

The late Prof. Hardy Cross published the moment-distribution method in the *Proceedings of the American Society of Civil Engineers* in May, 1930, after having taught the subject to his students at the University of Illinois since 1924. His paper, entitled "Analysis of Continuous Frames by Distributing Fixed-End Moments" began a new era in the analysis of indeterminate frames and gave added impetus to their use. The moment-distribution method of analyzing continuous beams and frames involves little more labor than the approximate methods but yields accuracy equivalent to that obtained from the infinitely more laborious exact methods previously studied.

The analysis of indeterminate structures in the preceding chapters frequently involved the solution of inconvenient simultaneous equations. These equations are not necessary in solutions by moment distribution except in a few rare situations for complicated frames. The Cross method involves successive cycles of computation, each cycle drawing closer to the exact answers. The calculations may be stopped after two or three cycles, giving a very good approximate analysis, or they may be carried on to whatever degree of accuracy is desired. When these advantages are considered in the light of the fact that the precision obtained by the lengthy "classical" methods is often of questionable value, the true worth of this quick and practical method is understood.

23–2. Introduction

The beauty of moment distribution lies in its simplicity of theory and application. The student will be able to grasp quickly the principles involved, and he will clearly understand what he is doing and why he is doing it.

The following discussion pertains to structures having members of contant cross section throughout their respective lengths (i.e., prismatic members). It is assumed that there is no joint translation where two or more members frame together, but that there can be some joint rotation (i.e., the members may rotate as a group but may not move with respect to each other). Finally, axial deformation of members is neglected.

Considering the frame of Fig. 23–1 (*a*), the joints *A* to *D* are seen to be fixed. Joint *E*, however, is not fixed, and the loads on the structure will cause it to rotate slightly, as represented by the angle θ_E in Fig. 23–1 (*b*).

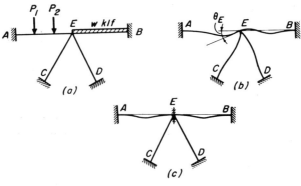

FIG. 23–1.

If an imaginary clamp is placed at E, fixing it so that it cannot be displaced, the structure will take the shape of Fig. 23–1 (c). For this situation, with all ends fixed, the end moments can be calculated with little difficulty by the usual expressions ($wl^2/12$ for uniform loads and Pab^2/l^2 or Pa^2b/l^2 for concentrated loads).

If the clamp at E is removed, the joint will rotate slightly, twisting the ends of the members meeting there and causing a redistribution of the moments in the member ends. The changes in the moments or twists at the E ends of members $AE, BE, CE,$ and DE cause some effect at their other ends. When a moment is applied to one end of a member, the other end being fixed, there is some effect or carry-over to the fixed end.

After the fixed-end moments are computed, the problem to be handled may be briefly stated as consisting of the calculation of 1) the moments caused in the E ends of the members by the rotation of joint E, 2) the magnitude of the moments carried over to the other ends of the members, and 3) the addition or subtraction of these latter moments to the original fixed-end moments.

These steps can be simply written as being the fixed-end moments plus the moments due to the rotation of joint E.

$$M = M_{\text{fixed}} + M_{\theta_E}$$

23–3. Definitions

The following terms are constantly used in discussing moment distribution:

Fixed-end moments. When all of the joints of a structure are clamped to prevent any joint rotation, the external loads produce certain moments at the ends of the members to which they are applied. These moments are referred to as fixed-end moments.

Unbalanced moments. Initially the joints in a structure are considered to be clamped. When a joint is released, it rotates because the sum of the fixed-end moments at the joint is not zero. The difference between zero and the actual sum of the end moments is the unbalanced moment.

Distributed moments. After the clamp at a joint is released, the unbalanced moment causes the joint to rotate. The rotation twists the ends of the members at the joint and changes their moments. In other words, rotation of the joint is resisted by the members and resisting moments are built up in the members as they are twisted. Rotation continues until equilibrium is reached—when the resisting moments equal the unbalanced moment—at which time the sum of the moments at the joint is equal to zero. The moments developed in the members resisting rotation are the distributed moments.

Carry-over. moments. The distributed moments in the ends of the members cause moments in the other ends, which are assumed fixed, and these are the carry-over moments.

23–4. Sign Convention

The moments at the end of a member are assumed to be positive when they tend to rotate the member clockwise about the joint (the resisting moment of the joint would be counterclockwise). The continuous beam of Fig. 23–2, with all joints clamped, has clockwise (or +) moments on

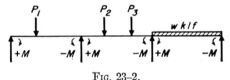

Fig. 23–2.

the left end of each span and counterclockwise (or −) moments on the right end of each span. (The usual sign convention used in strength of materials shows fixed-ended beams to have negative moments on both ends for downward loads, because tension is caused in the top fibers of the beams at those points.)

23–5. Basic Relations

There are two questions which must be answered in order to apply the moment-distribution method to actual structures. They are:

1) What is the moment developed or carried over to a fixed end of a member when the other end is subjected to a certain moment?

2) When a joint is unclamped and rotates, what is the distribution of the unbalanced moment to the members meeting at the joint, or how much resisting moment is supplied by each member?

Carry-Over Moment. To determine the carry-over moment, the un-loaded beam of constant cross section in Fig. 23–3 (*a*) is considered. If a moment M_1 is applied to the left end of the beam, a moment M_2 will be developed at the right end. The left end is at a joint which has been released and the moment M_1 causes it to rotate an amount θ_1. There will, however, be no deflection of the left end with respect to the right end.

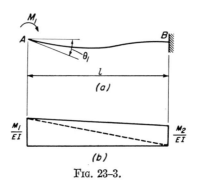

FIG. 23–3.

The second moment-area theorem may be used to determine the magnitude of M_2. The deflection of the tangent to the elastic curve of the beam at the left end with respect to the tangent at the right end (which remains horizontal) is equal to the moment of the area of the M/EI diagram taken about the left end and is equal to zero. By drawing the M/EI diagram in Fig. 23–3 (*b*) and dividing it into two triangles to facilitate the area computations, the following expression may be written and solved for M_2:

$$\delta_A = \frac{(\tfrac{1}{2} \times M_1 \times l)(\tfrac{1}{3}l) + (\tfrac{1}{2} \times M_2 \times l)(\tfrac{2}{3}l)}{EI} = 0$$

$$\frac{M_1 l^2}{6EI} + \frac{M_2 l^2}{3EI} = 0$$

$$M_2 = -\tfrac{1}{2}M_1$$

A moment applied at one end of a prismatic beam, the other end being fixed, will cause a moment half as large and of opposite sign at the fixed end. The carry-over factor is $-\tfrac{1}{2}$. The minus sign refers to strength-of-materials sign convention: a distributed moment on one end causing tension in bottom fibers must be carried over so that it will cause tension in the top fibers of the other end. A study of Fig. 23–11 shows that carrying over with a $+\tfrac{1}{2}$ value with the moment-distribution sign convention automatically takes care of the situation, and it is unnecessary to change signs with each carry-over.

Distribution Factors. Usually a group of members framed together at a joint have different stiffnesses. When a joint is unclamped and begins to rotate under the unbalanced moment, the resistance to rotation varies from member to member. The problem is to determine how much of the unbalanced moment will be taken up by each of the members. It seems reasonable to assume the unbalance will be resisted in direct relation to the respective resistance to end rotation of each member.

The beam and M/EI diagram of Fig. 23–3 are redrawn in Fig. 23–4, with the proper relationship between M_1 and M_2, and an expression is written for the amount of rotation caused by a moment M_1.

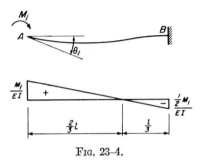

FIG. 23–4.

Using the first moment-area theorem, the angle θ_1 may be represented by the area of the M/EI diagram between A and B, the tangent at B remaining horizontal.

$$\theta_1 = \frac{(\tfrac{1}{2})(M_1)(\tfrac{2}{3}l) - (\tfrac{1}{2})(\tfrac{1}{2}M_1)(\tfrac{1}{3}l)}{EI}$$

$$= \frac{M_1 l}{4EI}$$

Assuming that all of the members consist of the same material, having the same E values, the only variables in the foregoing equation affecting the amount of end rotation are the l and I values. The amount of rotation occurring at the end of a member obviously varies directly as the l/I value for the member. The larger the rotation of the member the less moment it will carry. The moment resisted varies inversely as the amount of rotation or directly as the I/l value. This latter value is referred to as the *stiffness factor K*.

$$K = \frac{I}{l}$$

To determine the unbalanced moment taken by each of the members at a joint, the stiffness factors at the joint are totaled, and each member is assumed to carry a proportion of the unbalanced moment equal to its K value divided by the sum of all the K values at the joint. These proportions of the total unbalanced moment carried by each of the members are the *distribution factors*.

$$DF_1 = \frac{K_1}{\Sigma K} \qquad DF_2 = \frac{K_2}{\Sigma K}$$

23–6. Application of Moment Distribution

The very few tools needed for applying moment distribution are now available, and the method of applying them is described, reference being made to Fig. 23–5.

Fig. 23–5 (*a*) shows a beam and the several loads applied to it. In (*b*), the interior joints B and C are clamped, and the fixed-end moments are computed. At joint B the unbalanced moment is computed and the

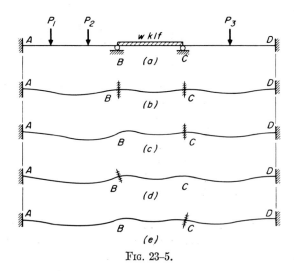

Fig. 23–5.

clamp is removed, as seen in (*c*). The joint rotates, thus distributing the unbalanced moment to the B ends of BA and BC in proportion to their distribution factors. The values of these distributed moments are carried over at the one-half rate to the other ends of the members. When equilibrium is reached, joint B is clamped in its new rotated position and joint C is released, as shown in (*d*). Joint C rotates under its unbalanced moment until it reaches equilibrium, the rotation causing distributed moments in the C ends of members CB and CD and their resulting carry-over moments. Joint C is now clamped and Joint B is released, Fig. 23–5 (*e*).

The same procedure is repeated again and again for joints B and C, the amount of unbalanced moment quickly diminishing, until the release of a joint causes only negligible rotation. This process, in brief, is moment distribution.

Examples 23–1 to 23–3 illustrate the procedure used for analyzing relatively simple continuous beams. The stiffness factors and distribution factors are computed as follows for Example 23–1.

$$DF_{BA} = \frac{K_{BA}}{\Sigma K} = \frac{\frac{1}{20}}{\frac{1}{20} + \frac{1}{15}} = 0.43$$

$$DF_{BC} = \frac{K_{BC}}{\Sigma K} = \frac{\frac{1}{15}}{\frac{1}{20} + \frac{1}{15}} = 0.57$$

A simple tabular form is given in the example problems for recording the steps involved in moment distribution. This procedure may be summarized as follows:

1) The fixed-end moments are computed and recorded on one line (line FEM in Examples 23–1 and 23–2).

2) The unbalanced moments at each joint are balanced in the next line (Dist 1).

3) The carry-overs are made from each of the joints on the next line (CO 1).

4) The new unbalanced moments at each joint are balanced (Dist 2), etc.

When the distribution has reached the accuracy desired, a double line is drawn under each column of figures. The final moment in the end of a member equals the sum of the moments opposite its position in the table. Unless a joint is fixed, the sum of the final end moments in the ends of the members meeting at the joint must total zero.

After the student has gained some proficiency in moment distribution, he may find it to his liking to balance the joints one at a time, make the carry-overs, and proceed to another joint (probably taking the joint each time with the greatest unbalance).

EXAMPLE 23–1. Determine the end moments of the structure shown in Fig. 23–6 by moment distribution.

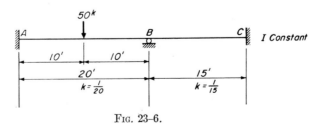

FIG. 23–6.

Solution:

	0.43	0.57		
+125	−125			FEM
	+ 53.8	+71.2		Dist I
+ 26.9			+35.6	CO I
+151.9	− 71.2	+71.2	+35.6	Final Moments

EXAMPLE 23–2. Distribute the fixed-end moments of the structure shown in Fig. 23–7.

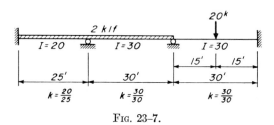

$$k = \frac{20}{25} \qquad k = \frac{30}{30} \qquad k = \frac{30}{30}$$

FIG. 23–7.

Solution:

	0.44	0.56		0.5	0.5		
+104.2	−104.2	+150.0		−150.0	+75.0	−75.0	FEM
	− 20.2	− 25.6		+ 37.5	+37.5		Dist I
− 10.1		+ 18.8		− 12.8		+ 18.8	CO I
	− 8.3	− 10.5		+ 6.4	+ 6.4		Dist 2
− 4.2		+ 3.2		− 5.3		+ 3.2	CO 2
	− 1.4	− 1.8		+ 2.7	+ 2.7		Dist 3
− 0.7		+ 1.3		− 0.9		+ 1.3	CO 3
	− 0.6	− 0.7		+ 0.4	+ 0.4		Dist 4
− 0.3		+ 0.2		− 0.4		+ 0.2	CO 4
	− 0.1	− 0.1		+ 0.2	+ 0.2		Dist 5
+ 88.9	−134.8	+134.8		−122.2	+122.2	− 51.5	Final Moments

EXAMPLE 23–3. Compute the end moments in the frame shown in Fig. 23–8.

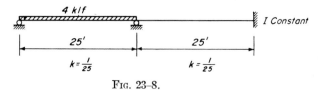

$$k = \frac{I}{25} \qquad k = \frac{I}{25}$$

FIG. 23–8.

Solution:

	0.5	0.5	
+208.3	−208.3		
−208.3	+104.2	+104.2	
+52.1	−104.2		+52.1
−52.1	+52.1	+52.1	
+26.0	−26.0		+26.0
−26.0	+13.0	+13.0	
+6.5	−13.0		+6.5
−6.5	+6.5	+6.5	
+3.2	−3.2		+3.2
−3.2	+1.6	+1.6	
+0.8	−1.6		+0.8
−0.8	+0.8	+0.8	
+0.4	−0.4		+0.4
−0.4	+0.2	+0.2	
+0.1	−0.2		+0.1
−0.1	+0.1	+0.1	
0	−178.4	+178.5	+89.1

23–7. Modification of Stiffness for Simple Beams

The carry-over factor was developed for carrying over to fixed-ends, but it is applicable to simply supported ends, which must have final moments of zero. The simple end of Example 23–3 was considered to be clamped; the carry-over was made to the end; and the joint was freed and balanced back to zero. This procedure repeated over and over is absolutely correct, but it involves a little unnecessary work which may be eliminated by studying the stiffness of members with simply supported ends.

Figure 23–9 (*a*) and (*b*) compares the relative stiffness of a member subjected to a moment M_1 when the far end is fixed and when it is simply supported. In part (*a*), the conjugate beam for the beam with far end fixed is loaded with the M/EI diagram, and the reactions are determined. The slope at the left end is represented by θ_1 and equals the shear when the conjugate beam is loaded with the M/EI diagram. Its value is $M_1 l/4EI$.

The conjugate beam for the simple end-supported beam is loaded with the M/EI diagram and its reactions are determined in Fig. 23–9 (*b*). The moment M_1 is found to cause a slope of $\theta_1 = M_1 l/3EI$; therefore, the slope caused by the moment M_1 when the far end is fixed is only three-fourths as large $(M_1 l/4EI \div M_1 l/3EI = 3/4)$ when the far end is simply supported. The beam simply supported at the far end is only three-

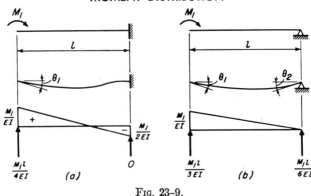

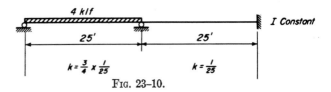

Fig. 23–9.

fourths as stiff as the one which is fixed. If the stiffness factors for end spans which are simply supported are modified by three-fourths, the simple end is balanced to zero, and no carry-overs are made to the end afterwards, the same results will be obtained. The stiffness modification is used for the beam of Example 23–3 in Example 23–4.

EXAMPLE 23–4. Determine the end moments of the structure shown in Fig. 23–10 by using the simple end-stiffness modification for the left end.

Fig. 23–10.

Solution:

	0.43	0.57	
+208.3 −208.3	−208.3 + 89.5	+118.8	
	− 104.2 + 44.7	+ 59.5	+59.4
			+29.7
0	− 178.3	+178.3	+89.1

23–8.   Shear and Moment Diagrams

The drawing of shear and moment diagrams is an excellent way to check the final moments computed by moment distribution and to obtain an over-all picture of the stress condition in the structure.

Before preparing the diagrams, it is necessary to consider a few points relating the shear and moment diagram sign convention to the one used for moment distribution. The usual conventions for drawing the diagrams will be used (tension in bottom fibers of beam is positive moment and upward shear to left is positive shear).

The relationship between the signs of the moments for the two conventions is shown with the beams of Fig. 23–11. Part (a) of the figure illustrates a fixed-end beam for which the result of moment distribution is a positive moment. The clockwise moment bends the beam as shown, causing tension in the top fibers or a negative moment for the shear and moment diagram convention. In Fig. 23–11 (b), the result of moment distribution is a negative moment, but again the top beam fibers are in tension, indicating a negative moment for the moment diagram.

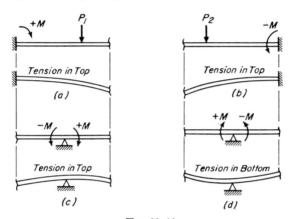

Fig. 23–11.

An interior simple support is represented by Fig. 23–11 (c) and (d). In part (c), moment distribution gives a positive moment to the right and a negative moment to the left, which causes tension in the top fibers. Part (d) shows the effect of moments of opposite character at the same support considered in part (c).

To draw the diagrams for a vertical member, the right side may be considered the bottom side. Moments are distributed for a continuous beam in Example 23–5, and shear and moment diagrams are drawn.

EXAMPLE 23–5. Distribute moments and draw shear and moment diagrams for the structure shown in Fig. 23–12.

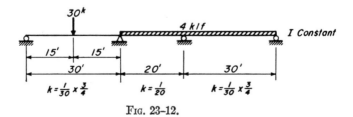

Fig. 23–12.

Solution:

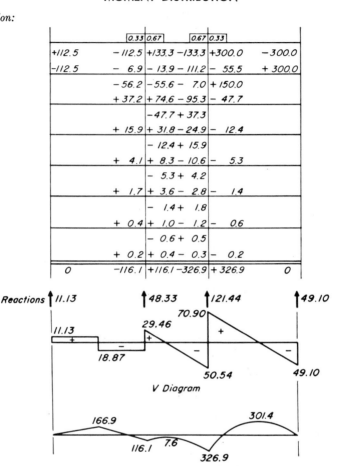

	0.33	0.67		0.67	0.33	
+112.5	− 112.5	+133.3	−133.3	+300.0	− 300.0	
−112.5	− 6.9	− 13.9	− 111.2	− 55.5	+ 300.0	
	− 56.2	−55.6 −	7.0	+ 150.0		
	+ 37.2	+ 74.6	− 95.3	− 47.7		
		−47.7	+ 37.3			
	+ 15.9	+ 31.8	− 24.9	− 12.4		
		− 12.4	+ 15.9			
	+ 4.1	+ 8.3	− 10.6	− 5.3		
		− 5.3	+ 4.2			
	+ 1.7	+ 3.6	− 2.8	− 1.4		
		− 1.4	+ 1.8			
	+ 0.4	+ 1.0	− 1.2	− 0.6		
		− 0.6	+ 0.5			
	+ 0.2	+ 0.4	− 0.3	− 0.2		
0	−116.1	+116.1	−326.9	+ 326.9	0	

Reactions ↑11.13   ↑48.33   ↑121.44   ↑49.10

V Diagram

23–9. Structures with Columns, Sidesway Prevented

Moment distribution is carried on in the usual manner for structures with columns if sidesway, or movement laterally, is prevented. Analysis of frames without sidesway is illustrated by Examples 23–6 and 23–7. Where sidesway is possible, it must be taken into account, because the movements or deflections cause twisting and affect the moments in the rotated members.

As the structures being analyzed become more complex, it is necessary to use some method of recording the figures so they will not interfere or run into each other. A system is used in the remaining examples whereby the moments are recorded below beams on their left ends and above them on their right ends. For columns the same system is used, the right sides being considered the bottom sides. As before, all joints are balanced, the carry-overs are made, the joints are balanced, etc.

EXAMPLE 23–6. Determine the end moments for the frame shown in Fig. 23–13.

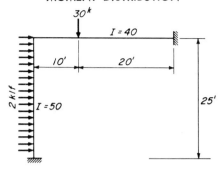

Fig. 23–13.

Solution:

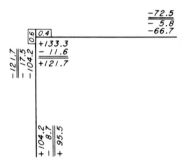

Example 23–7. Compute the end moments of the structure shown in Fig. 23–14.

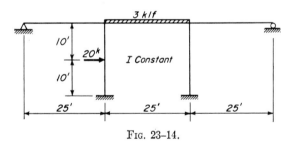

Fig. 23–14.

Solution:

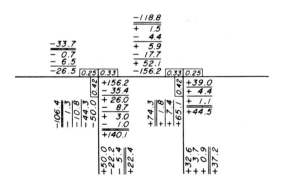

23–10. Structures Having Sidesway, Columns of Equal I's and Lengths

Structural frames, similar to the one shown in Fig. 23–15, are usually so constructed that they may possibly sway to one side or the other under load. The frame in this figure is symmetrical, but it will tend to sway because the load P is not centered. Analysis of the frame by the usual procedure, illustrated in the figure, gives inconsistent results.

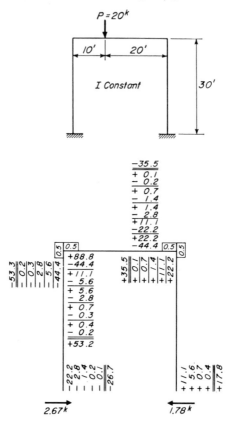

Fig. 23–15.

The values of the horizontal components at the supports are computed, and from the results obtained it can be seen that the sum of the horizontal forces on the structure is not equal to zero. The sum of the forces to the right is 0.89^k more than the sum of the forces to the left. If the structure were subjected to an unbalanced force system such as this one, it would not be in equilibrium.

The usual analysis does not yield consistent results, because the structure actually sways or deflects to one side, and the resulting deflections affect the moments. One possible solution is to compute the deflections caused by applying a force of 0.89^k acting to the right at the top of the bent. Moments could be obtained for the computed deflections and added to the originally distributed fixed-end moments, but the method is so difficult as to be impractical.

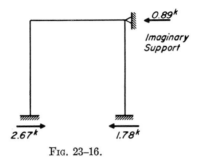

Fig. 23–16.

A much more convenient method is to assume the existence of an imaginary support which prevents the structure from swaying, as shown in Fig. 23–16. The fixed-end moments are distributed, and the force the imaginary support must supply to hold the frame in place is computed. For the frame of Fig. 23–15 the fictitious support must supply 0.89^k pushing to the left.

The support is imaginary and if removed will allow the frame to sway to the right. The ends of the columns rotate in a clockwise direction and produce clockwise or positive moments at the joints (Fig. 23–17).

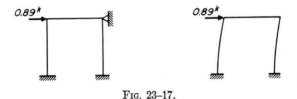

Fig. 23–17.

If convenient clockwise moments are assumed in the columns, they may be distributed and their effect on the reactions may be determined. This method is followed in Fig. 23–18 (a), and the assumed column moments of $+10'^k$ each are found to produce horizontal reactions to the left totaling 0.92^k. Only 0.89^k was needed, and if $0.89/0.92$ times the values of the distributed moments are added to the originally distributed fixed-end moments, the final moments will be obtained. The results are shown in Fig. 23–18 (b). Example 23–8 presents the solution of a similar problem.

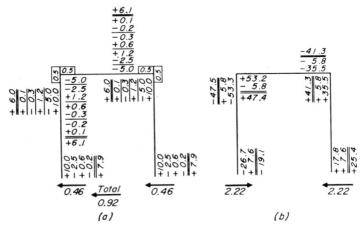

Fig. 23–18.

EXAMPLE 23–8. Determine the final moments of the structure shown in Fig. 23–19. Use the sidesway method.

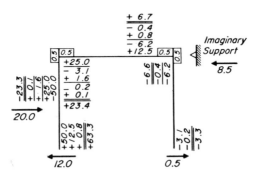

Fig. 23–19.

Solution:

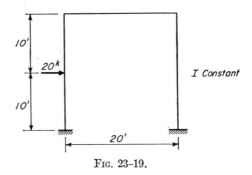

The imaginary support must supply 8.5^k acting to the left for equilibrium.
If the imaginary support is removed, the structure will lean or sway to the right

and produce clockwise moments at the joints; therefore, positive moments are assumed in the columns and distributed as follows:

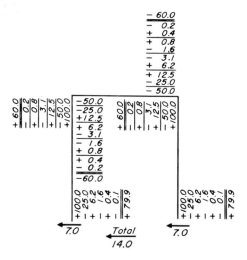

The assumed moments produce horizontal reactions totaling 14.0^k to the left, which is larger than the 8.5^k needed. The final moments equal the originally distributed fixed-end moments plus 8.5/14.0 times the results obtained from distributing the assumed sidesway moments, as shown.

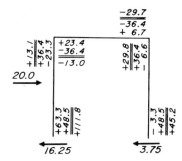

23–11. Structures Having Sidesway; Columns of Different I's and Lengths

When a structure has columns of varying lengths or different moments of inertia, the procedure for handling the analysis is different in one respect: the assumed sidesway moments. It will be proved in the following paragraphs that the assumed moments should vary from column to column in proportion to their I/l^2 values.

If the frame of Fig. 23–20 is pushed laterally an amount Δ by the load P, it will take the deflected shape of Fig. 23–21.

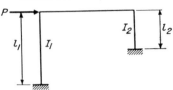

Fɪɢ. 23–20.

Theoretically both columns will become perfect S curves, the beam being considered rigid and unbending. At their mid-depths the deflection for both columns will equal $\Delta/2$. Mid-depths of the columns may be considered points of contraflexure; and the bottom halves may be handled as though they were cantilever beams.. The expression for deflection

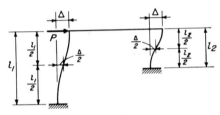

Fɪɢ. 23–21.

of a cantilever beam with a concentrated load at its end is $Pl^3/3EI$. Since the deflections are the same for both columns, the following expressions may be written:

$$\frac{\Delta}{2} = \frac{(P_1)(l_1/2)^3}{3EI_1} = \frac{P_1 l_1^3}{24EI_1} \qquad \frac{\Delta}{2} = \frac{(P_2)(l_2/2)^3}{3EI_1} = \frac{P_2 l_2^3}{24EI_2}$$

By solving these deflection expressions for P_1 and P_2, the forces pushing on the cantilevers, we have

$$P_1 = \frac{12EI_1\Delta}{l_1^3} \qquad P_2 = \frac{12EI_2\Delta}{l_2^3}$$

The moments caused by the two forces at the ends of their respective cantilevers are equal to the force times the cantilever length. These moments are written and the values of P_1 and P_2 are substituted in them.

$$M_1 = P_1 \frac{l_1}{2} = \left(\frac{12EI_1\Delta}{l_1^3}\right)\left(\frac{l_1}{2}\right) = \frac{6EI_1\Delta}{l_1^2}$$

$$M_2 = P_2 \frac{l_2}{2} = \left(\frac{12EI_2\Delta}{l_2^3}\right)\left(\frac{l_2}{2}\right) = \frac{6EI_2\Delta}{l_2^2}$$

From these expressions a proportion may be written between the moments as follows:

$$\frac{M_1}{M_2} = \frac{6EI_1\Delta/l_1^2}{6EI_2\Delta/l_2^2} = \frac{I_1/l_1^2}{I_2/l_2^2}$$

This relationship must be used for assuming sidesway moments for the columns of a frame. Any convenient moments may be assumed, but they must be in proportion to each other, as their I/l^2 values. Should their I and l values be equal, the assumed moments will be equal. Examples 23–9 and 23–10 illustrate the application of the method.

EXAMPLE 23–9. Find all moments in the structure shown in Fig. 23–22. Use the sidesway method.

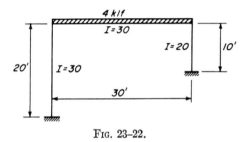

FIG. 23–22.

Solution:

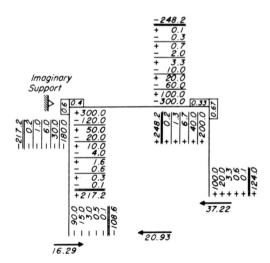

The imaginary support must supply a force of 20.93^k to the right. Removal of the support will allow the frame to sway to the left; therefore, counterclockwise or negative moments are assumed in the columns in proportion to their I/l^2 values.

$$\frac{M_1}{M_2}=\frac{I_1/l_1^2}{I_2/l_2^2}=\frac{30/20^2}{20/10^2}=\tfrac{3}{8}$$

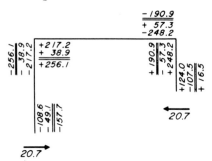

The assumed moments develop total reactions to the right of 10.58^k; however, 20.93^k was needed, and $20.93/10.58$ times these moments is added to the results obtained initially by distributing the fixed-end moments.

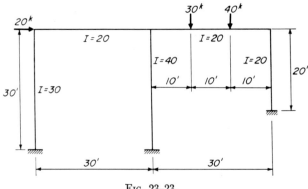

EXAMPLE 23–10. Compute the final end moments for the frame shown in Fig. 23–23.

FIG. 23–23.

Solution:

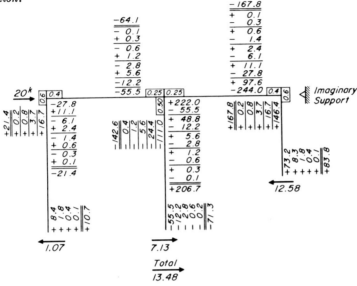

The structure sways to the right; therefore, positive moments are assumed in the columns in proportion to their I/l^2 values.

$$M_1 : M_2 : M_3$$

$$\frac{30}{30^2} : \frac{40}{30^2} : \frac{20}{20^2}$$

$$30 : 40 : 45$$

Final moments

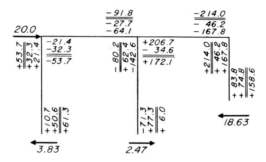

23–12. Multistory Frames

There are two possible ways in which the frame of Fig. 23–24 may sway. The loads P_1 and P_2 will obviously cause both floors of the structure to sway to the right, but it is not known how much of the swaying is going to occur in the top floor (x condition) or how much will occur in the bottom floor (y condition). There are two sidesway conditions that need to be considered.

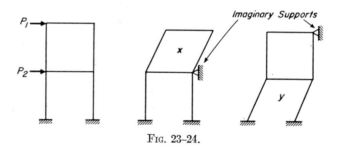

Fig. 23–24.

To analyze the frame by the usual sidesway procedure would involve 1) an assumption of moments in the top floor for the x condition and the distribution of the moments throughout the frame and 2) an assumption of moments in the lower floor for the y condition and the distribution of those moments throughout the frame. One equation could be written for the top floor by equating x times the horizontal forces caused by the x moments plus y times the horizontal forces caused by the y moments to the actual total shear on the floor, P_1. A similar equation could be written for the lower floor by equating the horizontal forces caused by the assumed moments to the shear on that floor, $P_1 + P_2$. Simultaneous solution of the two equations would yield the values of x and y. The final moments in the frame equal x times the x distributed moments plus y times the y distributed moments.

Office Building, 99 Park Avenue, New York City. (Courtesy of American Institute of Steel Construction, Inc.)

The sidesway method is not difficult to apply for a two-story frame, but for multistory frames it becomes unwieldy because each additional floor introduces another sidesway condition and another simultaneous equation.

Professor C. T. Morris of Ohio State University introduced a much simpler method for handling multistory frames which involves a series of successive corrections.[1] His method is also based on the total horizontal shear along each level of a building. In considering the frame of Fig. 23–25 (a), which is being deflected laterally by the loads P_1 and P_2, each column is assumed to take the approximate S shape shown in (b).

At the mid-depth of the columns there is assumed to be a point of contraflexure. The column may be considered to consist of a pair of cantilever beams one above the point and one below the point as

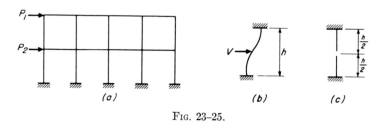

Fig. 23–25.

shown in (c). The moment in each cantilever will equal the shear times $h/2 = Vh/2$, and the total moment top and bottom is equal to $Vh/2 + Vh/2 = Vh$. The total moment in a column must be equal to the shear carried by the column times the column height.

Similarly, on any one level the total moments top and bottom of all the columns will equal the total shear on that level multiplied by the column height. The method consists in initially assuming this total for the column moments on a floor and distributing it between the columns in proportion to their I/l^2 values. The moment taken by each column is divided half to top end and half to bottom end. The joints are balanced, including the fixed-end moments, making no carry-overs until all joints are balanced. The column moments are corrected to their initial and final total, and the joints are balanced again, etc. Successive corrections work exceptionally well for multistory frames, as illustrated by Examples 23–11 and 23–12. The procedure used is as follows:

1) Compute fixed-end moments.

2) Compute total moments in columns (equal to shear on the level times column height) for each level and distribute between the columns in proportion to their I/l^2 values and divide each by half, one-half to top of column and one-half to bottom.

[1] *Transactions of ASCE*, Vol. 96, 1932.

3) Balance all joints throughout the structure, making no carry-overs.

4) Make carry-overs for entire frame.

5) The total of the column moments on each level has been changed and will not equal the shear times the column height. Determine the difference and add or subtract the amount back to the columns in proportion to their I/l^2 values.

6) Steps 3 to 5 are repeated over and over until the amount of the corrections to be made is negligible.

EXAMPLE 23–11. Determine final moments for the structure in Fig. 23–26. Use the successive-correction method developed by Professor Morris.

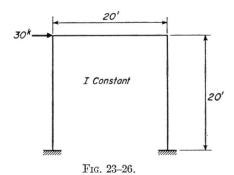

FIG. 23–26.

Solution:

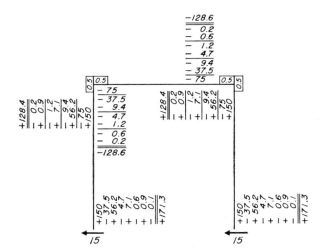

EXAMPLE 23–12. Determine the final moments for the frame of Example 22–7, reproduced in Fig. 23–27, by successive corrections.

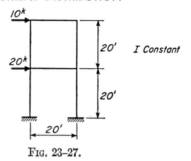

Fig. 23–27.

Solution:

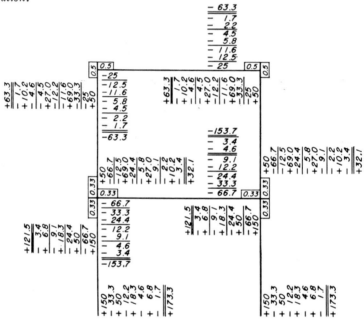

Problems

23–1 to **23–18.** Analyze the structures by the method of moment distribution. Draw shear and moment diagrams for Probs. 23–2, 23–4, 23–5, 23–9, 23–11, and 23–13. Problems 23–9 to 23–15 are to be worked by the sidesway method, while Probs. 23–16 to 23–18 are to be solved by the successive-correction method.

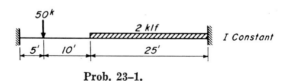

Prob. 23–1.

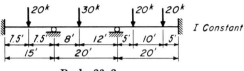

Prob. 23-2.

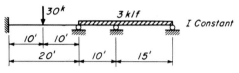

Prob. 23-3.

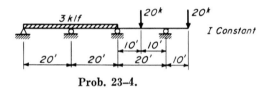

Prob. 23-4.

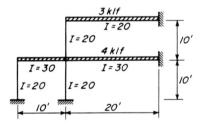

Prob. 23-5.

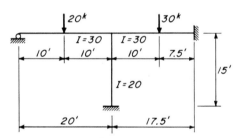

Prob. 23-6.

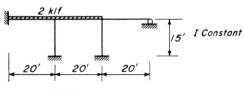

Prob. 23-7.

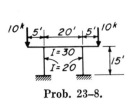

Prob. 23–8.

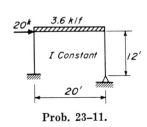

Prob. 23–9.

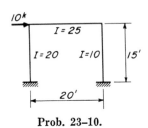

Prob. 23–10.

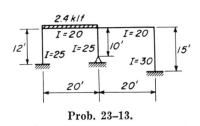

Prob. 23–11.

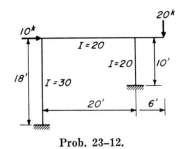

Prob. 23–12.

Prob. 23–13.

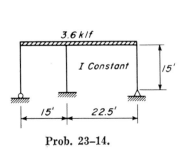

Prob. 23–14.

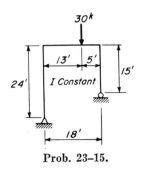

Prob. 23–15.

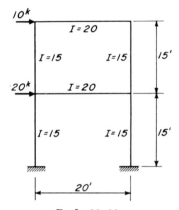

Prob. 23-16.

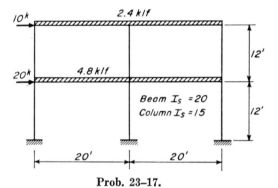

Prob. 23-17.

Prob. 23-18.

24 | COLUMN ANALOGY

24-1. General

The conjugate-beam procedure is an analogy in that a convenient viewpoint was taken of the mechanical operations involved in figuring the deflections in members subject to bending moment. The M/EI diagram was placed on a fictitious structure in which the resulting shear and moments coincided exactly with the slopes and deflections in the original structure.

In a similar manner, the column-analogy procedure takes a convenient view of the operations involved in figuring the moments in an indeterminate structure. The analogy pertains to the identities existing between the moments produced in an indeterminate structure and the stresses produced in an eccentrically loaded short column. The computations are reduced to a nearly mechanical procedure, and the comment, "I just put the figures in a table, turn the crank of the calculator, and out comes the answer," is sometimes heard.

Column analogy was the second outstanding contribution to the structural field made by the late Prof. Hardy Cross. The method is applicable to the analysis of structures indeterminate to not more than the third degree, including fixed-ended beams, single-span arches and frames, and closed boxes. Another application of column analogy, and perhaps the most useful today, is the calculation of the carry-over factors, stiffness factors, and fixed-end moments necessary for analyzing structures with members of varying moments of inertia by moment distribution.

24-2. Development of the Method

For the following discussion a short prismatic column, for which the deflections caused by bending are negligible, is considered. The column is shown in Fig. 24-1 loaded with an eccentric load P, and a stress diagram showing the variation of stress across the cross section of the column is drawn. The load is assumed to be applied at a point along the X axis of the cross section a distance e from the Y axis. The following expression may be written for the stress at any point a perpendicular distance y from the Y axis:

$$f = \frac{P}{A} \pm \frac{Mc}{I_y} = \frac{P}{A} \pm \frac{Pey}{I_y}$$

An important fact to notice is that the load P coincides with the cen-

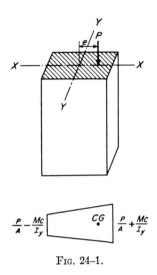

$$\frac{P}{A} - \frac{Mc}{I_y} \qquad CG \qquad \frac{P}{A} + \frac{Mc}{I_y}$$

Fig. 24-1.

troid of the forces produced in the column cross section or with the centroid of the stress diagram.

The fixed-ended beam of Fig. 24–2, which supports a concentrated load P, is now considered, and the magnitude of the end moments is desired. The beam is assumed to be replaced with a short column having a cross section with a center line the same in shape and length as the beam. Its width at any section equals the $1/EI$ value of the beam at the corresponding section.

The load P produces a bending-moment diagram which can be broken down into two parts as previously demonstrated in Example 17–6. These are the simple beam moment and the end moment. A review of the moment-area theorems will reveal the following two important points about these diagrams:

1) There is no change in slope of the tangent at A from the one at B; therefore, the total area of the M/EI diagram from A to B is zero. If the simple beam-moment diagram is considered as a downward load ($+$ moment), the end-moment diagram must act as an upward load ($-$ moment) and be equal in area.

2) The deflection of the tangent at one end of the beam from the tangent at the other is zero, as must be the moment of the total area of the M/EI diagram about either end; therefore, the centroid of the end-moment diagram must coincide with the centroid of the simple beam-moment diagram.[1]

[1] This discussion is quite similar to the one presented in Williams, *Analysis of Statically Indeterminate Structures* (Scranton, Penna.: International Textbook Company, 1959), pp. 292–294.

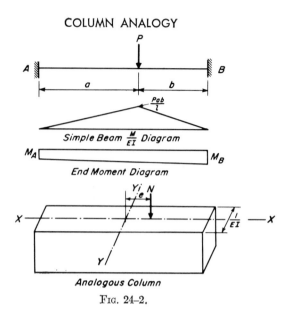

Fig. 24-2.

If the total area of the simple beam M/EI diagram, represented by N, is applied to the analogous column at a point corresponding to the centroid of the diagram, the "stress" at any point on the cross section will be:

$$f = \frac{N}{A} \pm \frac{Mc}{I_y} = \frac{N}{A} \pm \frac{Ney}{I_y}$$

The close relation of the moments in the fixed-ended beam to the "stresses" in the analogous column should now be evident. The load N is opposed by a stress diagram which coincides as to magnitude and centroid and has as ordinates stresses equal to the moments in the real beam.

Another method of developing the analogy between the stresses in an eccentrically loaded column and the moments in an indeterminate frame is the elastic-center method. For a thorough discussion of this subject the student may refer to *Analysis of Indeterminate Structures* by Parcel and Moorman.[2]

24–3.   Computation of Fixed-End Moments

Examples 24–1 and 24–2 illustrate the application of column analogy to the calculation of moments for fixed-ended beams. The calculations involved include obtaining certain properties of the analogous column and applying the bending and direct stress formula. The first of the two examples pertains to a beam which is prismatic, but the second one

[2] New York: John Wiley & Sons, Inc., 1955.

considers a beam with increased moments of inertia near the supports. It is necessary in this latter case to show the width of the cross section of the analogous cross section corresponding to the different $1/EI$ values present. If the size of the section should be constantly varying (see Example 24–5) over some little distance, it is necessary to divide the beam into short segments and figure the $1/EI$ widths for each of the segments.

EXAMPLE 24–1. Find the fixed-end moments of the structure in Fig. 24–3. Use column analogy.

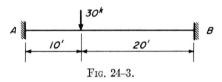

FIG. 24–3.

Solution:

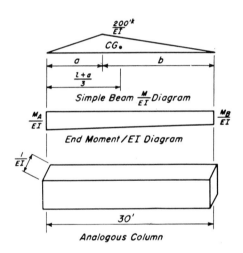

$$M_A = \frac{N}{A} + \frac{Ney}{I}$$

$$M_B = \frac{N}{A} - \frac{Ney}{I}$$

$$N = (\tfrac{1}{2})(30)\left(\frac{200}{EI}\right) = \frac{3000}{EI}$$

$$A = \frac{l}{EI} = \frac{30}{EI}$$

$$e = \frac{l}{2} - \frac{l+a}{3} = 15 - \frac{30+10}{3} = 1.67$$

$$I = \frac{l^3}{12EI} = \frac{30^3}{12EI} = \frac{2250}{EI}$$

$$y = \frac{l}{2} = 15$$

$$M_A = \frac{3000/EI}{30/EI} + \frac{(3000/EI)(1.67)(15)}{2250/EI} = 133.3'^k$$

$$M_B = \frac{3000/EI}{30/EI} - \frac{(3000/EI)(1.67)(15)}{2250/EI} = 66.7'^k$$

EXAMPLE 24–2. Compute the fixed-end moments for the beam shown in Fig. 24–4.

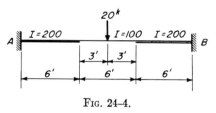

FIG. 24–4.

Solution:

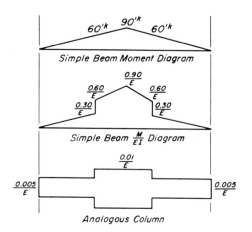

Simple Beam Moment Diagram

Simple Beam $\frac{M}{EI}$ Diagram

Analogous Column

$$N = (\tfrac{1}{2})(6)\left(\frac{0.30}{E}\right)(2) + (6)\left(\frac{0.60}{E}\right) + (\tfrac{1}{2})(6)\left(\frac{0.30}{E}\right) = \frac{6.30}{E}$$

$$A = (6)\left(\frac{0.005}{E}\right)(2) + (6)\left(\frac{0.01}{E}\right) = \frac{0.12}{E}$$

$$e = y = 0$$

$$M_A = M_B = \frac{N}{A} \pm \frac{Ney}{I} = \frac{6.30/E}{0.12/E} = 52.5'^k$$

24–4. Computation of Carry-Over and Stiffness Factors

The structures analyzed in Chapter 23 by moment distribution consisted of prismatic members for which the stiffnesses, fixed-end moments, and carry-over factors were easily obtainable (the carry-over factors were always $-\tfrac{1}{2}$). Although the application of moment distribution to structures containing nonprismatic members is exactly the same for those consisting entirely of prismatic members, the properties necessary for analysis are not so easily obtained. One of the better methods of computing these properties is the column-analogy procedure.

The calculations necessary for computing the fixed-end moments have been described in Sec. 24–3 and will be further illustrated in Example 24–5. The first problem considered in this section is the calculation of carry-over factors. With reference to Fig. 24–5, it is remembered that a moment M_A applied at the A end of the member shown will induce a moment in the B end equal to the carry-over factor times M_A or $C_{AB}M_A$. In this figure, the A end is considered to be hinged so that it may rotate. A hinge is theoretically a point of no stiffness and the moment of inertia is zero; therefore, the width of the analogous column (I/EI) is infinite and the Y axis of the cross section will pass through the hinge.

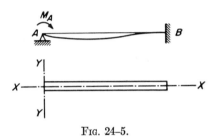

Fig. 24–5.

The A end of the member is assumed to be rotated through an angle of 1 radian; therefore, the total area of the M/EI diagram from A to B must be 1.0. Since point A does not deflect vertically with respect to B, the moment of the M/EI diagram about A must be zero. The effect of the facts stated in the preceding two sentences is that an equivalent load of 1.0 can be placed on the analogous column at point A because it represents the net effect of the diagram. This load could not be placed anywhere else because the effect would be a moment about A, falsely indicating deflection. Whatever the shape of the beam, 1.0 is placed at the end which is rotated. The moments or "stresses" at each end of the analogous column are determined; and from a ratio of the two, the carry-over factor is found.

The stiffness of one end of a member may be defined as the moment required to rotate that end of the member through a unit angle when the other end is fixed. This value is computed in making the carry-over calculations.

Examples 24–3 to 24–5 illustrate the calculations necessary for computing these beam properties. Fortunately, there are available in various publications tables and curves that give the properties needed for some groups of beams. The *Handbook of Frame Constants,* published by the

Portland Cement Association, is probably the most widely known. Example 24–6 illustrates the analysis of a continuous beam of constantly varying moments of inertia by moment distribution.

EXAMPLE 24–3. Compute the carry-over factor from A to B for the beam of Fig. 24–6, which has a constant moment of inertia.

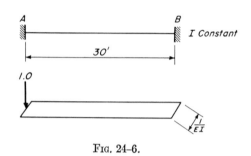

FIG. 24–6.

Solution:

$$N = 1.0$$

$$A = \frac{30}{EI}$$

$$I = \frac{l^3}{12EI} = \frac{2250}{EI}$$

$$e = \frac{l}{2} = 15$$

$$y = \frac{l}{2} = 15$$

$$M_A = \frac{N}{A} + \frac{Ney}{I} = \frac{1.0}{30/EI} + \frac{(1.0)(15)(15)}{2250/EI} = +0.1333EI$$

$$M_B = \frac{N}{A} - \frac{Ney}{I} = \frac{1.0}{30/EI} - \frac{(1.0)(15)(15)}{2250/EI} = -0.0667EI$$

$$C_{AB} = \frac{M_B}{M_A} = \frac{-0.0667EI}{0.1333EI} = -\frac{1}{2}$$

EXAMPLE 24–4. Compute the stiffness at A and the carry-over from A to B for the beam of Example 24–2, which is reproduced in Fig. 24–7.

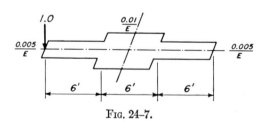

FIG. 24–7.

Solution:

$$N = 1.0$$

$$A = \frac{0.12}{E}$$

$$I = \left(\frac{1}{12}\right)\left(\frac{0.005}{E}\right)(18)^3 + \left(\frac{1}{12}\right)\left(\frac{0.005}{E}\right)(6)^3 = \frac{2.52}{E}$$

$$e = 9.0$$

$$M_A = \frac{1.0}{0.12/E} + \frac{(1.0)(9.0)(9.0)}{2.52/E} = +40.47E$$

$$M_B = \frac{1.0}{0.12/E} - \frac{(1.0)(9.0)(9.0)}{2.52/E} = -23.81E$$

$$C_{AB} = \frac{M_B}{M_A} = \frac{-23.81E}{+40.47E} = -0.588$$

$$K_A = 40.47E$$

Note: For members which are not symmetrical, Maxwell's law presents an interesting method of checking the carry-over and stiffness values obtained at the two ends. The twisting of the *A* end of a member through an angle of 1 radian produces a moment at the *B* end equal to the moment produced at the *A* end if the *B* end is twisted through an angle of 1 radian. This relationship may be expressed as $C_{AB}K_A = C_{BA}K_B$.

EXAMPLE 24–5. Compute fixed-end moments, carry-over factors, and stiffnesses for the beam shown in Fig. 24–8. The beam has a rectangular cross section with a constant thickness of 6 in. Divide the analogous column into 2-ft sections for computing values of *I* and *A*, although more precise values could be obtained by using smaller divisions.

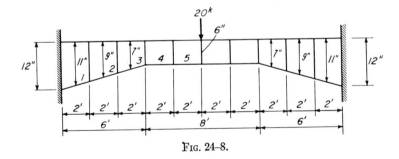

Fig. 24–8.

Solution:

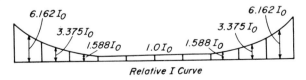

Relative *I* Curve

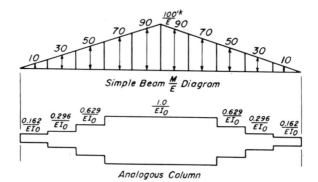

Simple Beam $\frac{M}{E}$ Diagram

Analogous Column

Section	N	A
1	$\dfrac{(10)(2)(\frac{1}{2})}{6.162EI_0} = \dfrac{1.62}{EI_0}$	$\dfrac{(2)(0.162)}{EI_0} = \dfrac{0.324}{EI_0}$
2	$\dfrac{(30)(2)}{3.375EI_0} = \dfrac{17.80}{EI_0}$	$\dfrac{(2)(0.296)}{EI_0} = \dfrac{0.592}{EI_0}$
3	$\dfrac{(50)(2)}{1.588EI_0} = \dfrac{63.00}{EI_0}$	$\dfrac{(2)(0.629)}{EI_0} = \dfrac{1.258}{EI_0}$
4	$\dfrac{(70)(2)}{1.0EI_0} = \dfrac{140.00}{EI_0}$	$\dfrac{(2)(1.0)}{EI_0} = \dfrac{2.000}{EI_0}$
5	$\dfrac{(90)(2)}{1.0EI_0} = \dfrac{180.00}{EI_0}$	$\dfrac{(2)(1.0)}{EI_0} = \dfrac{2.000}{EI_0}$
Σ	$\dfrac{402.42}{EI_0}$	$\dfrac{6.174}{EI_0}$

$$N = 2 \times \frac{402.42}{EI_0} = \frac{804.84}{EI_0}$$

$$A = 2 \times \frac{6.174}{EI_0} = \frac{12.348}{EI_0}$$

$$I = \left(\frac{1}{12}\right)\left(\frac{0.162}{EI_0}\right)(20)^3 + \left(\frac{1}{12}\right)\left(\frac{0.134}{EI_0}\right)(16)^3 + \left(\frac{1}{12}\right)\left(\frac{0.333}{EI_0}\right)(12)^3 +$$
$$\left(\frac{1}{12}\right)\left(\frac{0.371}{EI_0}\right)(8)^3 = \frac{217.3}{EI_0}$$

Fixed-end moments:

$$e = 0$$
$$M_A = M_B = \frac{804.84/EI_0}{12.348/EI_0} = 65.2'^k$$

Carry-overs and stiffness factors:

$N = 1.0$

$e = 10.0$

$$M_A = \frac{1.0}{12.348/EI_0} + \frac{(1.0)(10.0)(10.0)}{217.3/EI_0} = +0.081EI_0 + 0.46EI_0 = +0.541EI_0$$

$$M_B = +0.081EI_0 - 0.46EI_0 = -0.379EI_0$$

$$C_{AB} = C_{BA} = \frac{-0.379EI_0}{+0.541EI_0} = -0.702$$

$$K_A = K_B = 0.541EI_0$$

EXAMPLE 24-6. Distribute the fixed-end moments for the beam shown in Fig. 24-9, for which stiffnesses, carry-over factors, and fixed-end moments háve been calculated.

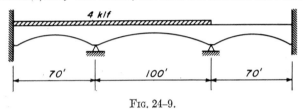

FIG. 24-9.

Solution:

← −0.75	0.78 →	← −0.78	0.75 →	CO
17.1	22.8	22.8	17.1	K
+2100	−2100	+4400	−4400	FEM

	0.43	0.57	0.57	0.43	
+2100	−2100	+4400	−4400		
	− 990	−1310	+2510	+1890	
− 740		+1970	−1030		+1410
	− 850	−1120	+ 590	+ 440	
− 635		+ 462	− 880		+ 330
	− 200	− 262	+ 500	+ 380	
− 150		+ 390	− 205		+ 285
	− 170	− 220	+ 115	+ 90	
− 127		+ 90	− 172		+ 67
	− 39	− 51	+ 98	+ 74	
− 29					+ 55
+ 419	−4349	+4349	−2874	+2874	+2147

NOTE: A booklet entitled *Continuous Concrete Bridges*, published by the Portland Cement Association, presents an excellent method of analyzing and designing concrete bridges whose floors or girders have parabolic soffits such as the ones of this problem.

24–5. Analysis of Frames

The analogous columns which would be used for several types of frame are shown in Fig. 24–10. Each member of the frame is drawn to

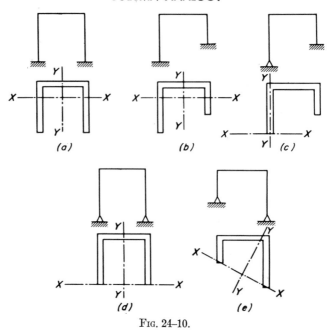

Fig. 24–10.

a width equal to its respective $1/EI$ value, and the centroidal axes are placed according to the principles previously discussed.

The center of gravity of the loads (i.e., the center of gravity of the simple beam moment diagrams) will rarely fall along one of the centroidal axes, and the stress developed is caused by bending about both axes. The stress may be calculated with the following formula, in which x is the perpendicular distance from the point where "stress" is desired to the Y axis and y is the perpendicular distance from the point to the X axis.

$$M = \frac{N}{A} \pm \frac{Nex}{I_y} + \frac{Ney}{I_x}$$

The analogous column is drawn with the proper dimensions, and its properties (A, I_x, I_y, etc.) are computed. The real frame is indeterminate and the number of reaction components required to leave a determinate and stable structure are removed. A moment diagram is drawn for the structure remaining, and its parts are placed in the appropriate position along the center lines of the analogous column. It is again obvious that for equilibrium the resultant of the simple beam moment diagrams and the end-moment diagrams must be equal and opposite and their center of gravities must coincide. The final moment at any point equals the sum of the moment at the point in the simple beam moment diagram and the stresses it causes at the point in the analogous column. Only one example (24–7) is given, but it should be sufficient to illustrate the procedure. The procedure is rather lengthy and tedious for structures consisting of prismatic members as compared to a solution by the moment-distribution method, but it has a considerable advantage for frames of varying moments of inertia. A simple beam moment diagram causing tension on the outside of the frame is considered to be a positive load.

The centroidal axes for the analogous columns for some frames are not vertical and horizontal, and symmetry is not present about either axis. The frame of Fig. 24–10 (e) falls into this class. For this situation it is necessary to use the principal moments of inertia and the products of inertia in the solution.

EXAMPLE 24–7. Determine the moments at C and D in the frame shown in Fig. 24–11. Remove the fixed end at A to leave a determinate structure.

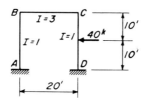

FIG. 24–11.

Solution:

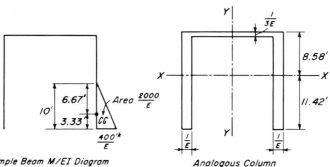

Simple Beam M/EI Diagram   Analogous Column

Properties of analogous column

$$A = (20)\left(\frac{1}{E}\right) + (20)\left(\frac{1}{E}\right) + (20)\left(\frac{3}{E}\right) = \frac{46.67}{E}$$

$$\bar{y} = \frac{(20/E)(10) + (20/E)(10)}{46.67/E} = 8.58 \text{ ft}$$

$$I_x = \left(\frac{1}{3}\right)\left(\frac{1}{E}\right)(8.58^3 \times 2 + 11.42^3 \times 2) + \left(\frac{20}{3E}\right)(8.58)^2 = \frac{1904}{E}$$

$$I_y = \left(\frac{1}{12}\right)\left(\frac{1}{3E}\right)(20)^3 + (2)\left(\frac{20}{E}\right)(10)^2 = \frac{4222}{E}$$

Mackinac Bridge, St. Ignace, Michigan. (Courtesy of H. D. Ellis, St. Ignace, Michigan)

Moment at C:

$$M_C = \frac{2000/E}{46.67/E} + \frac{(2000/E)(10)(10)}{4222/E} - \frac{(2000/E)(8.09)(8.58)}{1904/E} + M_{\text{simp. beam}}$$

$$M_C = +42.8 + 47.4 - 72.8 + 0 = 17.4'^k$$

Moment at D:

$$M_D = \frac{2000/E}{46.67/E} + \frac{(2000/E)(10)(10)}{4222/E} + \frac{(2000/E)(8.09)(11.42)}{1904/E} - 400$$

$$M_D = +42.8 + 47.4 + 96.9 - 400 = -212.9'^k$$

24–6. Conclusion

The heading of this section is entitled Conclusion, but a more appropriate title might be End of the Beginning, because there are so many topics of further possible study in the field of structural analysis. To mention a very few there are secondary stresses, model analysis, indeterminate space frames, plastic analysis, and suspension bridges.

The use of continuous structures becomes more common each year, while the emphasis of their analysis in undergraduate schools does not increase correspondingly. Some civil engineering schools are transferring all or part of indeterminate study from the required to the elective lists to permit the inclusion of more of the so-called broadening courses.

This trend makes it more difficult for the student to have a thorough background in the subject upon graduation. Only a small percentage of those persons entering the structural field can continue to graduate school to remove the deficiency. The solution to the problem lies in a program of continuing study by the individual. It is difficult to believe that the knowledge displayed by the outstanding engineers of our time was achieved only in the classroom and during the forty or so hours spent on the job each week. Their accomplishments are surely based to no small extent on many hours of painstaking *self-instruction.*

Problems

24–1. Determine the fixed-end moments, carry-over factors, and stiffnesses for the beam shown in the accompanying illustration.

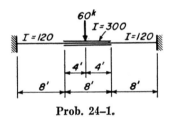

Prob. 24–1.

24–2. Repeat Prob. 24–1 for the 60^k load moved to a point 8 ft from the left end of the span.

24–3. Determine the fixed-end moments, carry-over factors, and stiffnesses for both ends of the beam shown in the accompanying illustration.

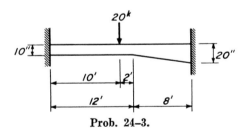

Prob. 24–3.

24–4. Compute the fixed-end moments in Prob. 24–3 for the 20^k load removed and the beam loaded with a 4-klf uniform load for the entire span.

24–5. Compute carry-over and stiffness factors for the beam shown in the accompanying illustration. Divide the beam into 2-ft sections for the calculations. The beam soffit is laid out on a curve in accordance with the formula $y=ax^2$.

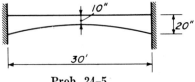

Prob. 24–5.

Calculate the moments at the ends of the members for the frames of Probs. 24–6 to 24–10 by the column-analogy method.

24–6. Problem 22–5.

24–7. Problem 22–7.

24–8. Problem 22–8.

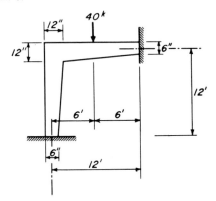

Prob. 24–9.

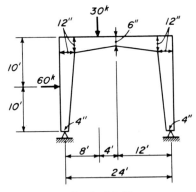

Prob. 24–10.

INDEX